THE NEW RUSSIAN SPACE PROGRAMME
From Competition to Collaboration

WILEY-PRAXIS SERIES IN SPACE SCIENCE AND TECHNOLOGY
Series Editor: **John Mason, B.Sc., Ph.D.**
Consultant Editor: **David Sloggett, M.Sc., Ph.D.**

This series reflects the significant advances being made in space science and technology, including developments in astronautics and space life sciences. It provides a forum for the publication of new ideas and results of current research in areas such as spacecraft materials, propulsion systems, space automation and robotics, spacecraft communications, mission planning and management, and satellite data processing and archiving.

Aspects of space policy and space industrialization, including the commercial, legal and political ramifications of such activities, and the physiological, sociological and psychological problems of living and working in space, and spaceflight risk management are also addressed.

These books are written for professional space scientists, technologists, physicists and materials scientists, aeronautical and astronautical engineers, and life scientists, together with managers, policy makers and those involved in the space business. They are also of value to postgraduate and undergraduate students of space science and technology, and those on space-related courses (including psychology, physiology, medicine and sociology) and areas of the social and behavioural sciences.

SATELLITE CONTROL: A Comprehensive Approach
John T. Garner, Aerospace Consultant, formerly Principal Ground Support Engineer, Communications Satellite Programmes, ESA-ESTEC, Noordwijk, The Netherlands

THE NEW RUSSIAN SPACE PROGRAMME: From Competition to Collaboration
Brian Harvey, M.A., H.D.E., F.B.I.S.

Forthcoming Titles

METALLURGICAL ASSESSMENT OF SPACECRAFT PARTS AND MATERIALS, Second edition
Barry D. Dunn, Head of Metallic Materials and Processes Section, ESA-ESTEC, The Netherlands

LIVING AND WORKING IN SPACE: Human Behaviour, Culture and Organization, Second edition
Philip Robert Harris, Executive Editor, *Space Governance* Journal; Vice President, United Societies in Space, Inc.

AEROSPACE POLYMERS AND COMPOSITES: Fundamentals and Applications
Sanjay Palsule

SOLAR POWER SATELLITES: A Space Energy System for Earth
Peter E. Glaser, Vice President (retired), Arthur D. Little Inc, USA, Frank P. Davidson, Coordinator, Macro-Engineering Research Group, Massachusetts Institute of Technology, USA, Katinka I. Csigi, Principal Consultant, ERIC International, USA

THE NEW RUSSIAN SPACE PROGRAMME

PROGRAMME

From Competition to Collaboration

Brian Harvey, M.A., H.D.E., F.B.I.S.

JOHN WILEY & SONS

Chichester • New York • Brisbane • Toronto • Singapore

Published in association with
PRAXIS PUBLISHING
Chichester

First edition published in 1988
This new edition published in 1996 by
John Wiley & Sons Ltd
in association with Praxis Publishing Ltd

Wiley Editorial Offices

John Wiley & Sons Ltd, Baffins Lane,
Chichester, West Sussex PO19 1UD, England

John Wiley & Sons, Inc., 605 Third Avenue,
New York, NY 10158-0012, USA

Jacaranda Wiley Ltd, G.P.O. Box 859, Brisbane
Queensland 4001, Australia

John Wiley & Sons (Canada) Ltd, 22 Worcester Road,
Rexdale, Ontario M9W 1L1, Canada

John Wiley & Sons (Asia) Pte Ltd, 2 Clementi Loop #02-01,
Jin Xing Distripark, Singapore 0512

A catalogue record for this book is available from the British Library

ISBN 0-471-96014-4

Printed and bound in Great Britain by Hartnolls Ltd, Bodmin

To Judith, Valerie and Alastair

Table of contents

Author's introduction

This book is based on *Race into space: the Soviet space programme* (Ellis Horwood, 1988). Since that book was written, many of the hidden pages of the Soviet space programme have been filled in. This book uses to the full the revelations of the *glasnost* period and those archives which have opened since the fall of the Soviet Union in 1991. It narrates developments in the Russian space programme since 1992, in particular how Russia had adapted to the new world economic order. Finally, this book relates how Russia, the rival of the United States during the Cold War, is now its partner in one of the most important scientific projects of all time, the international space station, due to be completed early in the new millennium.

The book is divided into three. The first part examines the early history of the space programme in Russia—from its theoretical and practical base (Chapter 1) to the golden years of Soviet rocketry (Chapter 2) leading to the climax of the Moon race (Chapter 3). Part 2 goes behind the scenes in the Russian space programme to describe its organization, structure, rocketry and engine technology, reporting how the programme has adapted to new pressures (Chapter 4), before studying the wide range of unmanned programmes (Chapter 5) and efforts to explore the Moon, Mars and Venus (chapter 6). Part 2 concludes with a look at the level of spaceplane development in Russia (Chapter 7). Part 3 takes up the main theme of current Russian space development—the creation of manned orbiting space stations. Chapter 8 describes the early Soviet space stations; Chapter 9 narrates how the Russians developed the skills necessary to keep cosmonauts in space for long periods. Chapter 10 gives an account of the greatest achievement of Soviet cosmonautics, the Mir orbiting space station. Chapter 11 concludes Part 3 by looking at how Soviet–American cooperation in space began, leading to the joint missions of the mid-1990s and the space station scheduled for 1997–2001.

Russian names have been standardized to those most commonly in use. Russian rockets present a particular problem, since there are four possible means of describing them—the NATO codename, the US Department of Defense coding system, the method devised by American analyst Charles Sheldon, and those used by the Russians themselves in the post-*glasnost* period. I have opted for the last-mentioned, though at appropriate points in the text the other systems will be referenced.

Acknowledgements

I wish to thank all those who contributed to this edition. I wish to especially thank those who provided photographs and gave permission for their use—Dr John Mason; Dr Nigel Evans; the National Aeronautics and Space Administration (NASA); and the Novosti Press Agency, which supplied photographs first used in the original edition of this book. I also wish to thank Rex Hall, for his advice on members of the cosmonaut teams and for sharing with me his considerable knowledge, interest and expertise.

List of illustrations

Chapter 11

Part 1: Origins

1

Beginnings

A hypothetical sputnik, similar to our Moon but nearer to our planet, could orbit at about 300 versts (270 km) free of Earth's gravity.
                        Konstantin Tsiolkovsky, *Dreams of Earth and sky*, 1895.

Russia's exploration of space began in a small village called Izhevskoye near the city of Ryazan, 200 km southeast of Moscow. On 17 September 1857 a small boy was born. His father, Eduard Tsiolkovsky, was a forest ranger and he named his son Konstantin.

He was a bright, active child until he was ten, when one disaster followed another. He was struck down by scarlet fever and he became almost totally deaf. For three years his mother nursed him and despite his affliction taught him to read and write and manage at boys' high school. Then, when he had reached thirteen, she died suddenly. Konstantin Tsiolkovsky's life is the story not only of one man's effort to cope with a terrible disablement. For despite it he became a self-taught scientist, a practical person and a theoretician of space flight. He was the one person who inspired the idea of a Russian space programme from the very beginning. Without him, it might never have happened at all.

By the age of 14, Tsiolkovsky was well able to read, and he read books endlessly. It was one thing he was able to do, deprived as he was of the normal channels of human contact and communication. Financially supported by his father, he moved to Moscow when he was 16, rented rooms, and spent day after day in the city's public libraries. By 17 he had begun to master higher mathematics, differential calculus and spherical trigonometry. After three years in Moscow, Tsiolkovsky took up a teaching post in Kaluga, a town southwest of Moscow. In the Tsar's Russia it was probably the most obvious career for him. His life was hard and he found deafness a terrible torment. He even designed tin funnels as hearing aids so he could try pick up what people were saying.

In 1883, in the course of the long summer school holidays, Tsiolkovsky turned his mind to something which had obsessed him—travel through space. We do not know where the inspiration came from and history gives us no clue. It may have been his deafness which, while depriving him in so many other ways, made him contemplative and all the more imaginative.

Free space, his book from 1883, took the creative leap from the earth-bound solid practical world to that of fantasy, yet without cutting scientific corners. He described what a human being would see and experience if flying around the Earth in a space ship. He would be weightless; and he would get up there by a 'reactive' interplanetary ship with a rocket engine using spherical projectiles fired by an on-board cannon. Gravity and weightlessness intrigued Tsiolkovsky. He rigged up devices that could create zero-gravity on the ground and a primitive centrifuge to test overloading, which he verified using chicken and mice. They could stand loads of six gravities (6 g) but died at much higher g—just like humans would.

Free space was followed by *On the Moon* (1887) and *Dreams of Earth and sky* (1895). In the last-mentioned he described how a small moon or artificial Earth satellite could be launched and circle the Earth at an altitude of 270 km. It would be a mistake to regard Tsiolkovsky as simply a Russian equivalent of the French novelist Jules Verne, inspired by him though he was. He was also an inventor. He designed and built a wind tunnel in his home to study air resistance; and he designed a monoplane with a gasoline engine, enclosed cockpit, autopilot and retractable landing gear.

Konstantin Tsiolkovsky, the man who was the inspiration for the Soviet space programme. In the year the Wright brothers made their first flight, he wrote of liquid-fuelled rockets, soft-landings on other planets and the colonization of space.

In 1903, Tsiolkovsky, in Kaluga, produced his most important paper 'Exploring space with reactive devices'. In it he spelt out the advantages of rocket flight and of liquid-fuelled rockets; and he explained how it might be possible to soft-land on other planets. Eventually, he predicted, poetically, 'people will ascend into the expanse of the heavens and found a settlement there'.

His ideas gained ground and won gradual acceptance. Papers were taken by the Petro-grad journal *Scientific Review* (1911). By then his mind had moved on. In the same year he proposed that, due to the possible inefficiency of liquid-fuelled rockets, some kind of atomic power would have to be considered for really distant space journeys!

PROBING THE ATMOSPHERE

Tsiolkovsky found some form of financial security when in 1918 the new revolutionary government awarded him a life pension. He continued writing, to produce in 1924 *Cosmic rocket trains*, advocating multi-stage rockets in which one used the thrust gained by a lower stage to fly to ever greater altitudes. He then designed a 'stellar ship', complete with closed ecocycle to resupply itself with air, plants and water. His spaceship designs would be considered conventional enough today in any technical journal dealing with future space travel : but liquid-fuelled engines, solar batteries, wheel-shaped space stations, these were all part of his thinking seventy years ago. In the same year the government republished all his old works.

In his later days, his home in Kaluga became a place of pilgrimage. Inventors, designers, journalists, aviators, and scientists beat their path to Tsiolkovsky's door. The now old, bearded, hollow-chested prophet lived in a two-storey house with a large veranda, where he sat out to reflect the summer. Books, manuscripts, and the odd globe were piled in his study.

The house in which Konstantin Tsiolkovsky lived and worked at Kaluga, a town to the south-west of Moscow.

Konstantin Tsiolkovsky's health gave way in August 1935. Newspapers carried accounts of his collapse and his subsequent death in September 1935. In his will he bequeathed all his papers to the Communist Party of the Soviet Union (CPSU).

His home was at once turned into a national museum and since then it has been a shrine and a tourist attraction. An obelisk has been erected, as has a shining 20 m high silvery rocket against a bronze bust of his figure. In 1954 the Tsiolkovsky Gold Medal was struck, to be awarded every three years to the most outstanding contributor to space flight.[1]

For good reasons, the 1920s and 1930s are universally considered to be a dark period in Russian history. But the revolutionary government also provided conditions under which rocket development and similar endeavours could develop. For the entire period until the late 1940s, the Soviet government was not only a socialist state: it was the only one. The eyes of the world were very much on it. Supporters were quick to focus on its achievements; sceptics and those hostile were quick to find fault. During the early years, there was much genuine enthusiasm and optimism concerning the building up of Russia as a modern, scientific, industrial power.

Scientific achievement became an acid test of the validity of socialism. The USSR simply had to progress faster and further—its science was unsullied by the profit motive or the corruptions of commercialism and it was open to all citizens in a socialist society to be great scientists. Science became part of the trial of strength between capitalism and socialism, in the same way that the figures of industrial and agricultural output, literacy, the numbers of doctors per thousand, coal output per pithead and so on.

In Tsarist Russia, many scientists had found themselves among the intelligentsia who opposed the régime. An example is the story of Nikolai Kibilachich. Independently of Tsiolkovsky, he drew up ideas for jet engines in the late 1870s and early 1880s. He devised a heavier-than-air flying platform, propelled by a rocket whose engine swivelled or gimballed. But he was also a revolutionary and he was executed for designing a bomb that killed the Tsar. His writings were impounded immediately—his last drawings were made in the condemned cell the night before he was hanged—and did not see the light of day until August 1917. They were then published at once.

The Soviet government was anxious to secure, maintain and develop the goodwill of the scientific community. Its plans were ambitious and they were pursued at a reckless pace throughout the 1920s and 1930s: they included electrification, air transport, heavy industry, a modern defence force, full employment and the ending of illiteracy. Theoreticians and rocketeers were included in this march of progress. On his 75th birthday in 1932, Tsiolkovsky was awarded the title "Red banner of labour" by the government, and a special session of the Academy of Sciences was called to honour him.

By contrast, right up to the late 1950s, Western governments were uninterested and sceptical about travel in space, insofar as they spent any time thinking about it at all, which they did not. They tolerated scientists like Goddard in the United States and the British Interplanetary Society in Britain. Yet in the USSR, government supported theoretical and practical rocket development from the foundation of the State.

Two theoreticians from the 1920s stand out: Friedrich Tsander and Yuri Kondratyuk. Friedrich Tsander (1887–1933) was an engineer from Riga Polytechnic in Latvia and had read Tsiolkovsky in 1906. In his designs, which date to 1912, he attempted to combine rockets and aircraft. His spaceship would take off and ascend like a plane, but rocket power would be used once the air became too thin to use. In his design are the antecedents of the space shuttle. He specifically suggested the use of liquid hydrogen as a high-energy rocket fuel, long before hydrogen was widely used either in science or in engineering. In the midst of testing a 50 kg liquid-fuelled rocket in 1933 he went down with typhoid fever and died. But he had already made his mark, both as a designer and a builder of small rockets, and as a theoretician. His obsession was flight to Mars, and he even did a schedule of a manned journey there. He ended it with the resounding words: 'One day we *shall* fly to Mars!'

Yuri Kondratyuk (1897–1942) wrote on space travel between 1916 and 1929, composing *The conquest of interplanetary space* (Novosibirsk, 1929). His book described multi-staged rockets which utilized solar energy. He invented the idea of slingshot maoeuvres—using the gravity of one planet to travel on to another. He described orbiting space stations, nozzles and turbine pumps, thermal protection systems, landing stages as a base for lunar takeoff and return to Earth by atmospheric braking. Writing on space travel in the 1920s had reached such a pitch that in 1929 Professor Nikolai Rynin was able to publish a nine-volume encyclopedia called *Space Travels,* which summarized all the main papers, ideas and concepts of the day.

Yuri Kondratyuk, who wrote about space travel between 1916 and 1929. He described multi-stage rockets, the use of solar energy for power and orbiting space stations.

ORGANIZING THE ROCKET EFFORT

Rocket and space organizations sprouted everywhere: a Society for the Study of Interplanetary Communications (OIMS, 1924); a Kiev Society for the Study and Conquest of Space (1925); and to top it all 1927 saw the first-ever 'Exhibition of interplanetary machines', held for three months in Moscow. Foreign exhibitors came from Britain, the USA (Goddard), France, Germany and Austria. The exhibits included designs, models, drawings, pictures and even a mockup spacesuit.[2]

The seriousness with which amateur space scientists took themselves was matched by government. In April 1924 a Jet Propulsion Section was established in the Zhukovsky Military Air Academy. Its first tasks included a competition to launch a rocket that would fly 100 km; and it had a journal called *Raketa* which would, it proclaimed, 'distribute information on interplanetary navigation'. Its work was linked to the Central Institute of Aerohydrodynamics, TsAGI, the technical institute which carried out research and development work for the Red Air Force.

The Soviet space programme produced its first hardware in the 1920s and it came from two groups with the names GIRD and GDL. Both started under the auspices of the most senior military man in the Soviet Union—the young, ambitious and ultimately doomed Red Army Marshal, Mikhail Tukhachevsky, who was intrigued with the idea of space flight and even more keen to see rocketry harnessed to the needs of the Red Army.

The Gas Dynamics Laboratory (GDL) dates to Moscow in 1921 but was formally set up in Leningrad in 1928 by Nikolai Tikhomirov, its first director. Within five years it had produced a liquid-fuelled rocket on a test stand. Thousands of static tests were made: the engines had variable thrusts and achieved rates of efficiency that the west did not match till the 1950s. The burn marks from these early tests are still there—in the old Petropavlovskaya fortress, the only safe site the experimenters could find. The roar from the fortress as the static tests went on startled passing citizens and probably mystified them too. GDL itself expanded from its initial staff of ten to 200 people by 1933.[3]

GDL was the apprenticeship of Valentin Pavlovich Glushko (1908–89), the man who was to become Russia's greatest rocket engine designer. Glushko came from Odessa, Ukraine. His mother was a nurse. As a boy, he made his own observations of Venus, Jupiter and Mars at the astronomical observatory of Odessa, which were published in the *Astronomical Bulletin* and in the magazine *Mirovedenie*. As a 15-year-old schoolboy, Glushko wrote about space travel to, and received replies from, Konstantin Tsiolkovsky, then aged 67.

Glushko was not simply an engine designer. His wider interest was evident when at 16 he had published 'The conquest of the Moon' and at 18 'Station beyond the Earth' in local newspapers. He entered the physics and mathematics department of Leningrad University (1929–33) with the aim of designing electric rocket engines. This became the topic of his graduation paper, which he later sent to GDL director Nikolai Tikhomirov, who was sufficiently impressed to recommend that Glushko be admitted to GDL. In 1930, Glushko first experimented with toxic, storable fuels, such as nitric acid; then in the following year, with fuels which ignited spontaneously on contact with one another. In 1931 he designed and static-tested his first engine, the ORM-1, the first proper liquid-propellant rocket engine. The first version had a thrust of only 20 kg, but later ones were more powerful, at 300 kg. By 1933 he had developed a technique of regenerative cooling which ensured that liquid-fuelled engines could fire for a long duration without overheating. In 1936 he developed the first throttleable liquid-fuelled engine. He developed new turbine pumps and engines on gimballs.

GIRD was a larger but parallel organization functioning in Moscow from 1931. Composed of TsAGI scientists, GIRD (Group for the Study of Reaction Propulsion) set up in Moscow's city centre in 1932. It always saw itself as a national, not just a Moscow, organization, and its founders were Friedrich Tsander and Sergei Korolev.

GIRD was the apprenticeship of the man who became Russia's greatest rocket designer, Sergei Pavlovich Korolev (1906–66). From Zhitomir, Ukraine, Sergei Korolev developed a fascination with aircraft, went to Kiev Polytechnic and (far from easy) got into the Moscow Higher Technical School. Some of its students were in GIRD, and this was Korolev's link to rocketry. A visit to Tsiolkovsky in 1929 converted him. Once noticed, his rise was rapid. In 1932 he became leader of GIRD's design and production section. In 1934 the Soviet Ministry of Defence published *Rocket flight in the stratosphere*, which was written by Korolev. In the following year, Korolev sat in the passenger seat of a rocket glider that he designed himself. It made a test flight in tow from Moscow to the Crimea.

GIRD's claim to lasting fame was that it designed and flew the first modern liquid-fuel rocket in the USSR. The '09' rocket was 2.4 m long, weighed 19 kg divided between payload and fuel, and went up on 17 August 1933. It was designed by Mikhail Tikhonravov; Korolev lit the fuse. Its successor, GIRD-X, is still impressive as a black needle hurling skywards on the jerky black-and-white film of the time. This time, Tsander was the designer.

At one stage in 1934, Korolev fought a bitter argument with his colleague, Arvid Pallo, about whether they should launch a new rocket. Pallo, who doubted the piping system, urged more tests. Korolev refused and went ahead with the launch. In the explosion which followed, Korolev ended up in hospital, blood pouring from his forehead.

Marshal Tukhachevsky was critical of the division of effort between the GDL in Leningrad and the GIRD in Moscow. So in 1933 he ordered that these be merged as the RNII (Scientific Rocket Research Institute). Two of his deputies, Ivan Kleimenov (director of GDL, 1932-3) and Georgi Langemak, ran RNII along with Korolev. Glushko was also assigned there from GDL. Langemak, born in Starobelsk in 1889, was a university-educated army officer, who had crushed the Kronstadt uprising for the Red Army. At RNII he specialized in the development of solid-fuelled rockets, writing, with Valentin Glushko, a book called simply *Rockets* (Leningrad, 1935).

The merger of 1933 led to a change of direction. The liquid-fuelled rocket programme was abruptly halted: emphasis was switched to winged rockets. Korolev in particular was involved in fitting rocket motors to gliders and there are many pictures from this time showing him in flying gear with gliders in the background. This change of tack—it is glossed over in the histories of the period—was a portent of things to come. Tukhachevsky saw in winged rockets, rocket gliders and rocket planes a more effective weapon of war and that was where his first loyalty lay. Glushko's rocket's were adapted to torpedoes, planes and missiles. Korolev's designs became the basis of a rocket glider first flown in 1940.

Early Soviet rocket organizations

Name	Date founded
GDL	1921
OIMS	1924
GIRD	1931
RNII	1933

FLIGHTS IN THE STRATOSPHERE

Even as work on rockets progressed, the Soviet Union began exploring near-Earth space with balloons.[5] Flights by aerostats in Russia dated back to 1804, when the first balloon flew over St Petersburg. In 1933, the Ministry of War and the Society for the Promotion of Air Travel, OSOVIAKHIM, proclaimed a programme for the balloon exploration of the atmosphere at the same time as the United States and European countries were developing high-altitude scientific flights. These were serious scientific missions designed to study cosmic rays, temperature, wind, the atmosphere, ozone, the stars and optical waves. On 30 September 1933, the Red Army launched the USSR 1, with three balloonauts on board—Prokoviev, Birnbaum and Gudunov. The balloon ascended from Moscow airport, the balloonauts being equipped with special coats and communications soft-hats. As they rose, they noted the sky turn to deep violet and that they could see as far as 80 km. They flew 18 km, higher that the previous altitude record (17.2 km, set by the great Swiss explorer Picard), and landed 100 km from Moscow 8 h later.

On 30 January 1934, the larger OSOVIAKHIM 1 balloon, with balloonauts Fedosenko, Vasenko and Ousyskin on board, climbed from Moscow airport. The air-sealed gondola had electric controls so that the crew could engage in science. The crew had parachutes should they need to escape. OSOVIAKHIM reached 22 km, but during the descent the gondola tore free and it crashed to destruction 16 km east of the Moscow radio tower. The crew was unable to evacuate the plunging gondola and died on impact. Two days later, they were buried in the Kremlin wall.

Despite this disaster, two more ascents were made. USSR 1 flew a second time on 26 June 1935. On 12 October 1938, the *Komsomol*, with AI Fomin, AF Krikun and MI Volkov on board, reached 16.8 km, but they had to bail out during the descent at 9 km. Two long-distance balloon journeys were made just before the outbreak of war, the longest being 2700 km in 1941, but it is not known if this was part of a scientific programme or part of sports ballooning.

Early Soviet balloon flights

Date	Name
30 Sep 1933	USSR 1
30 Jan 1934	OSOVIAKHIM 1
26 Jun 1935	USSR 1
12 Oct 1938	*Komsomol*

TERROR AND WAR

On 11 June 1937, Marshal Tukhachevsky was arrested on Stalin's orders. He and seven other generals were shot in a prison yard later that night. This heralded a ferocious purge of the armed forces: 35,000 were shot, half the entire officer corps of the Red Army. An equally ruthless purge of the communist party itself had begun the previous year. Stalin's purges had broken.

Soviet rocket development was hit as much as any other sector of Russian society. The rocket programme, simply and for no other reason than that Tukhachevsky had taken it under his wing, became automatically suspect. His two deputies in RNII, Langemak and Kleimenov, were shot in 1938. Worse, Langemak was persuaded to incriminate Korolev. The official histories of the programme from around 1937 are sketchy. We catch only glimpses, compared to the wealth of light and detail of the GIRD and GDL years. This is especially true of the key personalities, Korolev and Glushko.

Korolev, only 30 at the time, was arrested on 27 June 1938. He was one of many aircraft and rocket designers rounded up by the secret police, the NKVD. One of his prison colleagues was aircraft and later spaceplane designer Vladimir Myasishchev. Korolev was charged with selling his designs to Willi Messerschmitt in Germany. After a lengthy interrogation, he was sent in a boxcar to Siberia. After many days, the train reached the Pacific coast. Korolev spent some time at a seaport staging post before being transferred to the terrible Maydek, Kolyma, goldmine from which most people never returned. He was there for a year. In late 1939, aircraft designer Andrei Tupolev, under guard but not sentenced to hard labour, got authority to ask him to join him in designing bombers in a special design bureau run by the NKVD in Radio st, Moscow. Had Korolev stayed in Kolyma, he would probably have succumbed to the cold and the hard labour. Korolev may also have been protected by Dmitri Ustinov, one of Stalin's entourage. Tupolev worked in a seven-floor building, of which four floors were design offices and two were cells.

ATTACK

In 1941, Hitler's armies invaded Russia. On 15 July 1942, Tupolev's bureau was evacuated to the Ural mountains, where Korolev was made assistant floor manager. In November, the bureau was transferred to Kazan, where it came under the authority of Valentin Glushko. Glushko had been arrested just before Korolev, on 23 March 1938, but was sent to a *sharashka* (a form of house arrest), rather than hard labour. The role of the Kazan bureau was to design small rockets which could be fitted to heavy bombers so that they could take off from short or snow-bound airfields.

After the war, Korolev and Glushko both received awards in the Kremlin in 1945. They were honoured with the Order of the Red Banner of Labour. Korolev's criminal record was expunged: he was formally declared not guilty in 1944, and was fully rehabilitated in 1948. Even as these events unravelled, they were shattered to learn of the progress made by the Germans during the war.

Prompted by a message from Churchill to Stalin, the Russians first found some rocket remains in Poland. In April 1944, the Russians appointed a secret commission to find out about German rockets. When the Germans retreated westwards they abandoned the Peenemünde station on the Baltic coast. The Russians lost no time in realizing just what a treasure trove they had stumbled across. Peenemünde was a real rocket range and its prize exhibit, the A-4, a real rocket.

The A-4 was 14 m high and weighed 12.8 tonnes at launch. On the autumn day of 3 October 1942, the first A-4 lifted off the sandy Baltic launch site, curved over gently into a clear blue sky, and disappeared from view. Tracking showed that it went as high as 85 km and splashed down 190 km away. Programme director Dornberger, turned to his chief rocket designer, Wernher von Braun and said: 'Do you realize what we have accomplished today? Today the spaceship was born!'

The A-4 was larger, more powerful and sophisticated than anything that had gone before. The military version of the A-4, called the V-2, was swiftly put to military use by Hitler against Britain. 1115 were fired: 3000 civilians died. Von Braun's ambitions went further than what the A-4 could achieve. The Peenemünde team flew a winged A-4b: its range, employing aerodynamic skip over the atmosphere, was no less than 595 km. The two-stage A-10 was to fly 5000 km, enough to have hit New York.

GERMAN ROCKET ENGINEERS

An undignified scramble was the only way to describe the efforts of the Russians and Americans to get hold of the A-4 hardware and the scientists who designed it. Later, the rumour circulated that the Americans had somehow got the 'wrong' Germans and the Russians had got the 'right' ones. In fact, the more talented ones went west.

Although the Russians took Peenemünde, von Braun and his colleagues arranged and, in some cases, tried desperately to ensure that they were captured by the Americans. Von Braun tipped off the Americans as to the whereabouts of the A-4 components, parts and designs. Enough parts for 100 A-4s were found, shipped off to the Unites States and were soon blasting off from the White Sands deserts in New Mexico, to von Braun's delight and the pleasure of US Army engineers. When the Russians asked for their share of A-4 parts, the Americans crated them tractor parts.

The Russians took longer to get their act together. In October 1945, Korolev arrived in Germany direct from his *sharashka* in Kazan; Glushko not long afterward. Both attended a British-sponsored launch of an A-4 (Operation Backfire). For two years, the Russians worked in Bleicherode, Germany, with the German specialists and hardware in a project called Rabe (German word for 'Raven'). Director of Rabe was Prof. Boris Chertok, a rocketplane designer who had been transferred to RNII when the first A-4 remains arrived in 1944. In October 1946, 177 Peenemünde Germans, with their families totalling 500 men, women and children, were transported to a guarded island in Seliger lake between Moscow and St Petersburg, then called Leningrad. The most important German scientist in the group was Helmut Grötrupp, who had designed the guidance system of the A-4 for von Braun. Korolev remained in Germany until February 1947.

POST-WAR RUSSIAN ROCKET PROGRAMME

The German experience had shown how much progress could be made, and had been made, in rocketry. As the uneasy post-war peace turned to cold war, Stalin decided that Russia must be equipped with nuclear weapons and rockets with which to deliver them. First, Stalin gave orders for a rocket programme. He gave permission for A-4s to be tested, and Soviet rockets to be built, based on the A-4. Wingless rockets were once again back in business. On 13 May 1946, the Soviet government issued a decree for the development of ballistic missiles. An organization was set up in August 1946 to carry out the decree, the Scientific Research Institute 88 (NII-88) in Kaliningrad, near Moscow, under the authority of Dmitri Ustinov. One section of NII-88 was called a special design bureau and the director of the division for long-range missiles was Sergei Korolev. Working with him were Vasili Mishin, his deputy, and other engineers Boris Chertok, Konstantin Bushuyev, Dmitri Kozlov, Vyacheslav Kovturenko, Mikhail Tikhonravov and Pavel Tsybin. These men and their colleagues were destined to become the key personalities in the Soviet space programme for the next 40 years.

Separately from NII-88, other institutes were at work which would in time contribute to the post-war Soviet rocket effort. These were NII-885 (control systems, under Nikolai Pilyugin), NII-944 (gyroscopes, Viktor Kuznetsov), and OKB-456 (engines, Valentin Glushko). OKB is the abbreviation (in Russian, *Opitnoye Konstruktorskoye Biuro*) for special or experimental design bureau. To coordinate these efforts, a Council of Chief Designers was formed in 1946, chaired by Korolev.

Council of Chief Designers, 1946

Valentin Glushko, Chief Designer of Rocket Engines;
Nikolai Pilyugin, Chief Designer of Guidance Systems;
Mikhail Ryazansky, Chief Designer of Radio Control Systems;
Viktor Kuznetsov, Chief Designer of Gyroscopes; and
Vladimir Barmin, Chief Designer of Launch Complexes.

The initiative for forming this Council of Chief Designers appears to have been Korolev. His purpose was to link their work more effectively with that of his own division within NII-88.

A launch site was located. An isolated place near a railhead was sought—isolated because it was not a public programme and because failures should not crash down on populated areas. The railhead was essential because the Russian transport system was based entirely on rail, not road. Another consideration was a place where there would be good launching conditions—sunny, cloudless skies in other words. A point was selected on a bend in the river Volga in the south east. It was later called the Volgograd station (the nearest large city was Volgograd, then Stalingrad), but was closest to the small town of Kapustin Yar (in translation the words mean 'cabbage patch').

The Peenemünde Germans were split into different design groups. They were never integrated into the main Soviet design teams. They checked the Russian designs and double-checked the theoretical findings. Their work was mostly done by correspondence and they met their opposite numbers infrequently. Helmut Grötrupp did attend the subsequent launches at Kapustin Yar. They were packed home in 1952–3. Grötrupp was given passage to the west: the Americans interrogated him and offered him a contract in their rocket programme. His wife was adamant they would not leave the German Democratic Republic (GDR, or East Germany), so they stayed there. Grötrupp found work in electronics and computers, devised a machine to count bank notes, and died of cancer not long afterwards.

In a reversal of their wartime roles, Korolev became effectively the chief designer at this time—he was made responsible for the tests of the A-4—while Glushko was relegated to giving lectures to students at Kazan University and the Bauman Institute in Moscow.

FIRST ROCKET TESTS

Two years after the end of the war in Europe, the Soviet Union was close to testing Germany's rockets. The prospects of rocket development were assessed at a conference held in the Kremlin on 14 April 1947. After the meeting, Korolev met Stalin for the first time. The German rockets were fired from Kapustin Yar that autumn. Russia's A-4 tests did everything expected of them. The first one to be tested went up in October 1947 and flew 281 km. About 20 were fired altogether.

After the first batch of A-4s were dispatched, Korolev developed an improved version based on the A-4 called the R-1 short-range ballistic missile, (R for *raketa*, the Russian word for rocket). The first successful flight of the R-1 was 18 October 1948, an unsuccessful attempt having been made the previous 17 September. The North Atlantic Treaty Organization (NATO) called the R-1 the SS-1, or Skunner. Its RD-100 engine burned for 65 sec, the rocket impacting 300 km downrange. On 7 May 1949, a nosecone was separated for an independent landing. An improved version, the R-2, called Sibling by NATO, was introduced over 1949–52.

In 1951, Korolev completed the design of a single-stage, long-range ballistic rocket, the R-3. With a weight of 72 tonnes, it was designed to fly 3000 km. Korolev also calculated that three R-3s, grouped together, had just enough power to put a small satellite into orbit. However, he did not receive approval to build the rocket.

By 1953, Korolev had built the first rocket of wholly Soviet design, the R-5. The R-5 missile was first launched on 15 March 1953, with a range of 1200 km and was designed to carry a nuclear warhead. Like the A-4, the R-5A used alcohol and liquid oxygen. The take-off thrust was 43.8 tonnes. A modified version, the R-5M, was used to carry a nuclear warhead and was first tested in 1955, going into service with the rocket corps in 1956. Much later, geophysical versions were the R-5A (1958–61), R-5B and R-5V, also known as the Vertikal (1964–75).

FIRST FLIGHTS OF ANIMALS

At this stage, one of the most important themes of the Russian space programme emerges: the nature of its purpose. Korolev was sent to Kapustin Yar to develop rockets which would carry nuclear payloads. However, Korolev's real interest was human travel and the exploration of near-Earth space. He and his colleagues took advantage of the rockets the military required him to develop in order to begin the first scientific experiments. To do this, he built links with the scientific community, especially the Soviet Academy of Sciences and with its cooperation proceeded with atmospheric sounding and physiological flights. The atmospheric flights were supervised by A Blagonravov, head of the USSR Academy of Sciences Committee for the Study of the Upper Layers of the Atmosphere, and assisted by Norair Sisakyan. The R-1 was adapted for high-altitude sounding rockets carrying a basic scientific payload. These were called the *akademik* tests, because they were for academic, scientific purposes. There were five versions, the A, B, V, D, E, after the first letters of the Cyrillic alphabet. This was done by fitting two 65 kg payload containers to the side of the rocket. In 1949, two flights were made to 102 km. The V-1B, 1950–1, had a side-mounted payload which came off at 65 km and a top, finned payload, which came off at 100 km. The V-1E, in 1955, carried a 1819 kg payload of scientific instruments. On 16 May 1957, a V-2A reached an altitude of 200 km, taking pictures in space and measuring the chemical composition of the atmosphere. On 21 February 1958, the V-5A, 23.74 m high, reached 480 km. In its 1350 kg cone were animals and instruments for measuring pressure, micrometeorites, and air pressure.

The ballistic rockets also provided the first opportunities to examine what the early stages of space flight would be like, in particular the effects of vibration, noise, brief spells of weightlessness, acceleration and deceleration. Some test animals had to be selected. There was a lengthy debate as to what sort of animals would fly in space and which would be able to give the most accurate prediction as to how humans might respond. Rabbits, mice, reptiles, all were considered. Eventually the rocketeers settled on dogs. Canines had the advantage of being small in size and weight. They had to be even-tempered, and mongrels were chosen in preference to purebreds. Twenty-four dogs were selected by Korolev's teams of zoologists. They were given exhaustive tests in small capsules, in aircraft, in vibration chambers and in centrifuges. Eventually they were fired aloft. Initially they were in pressurized cabins. Then they were fitted with spacesuits and helmets. On some missions, the dogs were flown in their spacesuits but in exposed, unpressurized cabins. Cameras in the nosecone filmed their reactions to the strains and stresses of liftoff.

Some early flights by animals on ballistic missions, 1958–9

26 May 1955	Flight by two dogs
1 Jun 1956	Flight by two dogs
7 Jun 1956	Flight by two dogs
14 Jun 1956	Flight by two dogs
22 Jun 1956	Flight by two dogs
20 Jul 1956	Flight by two dogs
20 Dec 1956	Flight by two dogs
16 May 1957	Flight by two dogs
21 Feb 1958	V15A reaches altitude of 480km with animals on board
19 Sep 1958	Flight by two dogs
31 Oct 1958	Flight by two dogs
23 Dec 1958	Flight by two dogs
2 Jul 1959	Dogs Otvazhnaya and Snezhinka, rabbit Marfusha recovered from 'a great height'
10 Jul 1959	Flight by two dogs
13 Jul 1959	Two dogs recovered, including Otvazhnaya on second mission
29 Aug 1959	Dogs Belanka and Pyostraya recovered from height of 448 km
15 Jun 1960	Flight by two dogs and one rabbit
24 Jun 1960	Flight by two dogs
16 Sep 1960	Flight by two dogs
22 Dec 1960	Flight by two dogs

160 ascents took place between 1949 and 1960. In the first phase, 1949–52, involving six dogs, these rockets reached heights of 96 km, and in the later stages, 192 km. In the second phase, 1952–5, higher altitudes were reached. The most important animal ballistic tests were carried out during the third phase, 1958–60. The first systematic recruitment of dogs took place during this period. Zoologists and other specialists scoured Moscow for suitable dogs. According to one historian, phone calls were made to dog owners, and a number of mongrels were procured, either through purchase or 'by other means'. Seventeen dogs were trained for these flights. Some of these—Albina, Kozyavka, Malyshka and Tsyganka—made more than one flight. Others, such as Laika, Strelka, Belka, Chernushka and Zvedochka, later made orbital flights. These experiments gave the USSR valuable data: the dogs experienced g forces of 5 g. The dogs were filmed in flight, and their changing medical conditions were monitored. Flight times of 600 s provided weightlessness for up to 370 sec.[6]

CONCEPTS FOR AN EARTH SATELLITE

By the time Stalin died in 1953, the Soviet Union had developed indigenous rockets which far exceeded the performance of Germany's wartime A-4. The preliminary experiments that would test the physiological aspects of ascent through the atmosphere had also been conducted. The next logical step was to place a small Earth satellite into orbit. Despite the theoretical writings made in the Soviet Union in the 1920s and 1930s, most of these had concentrated on much more ambitious manned flights. Much less work had been done on the no less essential earlier steps which must be taken.

In 1953, the situation was similar in the United States. The Americans had also conducted A-4 tests, in White Sands, New Mexico. There, too, only a few studies were available about early small Earth satellites. Most had been made independent of one another. In 1945 the American Navy Bureau of Aeronautics had carried out a preliminary study of an artificial Earth satellite, as did the US Army Air Force in 1946. The RAND Organisation in 1948 suggested that satellites could demonstrate a nation's technological and political superiority. A more precise study was made by the British Interplanetary Society (BIS) in 1951, when a paper entitled 'Minimum satellite vehicles' was read out at one of its meetings . A small payload, put up by a three-stage rocket, was proposed.

Little, if any, of this came to public notice at the time, even though the RAND study was released by the Secretary of State for Defense. In fact, America's space effort would have remained dormant for many years but for the intervention of, ironically, a Russian emigré and nephew of the composer Rachmaninoff. Alexander Satin was Chief Engineer to the Office of Naval Research in Washington DC (ONR). He had a general brief of keeping up to date with technological developments. Satellites aroused his curiosity, no more, and he arrived in London one foggy night in November 1952. He located Arthur C Clarke, a leading authority in the BIS, to discuss the society's paper on minimum satellite vehicles. This paper was critical, for it bridged the gap between the fantasies of the space dreamers with their large-wheeled space stations and what the rockets of the day were actually capable of achieving. The BIS satellite was deliberately small. When Satin brought the paper to von Braun, the German reckoned that existing military hardware, if suitably modified, could get a 2.2 kg payload up to orbit and no further.

Satin spent the next two years working hard trying to persuade his colleagues to accept some kind of minimum satellite scheme. The admirals were brought round. The ONR was brought round. The Defense Department was persuaded. Project Orbiter was born. This was to be Wernher von Braun's project. He would convert the US Army's existing Redstone rocket, add solid propellant upper stages, and a 7 kg satellite which could make it to orbit. Von Braun and Satin's Orbiter project combined maximum use of existing hardware and the greatest possible speed.

President Eisenhower gave his approval to Project Orbiter on 15 July 1955. The satellite would probably have got into orbit within 18 months had a subsection of the same Office of Naval Research not intervened. Its own Naval Research Laboratory (NRL) persuaded the Secretary of State for Defense (who in turn persuaded Eisenhower) to adopt instead its own project called 'Vanguard'. Vanguard would also be a small satellite. It would be based on the Viking rocket, a descendant of the A-4; an Aerobee second stage; and a new third stage. It would be much more sophisticated than the Redstone. The advantages were that it used new technology and could be dressed up as a civilian rather than military project. The disadvantage—not then apparent—was that it would take time. President Eisenhower approved Vanguard in place of Project Orbiter on 9 September 1955. But the Americans were too late.

IDEA OF AN EARTH SATELLITE IN RUSSIA

A similar, though speedier, combination of factors brought about the construction of the first Earth satellite in Russia. These were the order by the military for an intercontinental ballistic missile, one which could deliver a nuclear warhead to the United States; a growing level of interest in the idea of an Earth satellite within the USSR Academy of Sciences and the scientific community; and Korolev's ability to take advantage of both to make progress in space exploration.

The A-4 rocket and its Soviet descendants, the R-1 to R-5, had only limited potential and could deliver nuclear warheads across land masses (nowadays these are termed medium-range ballistic missiles (MRBMs)). As the cold war intensified, Stalin ordered construction of the hydrogen bomb and a rocket which could deliver it on its superpower adversary (intercontinental ballistic missiles, or ICBMs). In December 1950, Korolev's OKB-1 was ordered to design a new rocket, much larger than the R-3, the seventh in his series, and which was labelled the R-7. It is worth saying a little about the R-7, not only because it launched the first satellite, but because its descendants, the Soyuz, the Molniya and the Rus, were the mainstay of the space programme for the next 50 years.

The R-7 had a central core with an RD-108 engine and four chambers (designed by Glushko) which burned at liftoff. Korolev's achievement was to add no less than four strap-on units to the side of the rocket, each with an RD-107 engine with four chambers (the central core is called the second stage, or block A; the strap-ons, the first stage, or blocks B, V, G and D). The use of strap-on rockets later surprised western observers, but it should not have, for the idea was well explored by Tsiolkovsky. A preliminary design of a modern system of clustered rockets was made by Mikhail Tikhonravov in 1947.[7] Thus no fewer than 20 nozzles burned simultaneously at liftoff. At a certain altitude the strap-ons came off and the central unit, the core, brought the payload into orbit. Mass production of the rocket was possible once its basic reliability was verified. Korolev designed the R-7 to have a total thrust of 600 000 kg and an orbital payload of 1350 kg. The R-7 was delivered to the pad horizontally on a huge railcar. It then tilted upwards to the vertical at the pad itself and was set in the restraining arms of the pad. It was then fuelled. A minute from launch the arms swung back and off it went.

Within the Academy of Sciences, the idea of an Earth satellite was aired from 1951 onward. The Academy of Sciences had little formal role within the power structure of the Soviet space industry, but it had significant influence in setting agendas, and was later frequently called in to offer opinions on competing space designs and proposals. In October 1951 Mikhail Tikhonravov declared that the creation of an Earth satellite was 'feasible'. On 27 November 1953, Alexander Nesmeyanov, President of the Academy of Sciences, announced that a satellite was 'a real possibility'. In 1954, Korolev wrote in a scientific journal the case for work to begin on an artificial Earth satellite:

> In my view it would be timely and advisable at this present moment to organize
> a research division to pioneer a satellite and more thoroughly analyze the range
> of related problems.

On 9 January 1955, a group of scientists, inspired by Korolev's paper, met to promote the project. They persuaded the Presidium of the Academy of Sciences to mail several hundred scientists the following terse instructions:

> Please comment on the use of artificial Earth satellites. What do you think they
> could carry? What experiments do you think could be conducted ?

The answers varied. Some were positive, some negative. Some said they would be no use at all. 'Fantasy: I visualize a space shot in the year 2000' was one reply.

It seems in retrospect that neither the Academy of Sciences nor their political decision-makers were much interested in replies: they had already made up their minds. On 15 April 1955, the Academy of Sciences set up a permanent commission on interplanetary travel, and gave this body, with such an all-embracing title, the modest task of developing an Earth satellite. A week later a team of design scientists was formed. Events began to move with increasing rapidity.

The final go-ahead was given at a closed meeting held in the Academy of Sciences in Moscow on 30 August 1955. Present were delegates of the Central Committee of the Communist party of the Soviet Union and on the scientific side, Sergei Korolev, Mstislav Keldysh and Valentin Glushko. Korolev promised that the new launcher would be ready in one to one-and-a- half years. 'We must not lose time', he said. His life's dream was nearing fulfilment.

The Soviet government immediately authorized the academy to develop a programme for artificial satellites and appointed Mstislav Keldysh as its chairman. Mstislav Keldysh (1911–1978) was an important personality in the early Soviet space programme. Born in Riga, Latvia in 1911, he was the son of VM Keldysh (1878–1965), chief engineer of the Moscow canal, the Moscow metro and the Dniepr Aluminium Plant. Young Mstislav entered Moscow University in 1931, becoming professor there before moving to the Central Institute for Aerohydrodynamics, TsAGI. In 1953, he became Director of the Institute of Applied Mathematics at the Academy of Sciences, where he developed the computer and calculating programmes that were essential to map the trajectories of the first satellites and for which he was justly awarded the Lenin prize in 1957. He became Vice-President of the Academy of Sciences in 1960 and its President from 1961 to 1975.

Korolev proceeded to design the satellite. Since his R-7 could lift over a tonne, he devised a large scientific observatory weighing over a tonne, called object D. His plan was approved on 30 January 1956.

BAIKONOUR COSMODROME

Already, on 31 May 1955, the first sod had been turned on the USSR's first purpose-built cosmodrome and space centre. That was probably too glamorous a title at the time—the construction workers lived in tents, shacks and caravans, and that was about all they had to start with. The decision to build a new cosmodrome had been taken in 1954. Thirty construction workers arrived on 12 January 1955. Supervisor of the project was Vladimir Barmin.

There were several reasons for the move from Kapustin Yar. First, it was too near to the Turkish border. American radar and listening posts installed there knew virtually everything that was going on. Second, the USSR needed a large new rocket pad for Korolev's forthcoming intercontinental R-7. Third, from the point of view of getting satellites into orbit, southerly locations were desirable. Baikonour was about as near to the equator as the USSR could get, and that was worth a 4% payload bonus compared to launching from Kapustin Yar.

So a new site was decided on at Tyuratam. The area designated for rocket development was adjacent to the Moscow–Tashkent railway line. German military maps from 1939 show that a British mining company once ran a railhead north-east from Tyuratam. It is a place of harsh climates. Metres of snow cover the steppe in winter from October to March. The winds howl and blizzards are frequent. In summer there is a long scorching desert heat and the ground is bleak yellow and stony brown. Only in April is it attractive, when the snow melts and the flowers thrust their way upward and blossom for their all-too-short days. Tyuratam had been used by the Tsars as a place of exile and in 1830 they had exiled there one Nikifor Nikitin for 'making seditious speeches about flying to the Moon'. And they called the new cosmodrome 'Baikonour'.

The name Baikonour was the first of many deceits of the early Soviet space programme. The new cosmodrome was a long way from Baikonour. The real Baikonour was a small mining town 370 km to the north-east. The deceit was a diversion to fool the Americans: if war broke out and the American missiles rained down on the real Baikonour they would be annihilating territory far from the real rocket base. All this time, the real Baikonour was, and remained what it is today, a sleepy railhead. In the event, it seems that the Americans were fooled for a few months at best.

The first thing the construction teams did was to run a spur off the old Tyuratam railway in a triangular shape 19 km north into the wasteland. It was flat, scrubby land with occasional bushes and grasses. Construction of the first launch pad, involving the digging of the launch pit, began in August 1955 and the first concrete was poured on 4 April 1956. The first engineers started with picks, shovels and their bare hands even. In the summer it was roasting hot and they must have lain out at night astride the old caravan routes to the east, gazing upwards to the stars that their descendants would one day reach from the launch sites they were building.

Two years after they started, the first stage of building was completed. An airport had been laid out beside Tyuratam; a large and long hangar-like assembly bay had been constructed; and a launch pad for the R-7 was completed on 4 March 1957. At the time, the pad was one of the world's largest engineering achievements. The foundation pit was 45 m deep, 250 m long, and 100 m wide—the 'biggest hole in the world', its designers believed.

Although Baikonour was the test site for the R-7, the first real base for the R-7 was far to the north. By joint resolution of the party and government on 11 January 1957 (resolution 61-39), codenamed Angara, the order was given to construct a four-pad missile base at Lake Plestsy on the Arctic Circle, to be in the best possible position to launch missiles over the North Pole toward the United States. The first launch pad went on combat duty in January 1960, the others following in July 1961.

Although during the American presidential campaign of 1960 there were allegations by the Kennedy camp of a missile gap and that Russia had hundreds, if not thousands, of ICBMs; in fact, the R-7 represented for many years the totality of the Soviet nuclear strike force. As an ICBM, the R-7 was quite unsuitable, easy to spot from the air, taking hours to fuel and fire. The military long argued with Khrushchev against the R-7, but his view was that it was the only missile available. Eventually, orders were given to Mikhail Yangel's design bureau to build a less visible rocket which could be readied more quickly.

Cosmodromes, location

Name and location	Date founded
Kapustin Yar, near Volgograd	First flight, October 1947
Baikonour, Tyuratam	First sod turned, 31 May 1955
Plesetsk, near Archangel	Party and government resolution, 11 January 1957

KHRUSHCHEV

The success of the Soviet space programme in its early years was very much due to two very different men with two very different purposes. Korolev was, as has been seen, a designer and visionary committed to the conquest of space. Khrushchev had other purposes. Nikita Khrushchev ruled the USSR from 1957 to 1964, seven brief years which are well remembered beyond what such a relatively short time span might merit. Nikita Khrushchev was short, fat, alternately angry and then wearing a giant grin from ear to ear, a man of cunning and short temper. While no liberal, he wanted to take the USSR out of the darkness of the Stalin era.

Khrushchev was both ambitious and adventurous. He believed the USSR could overtake and surpass America's rate of industrial and technological progress. The USSR had to be a superpower visibly equal to the United States. Visibility was all-important to Khrushchev, and if it reflected on him personally, all the better. He was attracted to large projects, like the ploughing up of the virgin lands, designed to produce a surge in agricultural production; like the Aswan High Dam in Egypt; and the space programme.

Korolev introduced Khrushchev to the R-7 in 1955. Khrushchev was awed:

> We gawked at what he showed us as if we were a bunch of sheep seeing a gate for the first time. We were like peasants at a market place. We walked round the rocket, touching it, tapping it to see if it was sturdy enough.

A space rocket combined Khrushchev's demand for visible progress and achievement as well as excitement in its own right. And, what also helped, the two men got on well together.

R-7 in silhouette

PREPARING FOR FLIGHT

By this stage, the R-7 was almost ready, but the 1.5-tonne scientific observatory was not. In December 1956, Korolev shelved his plans for the one-tonne observatory (ultimately this became Sputnik 3) and decided instead to develop the most simple design possible. He called it the PS (preliminary satellite), though his team called it the SP (after Sergei Pavlovich). In effect, the PS was little more than a radio transmitter in a spherical steel ball. Four whiplash aerials streamed out behind. The design team debated what sort of transmitter to use—a real issue when no one knew whether the Earth's atmosphere would distort transmissions. Korolev was adamant that the signals should be received by as many people as possible, including amateurs. He opted for one on a traditional waveband, 7.5 m and the other on 15 m, which he hoped could be received over wide distances. A further problem was that no one had ever built suitable antennæ before and no one in Korolev's bureau knew how to do so. So they asked the Moscow Institute for Education, where some technical students built the four antennæ—two short and two long. Lead designer of the Sputnik, under Korolev, was Yevgeni Frolov.

The Russians made no secret of their intentions of launching an Earth satellite. The day after Eisenhower announced Vanguard, the USSR too announced that it would put up a satellite. At the VIth International Astronautical Federation Congress in Copenhagen, Soviet delegates appeared for the first time, led by Leonid Sedov, Chairman of the Academy of Sciences Commission on Interplanetary Communications. He confirmed that a satellite would be launched—and within two years. A large new rocket launcher would be used. Soon after, a colleague, AG Karpenko, was reported in *Pravda* as saying that two satellites would be launched. One would fly between 200 and 1000 km, the other between 1516 and 2000 km.

On 6 March 1957, Radio Moscow confirmed that the first satellite would be small, spherical and weigh about 50 kg. The June 1957 issue of *Radio* magazine published full details of PS, emphasizing its radio transmission system. On 18 September 1957, Radio Moscow confirmed that the launching was coming soon. It was the centenary of Tsiolkovsky's birth.[8]

ALMOST READY

Meanwhile, back at the cosmodrome, things were going far from well. The Central Committee had only authorized building of the R-7 and the satellite—it insisted on final approval before anything actually happened. This nearly did not come. The R-7 had its first static tests in Zagorsk (now Sergiyev Posad) in the summer of 1956. The first version arrived at Tyuratam in December. The first R-7 was brought out to its pad on 5 May 1957. It lifted off on 15 May and crashed 50 s later. On 9 June, the second exploded on its pad. The third failed on 12 July. Korolev feared severe criticism, and other scientists began to demand his job: 'You think we are building ordinary machines? Or that only American Atlases explode?', he retorted.

Korolev was not an easy man to work with. Years later, top aide Konstantin Gringauz recalled: 'He was strong-willed and passionate. During meetings he often shouted and banged the table. But he never meant any harm: he just wanted to get the job done. He was able to build up strong teams and always insisted on the maximum scientific return.'[9] Finally, on 3 August 1957, Korolev's third R-7 was fuelled up. It flew. It went 6500 km and came down in the Pacific Ocean off the Kamchatka peninsular. A second suborbital test was made on 7 September. The USSR had the ICBM, and Korolev had something that could launch his satellite. The successful test was officially announced by the USSR later that month.

The countdown had begun. On 16 September 1957, Korolev addressed the 100th anniversary meeting of the birth of Konstantin Tsiolkovsky in Moscow's trade union house. Visibly excited, he told the audience that test satellites would be launched soon. But there was no reaction from the impassive audience, who seemed unable to take in what he was saying.[10]

On 20 September, Korolev left the design bureau in Moscow for Baikonour by aircraft. He lived at the launch site for the next two weeks in a small wooden-framed house in a wood. It was a ten-minute walk to the launch pad in one direction, a ten minute walk to the assembly building in the other.

Several days later, work was finally completed. In the huge assembly building, like a giant aircraft hangar, the time had come to fix the Preliminary Satellite into the nose-cone of the R-7 booster. The giant rocket, on its side and cradled by the rail-car, loomed and filled the room. At the front of the hangar were Korolev, the designers and engineers in their white coats.

A crane lifted the Preliminary Satellite into its grappling hook. The small glinting silver sphere was guided into the nosecone. The crane halted in the dim hall. Engineer Konstantin Gringauz gave the signal to the transmitter. And in the huge echo-filled room the 'beep beep beep' sound boomed off the walls. It would be the last time its signals would be heard on Earth. A contact was plugged into the satellite, and the beeping ceased abruptly. The contact was designed to be broken again only when the satellite reached orbit.

2 October. The starry darkness of a southern Russian night. The massive steel doors of the assembly building groaned open. The polished nozzles of the rocket were cold grey in the night. The railcar creaked its slow way down to the pad.

3 October. Sputnik was on the pad. One day to go. The sun blazed autumn sunshine over the bare steppe as the booster was fuelled up. As the day wore on the liquid oxygen began to boil off and cold compressed air had to be doused on the booster to cool it off. Korolev climbed the service tower to inspect his rocket for the last time.

4 October. Several attempts to count the rocket down failed. There were exasperating delays. The Sun set and it had turned dark when Korolev decided on one last attempt. With a white lab coat covering him he took his place in the underground command bunker 100 m from the rocket itself, protected by steel doors and thick reinforced concrete.

He waited, microphone in hand, watching through a submarine-style periscope. Not far from the final minutes of the count, a lone bugler, identity still unknown, ventured onto the concrete apron and blew a long series of trumpet blasts before vanishing. His long tones resounded around the pad and the booster bathed silently in floodlights in the background.

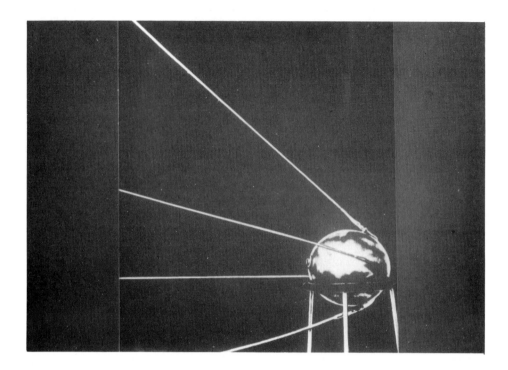

The Preliminary Satellite 1 (PS 1), Sputnik 1

Finally it happened. Blinding flames shot out through the trench. Clouds of vapour surrounded the rocket. Its body quivered and it began to rise. It dazzled and deafened the watchers, and lit up the periscopes and the bunkers and service towers for miles around. Twenty separate chambers fired in unison.

The R-7, with the precious PS in its cone, rose rapidly and ever more rapidly. It headed off into the night sky in the north-east, and became more and more blurred and hard to follow as each second passed. The strap-on boosters peeled away and dropped silently down to oblivion. Soon it was nothing but a speck in the night sky, just one of a million constellations. It was well after midnight, 10.30 pm by the Kremlin clock tower. The launch team clapped and cheered wildly. All had gone well, but there was no way of telling for sure. Just 50 km/h too little energy and the sputnik would tumble to Earth after a mere half hour's flight.

There was only one way to know, and that involved a wait of 90 minutes. When the sputnik had completed its first orbit it would be back over the launch site. Its transmitter should then be working with its familiar 'beep beep beep' characteristic: if the sound was heard, success would be total. Silence would mean failure, and the reason would perhaps never be known.

Korolev, the scientists, designers, engineers and launch team returned from the launch site in the bus and gathered outside the assembly hangar. They held their breaths and listened. Loudspeakers had been rigged to the satellite receiver.

Against the infinite crackle of radio space it came. An audible, distinct and clear 'beep beep beep' was heard—there was no mistaking it! It must have been an exhilarating moment. The joy and elation were total. Korolev was carried to an improvised speaker's platform. A squat, firm, square and thickset figure, Korolev's normal sternness broke down. He summoned exhausted energies, and, eyes-aflashing, spoke:

> The conquering of space has begun. Today we have witnessed the realization of a dream nurtured by some of the finest minds who ever lived. Our outstanding scientist, Tsiolkovsky, brilliantly foretold that mankind would not forever remain on the Earth. This satellite is the first confirmation of his prophecy. We can be proud this was begun by our country.

PS began circling the Earth every 95 min between 228 and 947 km. A few days later, the engineers involved took the long train journey back to Moscow. They were astonished to find that wherever they went, people could do nothing but talk about the Sputnik.

REACTION

Khrushchev reacted casually at first. Later he recounted that when Korolev phoned him and told him that PS was in orbit, he, Khrushchev, congratulated him and the engineers involved and calmly went to bed.

That was not the reaction in the West. The satellite story was reported quietly at first, but grew as each day passed and its impact set in. The British Broadcasting Corporation (BBC) reported the satellite's launch with a peculiar mixture of astonishment, bemusement and uncertainty, not knowing how to cope with this new-found event:

> Moscow radio has announced within the past half hour that Russia has successfully launched an earth satellite. It is going round the earth in an elliptical trajectory at a height of about 560 miles. The launching was part of Russia's geophysical year programme.

The satellite was called Sputnik, the Russian word for 'companion'. The effect it produced in the United States varied between shock and panic. Subsequent surveys revealed that within months nearly all Americans had heard of Sputnik and that most people perceived that it conferred an advantage on the USSR and a disadvantage on the United States. Press reaction discussed Sputnik in terms of American prestige, and its scientific and military reputation being at stake. The transmitters which Korolev worried about exceeded their expectations and could be heard 12 000 km away, so that in no time, Sputnik had been heard by radio listeners and seen by sky-watchers. Watching for, or listening to, the Sputnik was a world-wide event, and newspapers gave predictions of its passes.

Virtually alone in not being swept along in this atmosphere of shock, fear and humiliation were the senior politicians of the Washington administration. President Eisenhower said:

> One small ball in the air does not raise my apprehensions, not one iota. We must...find ways of affording perspective to our people and so relieve the current wave of near hysteria.

Lyndon Johnson, the opposition Democratic Party's Congressional leader, did not see things that way at all. He heard the news of Sputnik at his ranch in Texas, and he had wires humming to Washington within the hour. Of course there was an element of political opportunism in Johnson: Sputnik was an easy stick with which to beat the administration and a complacent and ever more ineffective Eisenhower presidency. But Johnson was also motivated by what he saw as a threat to America's national security; by a belief in technology; and by a belief that America must always be first in everything. Johnson had nearly always voted for anything the military had wanted and took an equally generous view of the need for military research. He had tried to persuade the Pentagon to set up a space programme as far back as 1949.

Johnson set up a Congressional 'Preparedness Committee'. The title told it all. For the next six months, Johnson called a parade of scientists, generals and industrialists to testify to America's lack of preparedness. The administration was blamed, as were the schools and higher education.

ASSESSMENT

The Soviet space programme had a strong theoretical base. Unlike the efforts of their colleagues in the West, Soviet rocketeers found quick support from their government for military, political and scientific reasons. The Russians were quick to learn from, and apply the lessons of, German wartime rocketry. A combination of timely organization, military imperatives, scientific interest and the personalities of Korolev and Khrushchev gave the USSR an early lead in space exploration.

2

The golden years of Soviet rocketry

It is the task of the society to work for the achievement of flights beyond the atmo-sphere using reactive devices which are fundamentally sound.
    Charter of the Society for the Study of Interplanetary Communication, 1924.

Immediately after Sputnik 1, Korolev and his closest comrades travelled to the Crimea for a short rest. They had barely settled in when Khrushchev was on the phone, demanding a space spectacular for the 40th anniversary of the October revolution—only three weeks away! Thinking quickly, Korolev offered to put an animal and space. Khrushchev agreed, Korolev hurried back and the entire Sputnik 2 project was conceived and executed in less than three weeks. There were no 'designs' for Sputnik 2—only a few rough sketches. They used an analogue of Sputnik 1, attached a container used from the geophysical flights of the previous year and added a cosmic ray detector.[11] Even the animal was a veteran of previous ballistic flights.

On 9 October *Pravda* warned that:

> The Soviet Union will launch a sputnik carrying animals as passengers. De-tailed observations will be made of their behaviour.

On 3 November 1957, Sputnik 2 was duly launched. It weighed no less than 508 kg, five times more than its predecessor. The dog, Laika, was known for her even-tempered-ness. She was put in a harness inside the small pressurized cabin covered with soft mate-rial. There were widespread protests from dog lovers in the West over the mission. Offi-cially, Laika suffered no ill-effects from weightlessness and she died a week later when the air ran out. In reality, the insulation of Sputnik 2 came free at orbital insertion. Tempera-tures in Sputnik 2 must have risen rapidly, causing Laika to die painfully.

For the Americans, Sputnik 2 only added to the shock inflicted by Sputnik 1. Its size, the presence of an animal on board, the high altitude of the orbit (225 by 1671 km), the fact that it came only 30 days after the first launch—all these facts underlined the enormity of the Soviet lead. Although few people said so at the time, the flight of an animal could only mean the serious intention of putting a man into orbit, sooner or later.

By now, both Sputnik 1 and 2 were observable from the ground as small pinpoints of light crossing the sky just after dusk and just before dawn. Sputnik 1 made over 1400 revolutions over a period of 90 days before it burned up. Much was learnt about air density at Sputnik's altitude and how soon it would cause a satellite to slow down and burn up. Sputnik 2 was much easier to spot from the ground, since the rocket remained attached to the satellite. In its final orbits the cylinder turned end over end and flashed as a bright beacon in the night sky until it was incinerated. Sputnik 2 burnt up in April 1958 after 163 days and 2370 revolutions.

Both Sputniks had by then long since eclipsed the flagging American space programme. The Johnson hearings—which as coincidence had it, opened just after Sputnik 2—gathered momentum and heard warnings that became more and more apocalyptical each passing day, warnings that were exacerbated by the humiliating first American attempt to launch a satellite.

The slow but technically ambitious Vanguard programme eventually found its way to the launch pad at Cape Canaveral, Florida, on 6 December 1957. The countdown reached zero, the pencil-shaped rocket lifted off and for a brief intoxicating second it looked as if America might get a satellite into space in the same year as its rivals. But the joy lasted only an instant, for two seconds into the flight the thrust collapsed. Vanguard fell back on its pad and disappeared in an enormous cloud of smoke as it exploded like one of the old airship disasters. The tiny capsule was flung free of the holocaust on the pad. Pad personnel found it with its aerials sticking out of the sand in a nearby Florida beach, its radio chirping away, until someone put it out of its misery. The Kremlin offered its condolences. The press labelled it alternately Kaputnik, Flopnik, and Stayputnik.

This final humiliation galvanized the administration in Washington into action. Von Braun and his army team were given permission to launch their original satellite, for which they had sought approval in 1955 and which they could have put up in 1956. The Redstone–Jupiter C was made ready with a small pencil-shaped satellite on top, weighing 14 kg. The von Braun rocket rose flawlessly into the night sky on 31 January 1958. Not only that, it was a stunning scientific success. With a single geiger counter on board it discovered that the Earth had huge radiation belts around it, which were called the Van Allen belts, after the scientist involved.

SPUTNIK 3

More than this belated success was needed to expunge the memory of Sputnik. The ill-fated Vanguard project experienced further failures and did not know success until 17 March 1958, when Vanguard 1 achieved orbit. It was one of the smallest satellites ever launched—1 kg. By this stage, the Johnson hearings had nearly run their course. The timing was more than helpful to him: he had begun his own presidential campaign in January 1958. In his angriest Texan drawl, he summed up:

> The Roman Empire controlled the world because it could build roads. Later when men moved to sea, the British Empire was dominant because it had ships. Now the communists have established a foothold in space.

Already Johnson was seeing Sputnik in global and historical terms. If the USSR was going to take the high road to space, then so too would the United Sates, guided of course by the senior senator from Texas.

As if to add a riposte to Johnson's counter-attack, the USSR put up Sputnik 3 on 15 May 1958. This was Korolev's original plan for an Earth satellite, object D, though a first attempt had gone disastrously wrong on 27 April, the rocket exploding 88 s after launch. It was powered by solar cells and batteries, and orbited from 226 to 1880 km every 106 min. Sputnik 3 was shaped as a silvery shining perfect cone with aerials and protuberances. It returned information on micrometeorites, the Earth's radiation belts, cosmic rays, solar radiation, the density of the upper atmosphere and the effect of high energy particles. Well might Khrushchev deride Vanguard 1 as a mere 'grapefruit'.

Sputnik 3 was timed to coincide with parliamentary elections in Italy: Khrushchev hoped its success would impress voters to the point that they would vote for the communist party. As a result, the launching was rushed, even though the spacecraft's tape recorder had been giving trouble. The tape recorder duly failed in orbit, which meant that ground controllers received signals only when Sputnik 3 was in line with ground stations—there was no means of storing information collected during earlier parts of each orbit. As a result, although Sputnik 3 detected radiation belts, it had no means of storing and transmitting data about their extent. Credit for exploring the belts thus went to the Americans.[12] Sputnik 3 made 10 037 revolutions of the Earth, eventually burning up in 1960 after 691 days of flight.

First Russian Earth satellites

Sputnik	14 Oct 1957
Sputnik 2	3 Nov 1957
Failure	27 Apr 1958
Sputnik 3	15 May 1958

OFF TO THE MOON!

Khrushchev never attended a space launch, but he was well able to notice the consternation that the first three sputniks produced abroad and the public satisfaction evident at home. The impression spread of a thrusting Soviet technology under the progressive and efficient leadership of Nikita Khrushchev. He pressed Korolev to produce more spectacular spaceshots. Korolev was happy to oblige—indeed it enabled him to move faster and further than he could otherwise have imagined. More and more facilities and budgets were made available to him, and he became director of Special Design Bureau 1, OKB-1.

What was the next step? Mikhail Tikhonravov suggested that, by the addition of a small upper stage of 5000 kg thrust, it would be possible to send small payloads of about half a tonne to the Moon, Mars or Venus. Korolev commissioned Semyon Kosberg's design bureau the task of building the small upper stage. Semyon Kosberg, born in Slutsk in 1903, had come from the Moscow Aviation Institute. In 1941 he had been made chief designer of a bureau which made Red Air Force fighters. Kosberg had run a design bureau for the upper stages of rockets since October 1951. So, in early 1958, Korolev presented 'A programme for the investigation of the Moon'.

In the meantime, by mid-1958 the American programme was showing new signs of life. It took some time for the Americans to turn a disorganized space effort into a coherent rational and planned programme. Three things were to happen. First, the Americans realized in early 1958 that by using their Able booster they too could send very small payloads into space towards the Moon—perhaps before the Russians, if they moved fast enough. Second, a space agency was set up to plan ahead—the National Aeronautics and Space Administration (NASA), which was inaugurated on 1 October 1958. Third, within seven days, it in turn announced a man-in-space programme called Project Mercury. Its objectives were, precisely stated, 'to send a man into orbit, investigate his capabilities and reactions in space and return him safely to the Earth'.

Already a subtle form of space leapfrog had begun to dominate planning. It ran on the lines of: what kind of space activity could one side devise that might get that side ahead, albeit temporarily, of the other?

Korolev's first attempt at the Moon was made on 23 September 1958. It exploded after 92 s. A second failed at 100 s a month later on 12 October. Although launched a few hours after America's Pioneer 1, it would have followed a faster trajectory and reached the Moon first. The third, on 4 December, reached 245 s, when an engine failed.

The American Moon shots of 1958, also hastily put together, were equally disastrous. The probes varied in weight between 6 and 39 kg and were designed to pass close to the Moon. The first one (17 August) blew up after 16 km of flight. The next, called Pioneer 1, reached the then amazing altitude of 113 000 km and fell back to Earth (11 October). Their successors, Pioneer 2 and 3, never got that far.[13]

Despite these mishaps, the probes had a morale-boosting effect on American public opinion. There was huge press coverage. The Cape Canaveral range (all it had been to date was an air force and coastguard station) became part of the American consciousness. Boosters, rockets, countdowns, the Moon, missions—all of these words entered the vocabulary. America was fighting back, and if the missions failed, there were credits for trying.

MECHTA (DREAM)

The New Year was barely two days old when Korolev's third Moon probe left the pad at Tyuratam and hurtled skywards. With apparently effortless ease it achieved escape velocity (40 234 km/h) and headed moonwards. Designated Lunik 1 or *Mechta* ('dream' in Russian), the Moon probe was spherical in shape and weighed 361 kg. It carried instruments for measuring radiation, magnetic fields and meteorites. On 3 January, when 113 000 km out from Earth, Lunik 1 released a golden-orange cloud of sodium gas so that astronomers could track it. It was visible in the sky over the Indian Ocean.

By the second day, it was apparent that Lunik 1 would not hit the Moon as had been planned. On January 4 it passed by at a distance of 5995 km. Lunik 1 went on into orbit around the Sun between the Earth and Mars. En route it found that the Moon had no magnetic field and that the Sun emitted strong flows of ionized plasma—the 'solar wind'.

Lunik 1 was a dramatic start to Moon exploration: it ventured into areas of space never visited before. An unannounced attempt to launch another lunar probe on 18 June 1959 ended disastrously, when the guidance of the R-7 rocket failed.

Russia's third attempt at the Moon, Lunik 1, was the first to actually leave the Earth. It soared past the Moon in January 1959.

HITTING THE MOON

Lunik 2 was sent up on 12 September: it was very similar in design to Lunik 1 and at 390 kg carried similar instrumentation. A sodium vapour cloud released on the 13th told ground observers that its course was dead centre. Korolev and the designers gathered in the control room as Lunik 2 neared the Moon. Signals poured back loud and clear from Lunik 2 against the eternal static of deep space. Then in an instant they were cut short and there was dead silence! Lunik 2 had made it, reached the Moon and impacted onto it at great speed. There was celebration all round.

Lunik 2 hit the Moon just after midnight on 14 September. It was a bull's eye. It crashed somewhere between the craters Archimedes, Aristillus and Autolycus. To the Americans this knife-like precision only added insult to injury. Not that they were given much time to recover. Three weeks later, and on the second anniversary of Sputnik 1, Lunik 3 lifted off the pad. It weighed 434 kg.

CIRCLING THE MOON

The Lunik 3 mission caused mystery at first. Far from taking a rapid course out to the Moon, Lunik 3 swung lazily round the far side after a longer transit time and passed under it at a distance of 6200 km. As it pulled round the far side—that side perpetually turned away from Earth—the Sun angle was behind Lunik and shining on the far side.

It was then that Lunik 3's unique design came into its own. Cylindrically shaped, Lunik 3 carried solar cells for energy, photoelectric cells to orientate one side to the Sun and the other to the Moon, gas jets for stabilization and a transmitter. Lunik 3's cameras whirred into action. For a full 40 minutes the two lenses took 29 pictures of no less than 70% of the far side. These were vistas no human had ever before seen. Although coming less than a month after Lunik 2, the new probe was significantly more sophisticated than its predecessor. Project director was Yuri Mozhorin.

Lunik 3 swung around the Moon, taking a figure-of-eight trajectory back towards the Earth. Its return put it high in the northern sky and in an ideal position for Soviet ground-tracking stations. Lunik 3 was orientated towards Earth and the film was developed on board. The film was developed automatically in a developing unit, dried and wound into a special canister. A television device was brought into play to scan the film. It was then transmitted by radio to the ground.

Seventeen frames were sent. Within days the USSR released the historic first photograph of the Moon's far side. It was hazy and fuzzy, but it gave a bird's eye view of the Moon's hidden side. It was the first time the view from space had ever been presented to people on Earth; and the first time a space probe had ever obtained data that could never have been obtained any other way.

The photographs bore little relationship to the more-detailed maps accumulated during the 1960s, but that did not matter then. Lunik 3 was able to show that the far side was all mountainous, with the exception of two dark mare regions—the Mare Moscovrae and the Mare Desiderii (Moscow Sea, Sea of Dreams).

First Moonshots	
23 Sep 1958	Failure
12 Oct 1958	Failure
4 Dec 1958	Failure
2 Jan 1959	Lunik 1/*Mechta*
18 Jun 1959	Failure
12 Sep 1959	Lunik 2
4 Oct 1959	Lunik 3
15 Apr 1960	Failure
16 Apr 1960	Failure

Disappointingly, attempts to repeat the success of Lunik 3 with two more spacecraft, each carrying higher resolution cameras and making a closer pass to the surface, suffered launch failures on 15 and 16 April 1960. The first entered a highly elliptical orbit; during the second launch, the four strap-on blocks peeled apart, shooting out over the heads of the controllers, shattering the assembly hall and leaving the rails to the pad in a gnarled, tangled mess.

Meanwhile, the unfortunate Americans lurched from one more disaster to another. Pioneer 4 (March 1959), it is true, passed the Moon by 60 000 km, but four Moon probes during 1959–60 failed totally, none even reaching low Earth orbit. If there was indeed a space race, the gap between the two big powers was, if anything, widening. The appearance of a gap was exacerbated by the fact that Russian failures were neither announced nor publicly known.

NEW DESIGN BUREAUX

By this stage, the end of 1959, the space programme had grown in size. As it did so, new design bureaux came into existence. A military rocket design bureau under Mikhail Yangel, OKB-586, had already been set up in Ukraine in 1954 and was now significantly expanded. Yangel's design bureau in fact just pre-dated Korolev (9 May 1951). It was constituted as OKB-586 in April 1954. Yangel was ordered to produce an ICBM in December 1956, the R-16. To maintain the secrecy of the programme, Dniepropetrovsk, where his OKB was located, was closed to foreigners in 1959 and it remained closed until the late 1980s. In August 1960, OKB-586 was ordered to produce a small rocket for scientific payloads, the R-12, or small Cosmos rocket.

In 1959, three more bureaux were established: that of Mikhail Reshetnev for applications satellites; that of Alexei Isayev, for small rocket engines; and that of Dmitri Kozlov for unmanned recoverable spacecraft. Alexei Isayev, born in 1908 in St Petersburg, was a graduate of the Mining Institute in 1932 but worked in the Aviation Institute from 1934. From 1942 he developed rocket engines there, and from 1944 was put in charge of his own OKB.

Within the Ministry of Aviation Research, a new OKB, number 52, had been set up by a talented designer, Vladimir Chelomei, at Reutovo, outside Moscow. Although Vladimir Chelomei (1914–84) had cut his teeth in the 1950s on naval missiles, by the late 1950s he had begun to move into the space programme. He hired Nikita Khrushchev's son, Sergei. Vladimir Chelomei was a salesman. He had eloquence, he had charm, he knew how to read the political system and he invited in not just the grey cardinals but the scientists and the medium-level people for expositions on his space projects—presentations accompanied by mockups, colour charts and design drawings. With Khrushchev's blessing, he soon had the biggest project budget of all the bureaux in the Soviet Union (or, as it was referred to at the time, 'the most expensive mailbox in the Soviet Union', referring to the practice whereby secret installations were known only by postal code numbers). Because many of Chelomei's projects were classified, he never received the same attention, not to mention the posthumous adulation of Sergei Korolev.[14] His role in the Soviet space programme was at least as important and probably more controversial. His imaginative and versatile designs were still flying decades after his death.

Even as the new OKBs became established, Korolev was given new work. He was ordered to design a photoreconnaissance satellite, the Zenith; a generation of interplanetary space probes; and the ultimate assignment of a manned flight into space.

IDEA OF MANNED SPACE FLIGHT

Manned flight was the obvious, next, irresistible stage. A decision on this could not be put off much longer. In the R-7 rocket there existed sufficient rocket power, with a third stage, to put a four-tonne manned spaceship into orbit. Korolev had been working on possible designs for a manned space capsule since 1958. The Council of Chief Designers approved the project for a first manned space flight in November 1959. The next stage was to win political approval.

The same month, there took place a vital meeting of the Academy of Sciences, chaired by its president, Mstislav Keldysh. Also present were (naturally) Korolev, Valentin Glushko, Academician Vasily Parin, engineer Alexander Mrykin, General Nikolai Kaminin representing the Red Air Force, and Academicians Sisakayan and Stepnov. At least one senior scientist argued long and hard against the idea of manned flight at all. The rockets simply were not reliable enough. Unmanned flights were cheaper, safer and yielded just as good results. Would a man survive the radiation, meteorites, weightlessness?

A compromise proposal was put forward for a suborbital flight—up and down ballistically to a height of 200 km. That would really be up in space. There were none of the risks of orbital insertion, losing radio contact and retrofire. It would be over Soviet territory all the time. The flight would last 15 min, including 5 min of weightlessness. In the mid-1950s a number of designs had been presented for a manned ballistic flight. The only one published was Mikhail Tikhonravov's project, the WR-190, for a two-man suborbital flight; Korolev designed some projects too.

Korolev let the scientists fight it out, but it was Glushko's intervention that was decisive:

> Now that we have the chance to send a man into space, the ideas meet with opposition from certain comrades. I do not understand this.

Korolev quickly added:

> A ballistic flight will cost a lot of money and will be risky. The results will be very meagre. Science needs a flight around the Earth. Not a small step forward, but a stride forward that is decisive and daring.

Keldysh, who said little until the end, weighed in behind Korolev. No limit should be placed on man's desire to explore space, he pleaded. They were indeed ready for the next giant step. Sputnik had set going a force of irresistible momentum and any failure to take the next step, whatever that was, would be tantamount to a loss of nerve.

The academy's recommendation went straight to the government and it was to go all out for orbital flight. Khrushchev agreed. Vice-chairman of the Council of Ministers, Konstantin Rudnev, was appointed head of a State Commission for Space Flight, thus keeping a direct line to the Kremlin and Khrushchev himself. Sergei Korolev was deputy. The role of the Commission was a supervisory one, to check that government orders had been carried out and then to give the final go-ahead.

Mstislav Keldysh's intervention was decisive. This is the memorial to him in Moscow.

SHOOTING DOWN OF GARY POWERS

Korolev's team worked flat out to get the manned spaceship airborne. As of November 1959 a first piloted flight was still a year away. Detailed design work still had to be completed and a team of pilots recruited and trained to go into space. Korolev's leading assistant was Mikhail Tikhonravov (1900–74)—their collaboration dated back to their days in GIRD.

With his large, powerful, R-7 booster, Korolev had latitude with the design of his spacecraft. When the Americans were busily wind-testing bullet-shaped craft with special ablative heat shields, Korolev had a stroke of genius: make the spacecraft absolutely round, a perfect sphere. Weigh one end heavily with ablative material and just like a ball leaded at one end it would automatically turn that end head first into the searing heat of re-entry. This idea was lifted from the design of the Zenith photoreconnaissance satellite, then maturing in his bureau.

Mikhail Tikhonravov. Although he did not have a prominent public role, he was one of the great theoreticians of Soviet space flight, working closely with Korolev in the design of the R-7, Vostok and manned Moon projects.

By contrast America's Mercury was cone-shaped and the base had to be carefully pointed in the right direction if the craft were to come back. Korolev's sphere made those problems irrelevant. The R-7 booster was upgraded to prepare the way for the new manned spaceship, now to be called 'Vostok' or 'East'. The new upper stage had a thrust of 5600 kg. Three versions of Vostok were devised: an unmanned, non-recoverable version (Vostok-A); an unmanned, recoverable, biological version (Vostok-B) and the model designed for cosmonauts (Vostok-V). Vostok weighed 4700 kg.

The first tests took place in January 1960: a stripped-down Vostok forerunner was hurtled 10 000 km downrange from Baikonour, arcing 1000 km high in the process, and was lobbed into the Pacific Ocean. Great accuracy was achieved. The Soviet navy picked up the nosecones from the sea, but not without attracting some attention from the Americans, whose naval bases at Kwajelein Atoll, Hawaii, and Johnson Island were not far away.

The Americans realized that a new version of rocket was under test and may have suspected a manned link. Much of their information came from their spyplane, the U-2, which had been overflying the Soviet Union for four years. The U-2 had been developed by

Lockheed amidst great secrecy in the early 1950s. It was a small black jet plane with enormously long thin wings and gulping air intakes. It looked like a stranded seagull and could have been mistaken for a glider rather than a self-propelled aircraft. The analogy is not irrelevant, because the U-2 was designed to soar high in the atmosphere at 25 000 m where the air is thin and big intakes are essential to extract every molecule of oxygen that can be found. The U-2 was to soar silently, at great height, for enormous distances, over Russia, beyond the reach of the anti-aircraft flak guns.

Thus it was on 1 May 1960, that the CIA, picking up increased radio traffic from its listening posts in Turkey, believing that this might herald a new rocket test, ordered a U-2 into the air that summer's morning. The prize was to photograph the R-7 booster on the pad at Baikonour. The pilot was a young Air Force lieutenant called Gary Powers. His U-2 left the ground from an air force base in Afghanistan. The ungainly black plane climbed for height. It headed out across the Kazakhstan steppe and passed right over Baikonour. Cameras clicked and whirred as they caught sight of the R-7 booster sitting on its pad, almost ready for takeoff.

Gary Powers, breathing oxygen and in a heated pressure suit, turned his plane north to Sverdlovsk in a giant loop before he would turn back. That was as far as he got. His plane was suddenly buffeted by a thundering explosion in the tail. The plane rocked and shook and began to spin sickeningly to Earth. Before it was too late, Gary Powers bailed out, and parachuted into the forests of the Urals. He was captured and put on spying charges: Khrushchev stormed out of the Paris summit conference then under way. Angrily he denounced the Americans for spying and organized a well-publicized trial. It was the last spy flight of the U-2: the Americans never took on Russia's surface-to-air missiles again.

SPACESHIP 1 (*KORABL SPUTNIK 1*)

Whether delayed by the snooping U-2 flight or not, the manned prototype got away two weeks later. Spaceship 1 (In Russian, *korabl sputnik 1* or KS 1) reached orbit on 15 May 1960, flying from 312 km to 368 km, 91.1 min, 65 deg, and weighing almost five tonnes—another weight record. A sure indication of the designers' intentions was clear when it was announced that a dummy cosmonaut was aboard the cabin.

Spaceship 1 was the first of eleven 'Vostok'-type spaceships to go into orbit. The capsule itself consisted of a spherical cabin with heavy shielding on the outside. The pilot was to be placed on a large ejector seat fitted to rails: he could eject during ascent and eject by parachute during descent. In the cabin was a simple control panel and porthole, Earth globe to show position, clock, and Vzor orientation device. To the right was a control handle so that a pilot could orientate the spaceship. Clustered around the cabin walls were water and food containers, logs, radio, tape recorder and air purifiers. Parachutes were forward. Behind the cabin was a cylindrically shaped service module. This contained attitude control thrusters, oxygen and nitrogen storage bottles, aerials and, most importantly, the large retrorocket. Once this was fired to commence the descent, the two modules then separated.

It was a daring and simple design. But it all had to function flawlessly. Each Vostok contained 15 000 m of electrical wires, 240 valves, and 6000 transistors. An unheard of degree of reliability was being insisted upon in people already used to the standards required for jet planes. The chief designers of Vostok were, apart from Korolev himself, Oleg Ivanovsky and Yevgeni Frolov.

Spaceship 1 had no thermal coating, no parachutes and no ejector mechanism and was intended to burn up in the atmosphere. After 24 h the orientation system developed a fault. Boris Raushenbach, designer of the system, recommended to Korolev the use of the backup system, but he persisted in trying to use the primary system: in the event, the retro-rockets were orientated in the wrong direction and sent it into high orbit when they fired four days later on 19 May. Spaceship 1 and its dummy cosmonaut circled the Earth for another four years until October 1965 when they burnt up.[15]

ARRIVAL OF THE COSMONAUTS

Who would fly the first spaceships? There were no known ground rules and these had to be invented by Korolev and the others. It was decided to recruit an initial group of 20 cosmonauts—the word 'cosmonaut' was used to differentiate from the existing American term of astronaut. The cosmonauts had to be brave, reliable, physically fit, not prone to panic, capable of mental endurance and be familiar with the notion of 'things up there'. The last of these factors alone suggested that the selectors should look towards the Red Air Force, and so it was that the call went out for trainee cosmonauts in late 1959.

Air Force Pilots selected for first manned flight into space, March–June 1960

Pavel Belyayev
Valeri Bykovsky
Yuri Gagarin
Viktor Gorbatko
Anatoli Kartashov
Yevgeni Khrunov
Vladimir Komarov
Alexei Leonov
Andrian Nikolayev
Pavel Popovich
Georgi Shonin
Boris Volynov
Dmitri Zaikin
Valentin Bondarenko
Valentin Varlamov
Gherman Titov
Grigori Nelyubov
Mars Rafikov
Ivan Anikeyev
Valentin Filateev

The selection was handled by the Air Force. It went for fit, young pilots. Some had very little flying experience: one volunteer, Yuri Gagarin, had only 230 h, compared to the American average of 1500. The Air Force scrutinized over 3000 applicants. The selection took place from October 1959 to January 1960. On 11 January 1960, the decision was taken to set up the Cosmonaut Training Centre (TsPk), with an initial staff of 250. Responsibility for cosmonaut training went to Col Gen Nikolai Kaminin. Evgeni Karpov was the first director of TsPk. The cosmonaut group was formally selected on 25 February 1960, although some of the group did not arrive at TsPk until March and even later. Of the 20, nearly all were aged 25 to 35 and were Air Force test pilots.[16]

Of the first 20, only 12 flew and eight never got into space at all. Nelyubov, Anikeyev and Filateev were drummed out of the squad in late 1961 after a drunken brawl in a railway station. Nelyubov, brilliant, ambitious but ultimately unstable, later threw himself under a train and was killed. Mars Rafikov suffered from 'burn out', left the squad, continued test flying awhile, and ended up manager of a building cooperative in Alma Ata. Anatoli Kartashov, described by Titov as a 'splendid pilot', injured his spine on a centrifuge run that took him to eight times the force of gravity: the doctors dismissed him from the squad. Valentin Varlamov injured his spine in a swimming accident: he died suddenly of a brain haemorrhage in 1980. Dmitri Zaikin almost got his first flight, when in 1968 a medical review board failed him and he had to leave the programme.

The identities of the eight cosmonauts were not known until special articles about them were published by *Izvestia* in 1986.[17] Until then, these men appeared only eerily, from time to time, in photographs and film clips that somehow eluded the censors, scissors and airbrushes. Any of them could have been as famous as Gagarin or a Leonov, but fate decided otherwise.

Commanders of the cosmonaut squad

Yuri Gagarin	1961–3
Andrian Nikolayev	1963–8
Valeri Bykovsky	1968–9
Alexei Leonov	1976–82
Viktor Gorbatko	1982
Boris Volynov	1982–90
Alexander Volkov	1990–

BEST AND THE BRIGHTEST

Yuri Gagarin emerged as the most determined, energetic and ambitious of all the cosmonauts. Yuri Gagarin was born in 1934 near Smolensk, western Russia. In his youth he learned to be a foundryman and went to several industrial schools. He enlisted in the Saratov flying school in his spare time, went to pilot training school, joining the Soviet Air Force as a fighter pilot in 1956.

Because of his short height he always put a cushion on the seat of his MiG fighter. In 1957 he married a nursing student, Valentina, at his base and then transferred for arduous service in the Arctic. Their first baby, Lena, was born in 1958. In 1959, on his own initiative, he wrote to his superiors, applying to join a group of cosmonauts 'if such a group exists'. His application was filed. Gagarin was in time called up, put before a medical board and selected as a cosmonaut on his 26th birthday in March 1960. It is quite possible, granted what we know of him later, that he determined at this stage that he was going to be the first one to fly. But at first he was not permitted to tell anyone about his work, not even his wife Valentina, for it was so secret.

The school museum keeps with great care this photograph showing Yuri Gagarin (third from left, second row) in his school years.

Gagarin's stand-in, Gherman Titov, was a year younger. Curly-haired, Titov was a distinguished cadet from Volgograd Air Force pilots school. Unlike most American astronauts going into training at around the same time, whose spare-time interests tended to be vigorous and virile athletic sports, Gherman Titov was a sophisticated, widely read man with a special interest in poetry.

Andrian Nikolayev was older and known as the 'iron man'. Born in 1929 he was the first non-Russian member of the team (he was Chuvash) and spent his youth as a forester and lumberjack. Unlike the others he did not start his aviation career as a pilot but as a gunner and then a radio operator. Dark, serious, Andrian Nikolayev once found himself in a flaming crashing jet fighter. Rather than eject he insisted on bringing his plane down to the ground, walking away without a scratch when survival had seemed impossible. He was able to sweat out the isolation chamber longer than anyone else: it was a blacked-out room where cosmonauts were put for days on end without reading matter or clocks, and they were alternately frozen or baked to test their endurance.

Pavel Popovich was actually the first cosmonaut to arrive at the training centre. A veteran of military aviation school and an Arctic pilot too, he was the most extrovert member of the team. Extremely popular, he had a fine tenor voice and was constantly singing. His own flying record was eclipsed only by his wife, Marina, who was a colonel in the Red Air Force and had achieved numerous aviation records flying high-performance jet aircraft.

Valeri Bykovsky was the same age as Gagarin. A quiet and confident man, jet pilot, parachute instructor, he booked his flight by being the first person to test out the isolation chamber over a prolonged period. Over time, he became the man who always tested out training devices before others were let loose on them. Bykovsky was the only one to argue back about safety considerations. These were some of the first cosmonauts to get missions. Some of the others had to wait up to ten years—far longer than they or anyone else could have anticipated.

For project Mercury, the NASA people looked to the country's top 500 test pilots. Like their Russian opposite numbers they had to be in physically perfect shape, have superbly quick reactions, but unlike the Russians they had to be a graduate of military test school with over 1500 hours flight time and have college degrees in physical sciences or engineering. The 500 were narrowed to 110, then 36, largely by volunteers dropping out because of small medical flaws. Others were eliminated for suspect motivation like personal glory. Family background had to be impeccable—divorcees were out of the question. The final selection down to seven was a hard one for NASA, and by their own later admission a somewhat arbitrary one. The NASA seven were several years older than Russia's twenty.

NASA's seven heroes were subject to a special and unusual contract with *Life* magazine, which got sole publicity rights. Americans added the seven astronauts to their pantheon of film stars, war heroes, sports personalities, dynamic politicians, two years before any of them had even flown! These astronauts embodied the ideal American—adventurous, mature, family man, straight-talking, patriotic.

It was different on the Soviet side. There was no potential hero in the Russian squad. Once you flew, the world knew about you: until you did, you were quite unknown. Names were not released in advance, and like the Chief Designer the cosmonauts had the protection of total anonymity. After a flight, there was the abrupt transition to life before the public gaze in a country where heroes were few and far between. Soviet officialdom tended to be suspicious of heroes, who could too easily become a political threat. Cosmonauts were not perceived as one, and apart from the General Secretary of the Communist Party they became the best known public Russians both outside and inside their own country. They personified all that was best about the new Soviet state, celebrating its youth and scientific and technical prowess.

The cosmonauts began their training with theoretical lessons in aviation medicine. Noting their bored reactions, Korolev sent in his engineers to give them lectures about practical aspects of spaceship design. They were then brought off on a six-week parachute training course in the steppe. In the meantime, simulators were being built of the Vostok spacecraft.

Cosmonauts trained in centrifuges designed to simulate high gravity forces.

SPACESHIP 2

The summer of 1960. Training of the twenty cosmonauts got into its stride. The training itself consisted of flying jet fighters, parachuting, survival experiences, managing the centrifuge, enduring the isolation chamber, physical fitness and learning how a spacecraft works. Photographs from the period suggest that there was a fair amount of survival training. Cosmonauts would be deposited in the middle of nowhere and told to find their own way home, using their own navigation and resources. This was against the day that they might land badly off target.

Despite the failure of Spaceship 1 in May, it was time to proceed to the next stage, Vostok B, the recoverable biological version. The re-entry manoeuvre simply had to be got right or otherwise manned flight could not seriously be contemplated. What was required was that the spacecraft be orientated at exactly 45 deg to its flight path. With the wrong angle it would alternately shoot up into a higher orbit or descend too fast and be incinerated.

One hundred dogs were recruited for the Vostok-B dog missions, though this number included the surviving veterans from the ballistic missions of 1958–9. This time they were not recruited by the Moscow-based teams who had been responsible for the ballistic flights. They were taken this time from the research kennels of the Pavlov Institute at Pavlovo-Kultishi, near Leningrad. Head of research at this time was Dr Viktor Fyodorov.

Requirements were laid down that the dogs should be in good physical condition, aged 18 months to three years, and sufficiently small to be able to fit into the dog containers designed for the Vostok cabin (less than 8 kg).

The choice of dogs was a natural one for the USSR. Animal psychology had been pioneered in Leningrad by Ivan Pavlov. The institute explained this choice as follows:

> Dogs are highly organized, steady and easily trained animals. Monkeys on the other hand are capricious, highly strung and undisciplined. That is why experiments are best conducted with dogs—and that was why the founder of this institute used dogs for all his physiological experiments. We have plenty of chimpanzees here, but they are used for experiments where discipline and emotional stability are unimportant factors, and nothing to do with space research.

Although the Russians accepted that monkeys were closer to man on the evolutionary scale, they took the view that dogs were closer to man in emotional and physical reactions. Blood circulation and breathing in dogs under stress follow similar patters to humans. Dogs will undergo tests that nervier chimpanzees will reject. The first dog selection was brought to the Cosmic Physiological Research Station. The initial two months training included hours in enclosed spaces, centrifuge, water immersion in space suits, and parabolic curves in air force planes. The dogs were fitted out in bright orange zipper-fashioned nylon suits with globe-shaped helmets, and spent several weeks in a model spaceship. They were subjected to vibration, noise, high temperatures and g-loads.

The first Vostok-B mission took place on 28 July 1960, with dogs Chaika and Lisichka on board, but the mission was unsuccessful. The countdown reached zero, but nothing happened. No liftoff took place, the rocket was unfuelled and the cargo taken out.

The next, Spaceship 2, was put into orbit on 19 August 1960. There were two dogs on board. As if to encourage Korolev, only a week earlier, the Americans had recovered one of their own capsules, Discoverer 13, from the Pacific Ocean. It was one of the few things that the Americans had actually achieved before the USSR. It proved it could be done. The two dogs were huskies and were called Belka and Strelka. Belka was the Russian word for 'squirrel' and Strelka for 'little arrow'. Belka and Strelka went through training not dissimilar to the cosmonauts themselves. Aboard the spaceship, the ejector seat for the manned spaceship was converted into a giant ark for the two dogs and other animal cargo. This included two white rats, 28 mice, several hundred insects, plants and seeds from onion, peat, wheat and maize. Television cameras were fitted so that the dogs could be observed in flight.

The second objective of the flight—after recovery of the ark—was to study the ability of organisms to withstand zero gravity and radiation. The latter was the more feared, ever since the discovery of the Van Allen radiation belts in 1958. For every organism aboard Spaceship 2 there was a control one on the ground: the two would then be compared. What was not revealed at the time—not in fact till many years later—was that human specimens were also aboard. Three doctors from the Moscow Institute of Experimental Biology volunteered small flaps of their skin from their shoulders and thighs, which were placed in sterilized glass bottles. The question of manned flight was being approached with enormous care, both from an engineering and a biological point of view.

DOWN IN THE FIELDS

The noise and vibration were terrible as Spaceship 2 lifted off. The dogs, frightened, shifted restlessly around the cabin. Every movement was relayed back by TV. As the spaceship shot towards orbit, the pressure eased. Strelka and Belka settled down. After eight minutes, Spaceship 2 was in an orbit of 339 by 360 km, 65 deg, 90.7 min. News of the launch was immediately relayed to the world and to the Hall of Columns courtroom in Moscow, where Gary Powers was being found guilty of espionage. The judges were at that moment considering sentence.

Ground stations were able to pick up signals from the spaceship, which were heard in Paris and London, and sounded like dots and dashes. All went well. The environmental system provided air and kept the temperature at an even 18°C, with constant humidity and

The crew of Spaceship 2, Belka (pictured here) and Strelka. Belka was the first animal known to suffer from space sickness.

pressure. Radiation dosage seemed to be within the limits allowed for. The dogs sucked food and water from tubes and tapes at intervals. They got used to weightlessness after about five minutes hanging in the cabin apparently lifeless.

20 August: After 18 orbits, just a full day into the mission, it was time to begin the much-feared recovery sequence. The retrorockets blasted. Gravity gradually returned to the cabin. The descent cabin separated. Its skin glowed red hot, then white hot, as it headed into the fires of re-entry.

Down through the atmosphere. At 8000 m a pressure device in the cabin sensed the return to the atmosphere and parachutes popped out and unfurled. The ejector seat, carrying the ark, fired and the two cabins descended under parachute, gradually drifting apart. The sphere-shaped cabin was coming down at 10 m/s, the ark with its precious cargo at a gentler 6 m/s.

It was a classic scene. The two spacecraft were spotted coming down by farm workers, just as in science fiction stories. Both bumped down, the ark in a meadow. The farm workers gathered round. Silence. No aircraft. No suggestion as to where the strange container had come from. They peered closer and saw a printed metal message:

> Please inform the Soviet space centre immediately on discovery.

Cars were already bouncing over the fields towards the spot and to the surprised workers. So accurate was the landing that it came only 9 km from the place planned. Belka and Strelka had survived. They were alive and well. The flight was a technical triumph. Recovery was possible. Animals could successfully fly in space. Above all, the Vostok spaceship design was known to be sound. In an after-flight experiment, the flies and plants were crossed with ground samples to see if mutations developed as a result of radiation experienced in space.

The official medical and biological results of the flights were summed up by Academician Sisakyan:

> During the period of zero-gravity the animals did not display any signs of alarm, nor did they attempt to free themselves from the straps. Film showed that they jerked their heads up only when they entered the state of weightlessness ... during the first minutes of weightlessness, blood pressure, heart and respiration rates increased, but after four to six minutes they gradually returned to normal ... they were sufficiently calm after landing and had a hearty appetite.
> In other words, no noticeable deviations were detected in their behaviour.

What he did not report was the first case of space sickness. The medical director of the mission, Vladimir Yazdovsky, reported that Belka had been space sick on orbit 4 and had vomited. He recommended that the first flight of a man be limited to one orbit; the members of the State Commission agreed. The flight of the first man in space was set for December 1960.[18]

Despite the nervousness of the doctors, the public spin on the mission was upbeat. Spaceship 2 was clearly the manned spaceship in prototype and it was now only a question of time before it had human cargo. This was a point that the USSR made no effort to conceal:

Practical possibilities are now being created for man's flight into outer space (Radio Moscow, 21 Aug 1960).

A manned space flight could be made in the near future. Less than three years after the launching of the first spaceship we are on the immediate threshold of manned flight. (The Vice-President of the Academy of Sciences, quoted on Radio Moscow, 21 Aug 1960.)

To complement these tests, trials were carried out over a number of years in balloons of the life-support equipment and pressure suits required for Vostok cosmonauts in orbit as well as the ejector seat for the cosmonauts to use during the final stage of their return to Earth. Four men were assigned to what was called the Volga programme: Pyotr Dolgov, Yevgeni Andreyev, Vasili Lazarev, and Ivan Kamyshev. The Volga programme marked the resumption of the series of Soviet balloon flights begun in the 1930s. During one of these tests, on 1 November 1962, Pyotr Dolgov and Yevgeni Andreyev parachuted out of the Volga at 20 000 m. Dolgov's suit depressurized at once and he died during the descent.

TRANSITION FROM EISENHOWER TO KENNEDY

The American programme exhibited none of the apparent steadfastness of purpose of the Soviet one. President Eisenhower could only be described as extremely lukewarm if not downright sceptical about ventures into space. NASA soon realized that in the absence of presidential directives, indeed in the face of presidential scepticism, it would have to set its own space objectives. Accordingly, NASA published its first long-range plan in December 1959, proposing manned circumlunar flights in the mid-1960s and Moon landings around 1970. By July 1960, NASA had floated the name of a manned spacecraft which would accomplish the mission, Apollo. Requests for feasibility studies for Apollo were issued in October 1960.

Even while NASA was deliberating, the Army and air Force continued to be at each other's throats. The army, under von Braun, designed a huge booster-to-end-all-boosters, the Saturn. The air force designed something cheaper, the Titan, and a manned spaceplane to go on top, the Dynasoar. Called thus for 'dynamic soaring' it was a winged military reconnaissance plane which would circle the Earth with a single pilot.

Eisenhower, not to be hustled into anything, ordered a scientific study of all the manned projects. He was not impressed. In late 1960 he vetoed the Saturn programme, gave a tiny $30m to the post-Mercury missions, and privately stated his intention of scrapping Mercury after its first flight. The election of John F. Kennedy as President in November 1960 meant no immediate change. It is true that Kennedy regarded Eisenhower as weak, complacent, and pedestrian; but the Mercury programme was going so painfully slowly that Kennedy did not want any early association with it himself.

Kennedy was inaugurated as President on 21 January 1961. NASA's Mercury programme got off the ground successfully ten days later when Mercury-Redstone 2 carried the chimpanzee 'Ham' 280 km downrange in suborbital flight. The booster overheated and the capsule overshot its landing point badly. Washington ordered a further delay until 25 April so that the problems could be sorted out. On 22 March 1961, Kennedy had met with NASA director James Webb to discuss NASA's budget for 1962: Kennedy refused the request to increase funds for project Apollo. Kennedy was busily occupied with Laos and Cuba and did not want to be beset with space issues just yet. Little did he realize that Soviet scientists were making desperate efforts to get their manned spaceship in readiness.

DISASTERS

As NASA struggled with the transition to a new administration, the Russians were experiencing difficulties of their own. Noting the success of the Moon probes in 1959 and being informed that suitable opportunities existed to send spacecraft to Mars in October 1960 and Venus in February 1961, Khrushchev ordered Korolev to aim for the planets. With the Americans not even able to put up a Moon probe, a Soviet shot to the planets would demonstrate Russian prowess even more intolerably. Preliminary designs for Soviet interplanetary probes had begun in 1958. In August 1959, the Applied Mathematics Division of the Mathematical Institute of the Academy of Sciences had completed the necessary calculations for a flight to Mars in October 1960 and Venus in February 1961 (by happy coincidence, all would arrive at their respective targets, Mars and Venus, at the same time, during the third week of May 1961). On 15 March 1960, the Academy of Sciences Vice-President Mstislav Keldysh approved a paper called 'Designing spacecraft for Mars missions'. This laid down the objective of photographing Mars from a distance of between 5000 and 30 000 km and the carrying of instruments that might detect plant or animal life.[19]

The 1960 Mars probes weighed about 640 kg. Their scientific payloads included a magnetometer, ion traps for measuring solar plasma, cosmic ray counters and micrometeorite sensors. The energy required was beyond the capability of the R-7 and the upper stage used on the Lunik missions, so, for the first time, a new, fourth, upper stage was used. The launcher was called the 8K78 and subsequently became known as the Molniya, which is still in service almost forty years later.

The best date for a launch to Mars was 27 September, though in the event there were delays. Launch 'windows'' to Mars—times when the planets are suitably aligned for the minimal use of fuel and time—occur only every 25 months and last about several weeks. Opportunities to Venus are a little more frequent, being every 18 months. Because ignition out of Earth orbit toward Mars would have to take place over the Atlantic Ocean, three merchant ships were fitted out as tracking ships—the *Illchevsk*, *Krasnodar* and *Dolinsk*. They left their ports in August to take up station the next month.

Mars 1 failed on 10 October. The pumps in the third stage, hurriedly developed, did not develop enough thrust for ignition to begin. The Mars ship reached 120 km and then fell back into the atmosphere. Four days later, Mars 2 did likewise—an identical failure. *Illchevsk*, *Krasnodar* and *Dolinsk* returned to the Black Sea. Worse was to follow.

Three weeks later, a new rocket was prepared at the Baikonour cosmodrome. It was a military rocket and was quite unconnected to either the Mars shots or plans to put men into space. It was an R-16, ordered in 1956. The contract had gone to Mikhail Yangel's OKB in Dniepropetrovsk, Ukraine. The R-16 could be launched much more speedily than the clumsy R-7. It was prepared for its first flight on 23 October 1960 at launch pad 41. The preparations were observed at close hand by rocket troop trainees from the Felix

Dzherzhinsky Military Academy and by the commander of the Soviet Union's rocket troops, Marshal Mistrofan Nedelin. A fault occurred in the first-stage electrical system, which had to be rewired and rewelded. A valve in the first stage opened accidentally: it had to be fixed.

Launch was then set for 1700 the next day, 24th, but was delayed by leaks. The launch director later recalled that they simply tightened the joints to stop the leaks, ignoring the way that the fuel burned little holes in their rubber gloves. Rocketeers were gathered round the booster, still on the lookout for leaks. There were two further delays. To this day, there are rumours that Nikita Khrushchev was constantly telephoning to enquire if the rocket had yet been launched. Mikhail Yangel supervised from an underground bunker. At one stage, Nedelin retired to a distance of 17 m for a cigarette. At 1845, just 30 min before the new liftoff time, a current distributor fault on the second stage caused a fire which led to an immediate explosion of the first stage. Baikonour cosmodrome erupted in a cataclysmic volcano of fire.

Most of the victims were incinerated at once. Many tried to make a run for it, but were engulfed in the flames or fell down onto the boiling asphalt. As they did, the top of the rocket toppled over, spilling out fresh amounts of nitric acid onto the inferno. Others were overcome by fumes. The victims were terribly burned. Even the few survivors suffered appallingly, having had their outer clothes burnt off . The clean-up teams had to identify the bodies by their personal effects, such as apartment keys.

Of the launch team, 59 died on the day, 32 of burns later. Total deaths were 165, the others being officials from Yangel's bureau who had been on hand. The death of Marshal Nedelin was explained as an aircraft accident. The other, high-ranking officials also perished in a series of unconnected 'aircraft accidents' over the next several months.

The disaster was sufficiently serious for the first manned spaceflight, which had been scheduled for December, to be postponed. The committee of inquiry into the Nedelin disaster was headed by Soviet President Leonid Brezhnev. He recommended no further action be taken: people had already been punished and the priority should be to get the rocket into production.

The laying of wreaths on the graves of the victims was a secret activity requiring permission until 1990. With *glasnost*, a memorial was erected at launch pad 41 and at Mikhail Yangel's OKB. It was dedicated by the survivors' association. Nedelin's charred notebook is perhaps the most poignant item in the museum commemorating the disaster.[20] The R-16 was successfully launched on 2 February 1961 and entered service in the Soviet military arsenal. It was later called the Tsyklon 1 ('cyclone' in Russian) and became the basis of successful rockets still flying in the 1990s (the R-36, Tsyklon 2 and 3). The R-16 joined the nuclear strike force at Plesetsk.

The Nedelin disaster led to a loss of confidence in readiness for a manned flight into space, and a new test of the Vostok-B was ordered. On 1 December, Spaceship 3 climbed into the sky with dogs Pchelka and Mushka aboard. All proceeded perfectly. If it went well, then a manned flight would follow. The retrorockets fired on 2 December on schedule, but at too high an angle. The capsule plunged steeply into the atmosphere and burned like a fiery meteor. Pchelka and Mushka were no more.

It was a sobering moment. All the calculations had to be gone over again and all the systems checked. This was one of the key phases of the flight that simply could not be allowed to go wrong. The designers made two significant decisions. First, in order to reduce guidance risks, the first manned flight would be limited to just one orbit. Second, two dress rehearsals would be required before even that would be tried. Only then would they be sure.

Another Vostok-B mission was tried on 22 December 1960 with dogs Shutka and Kometa. During the ascent it was realized that the level of thrust was insufficient to reach orbit, so an abort was commanded. The cabin separated from the launcher at high altitude and made an emergency return. The cabin separated and came down near the Stony Tunguska river, near where the great meteorite had crashed in 1908, in the Soviet far east. This was only the start of the problem. To prevent the cabin falling into foreign hands, a self-destruct system had been installed to blow the cabin, dogs included, to bits in 60 h Knowing they had little time to find and retrieve the cabin, a gang of fourteen rescuers set off from Baikonour. Simultaneously, a bomb disposal team was summoned from Leningrad to disconnect the self-destruct system—if it got there in time. The two teams converged, flying across wintertime Siberia. The weather in Krasnoyarsk was so bad that the military commander denied them permission to fly, an injunction they ignored. But they found the Korabl Sputnik cabin. They were greeted by the dogs. Thankfully the bomb disposal team was not needed, for the cable connecting the self-destruct system had burned itself out.

ADRIFT ON THE OCEANS OF VENUS

Soon it was time for the first missions to Venus. Venus, a brilliant shining star in the cold dawn sky, was a tempting target. Virtually the same size as the Earth, it was shrouded in thick cloud. Its orbit inside the Earth's track brought it as close as 40 million kilometres: transit times for a space probe were only four months, half that of Mars. At the time, most Soviet astronomers believed Venus to be covered in oceans. They ignored one group of heretical scientists who said that Venus had a hot and rocky, arid surface.

The first Venus shot was only marginally more successful than the October Mars probes: unlike them it actually reached Earth orbit. But when after the first orbit the time came to ignite the fourth stage onwards toward Venus, nothing happened. The timer failed to give the necessary command for the fourth stage to ignite. The failed Venus shot was explained away as a 'heavy satellite' (in Russian, 'tyzhyolyi sputnik'). Orbiting at 223 by 328 km, weighing a record 6843 kg, it was announced that the mission was over soon after it completed its first orbit. There was much speculation in the West as to what the flight was all about, fuelling speculation that it was a manned flight that went wrong.

'Good morning Venus !' hailed the Western press as the Molniya rocket performed on schedule on 12 February. The fourth stage did everything it should have. From a parking orbit of 227 by 285 km, a small probe called at first an Automatic Interplanetary Station, and much later, more prosaically, Venera 1 (the Russian word for Venus), curved away from Earth in a circular orbit set to intercept Venus's path on 19 May.

Venera-1 was 2 m high, weighed 644 kg, with a domed top, a cylindrical body and two solar panels to soak in sunlight and turn it into electricity. A butterfly-net high-gain antenna picked up signals from a new deep-space-tracking station at Yevpatoria in the Crimea; a long-arm antenna sent information back. It had instruments to study cosmic radiation, micrometeorites and charged particles. There was no course-correction motor. A series of thermal shutters which opened and closed protected the hermetically sealed instruments from the heat and cold of deep space. The purpose of Venera 1 was to impact on Venus. Inside the dome of Venera 1 was a pressurized globe-float, which carried the inevitable pennant of the USSR. The float had been built so that it could drift on Venus's oceans.

Venera 1, the first probe to the planet Venus. In the dome was a globe designed to bob on the oceans of Venus.

The world watched as Venera 1 headed into regions of space never explored before. On 19 February it was nearly 2 million kilometres away from the Earth, travelling at 3.9 km/s. From early on it was known that Venera would come within 100 000 km of Venus—no mean achievement over a journey of 270 million kilometres. A stream of data was sent back over the airwaves.

It was a brave attempt. The planned communications session with the probe on 27 February never materialized (many years later, the Russians admitted that communications had been lost much sooner, only 2 million kilometres out). Venera 1 was lost. A team of scientists from the USSR travelled to the British radio observatory at Jodrell Bank, Macclesfield, to use its giant dish to regain contact, but to no avail.

First Venus and Mars probes

10 Oct 1960	Mars flyby	Failure
14 Oct 1960	Mars flyby	Failure
4 Feb 1961	Venus lander	'Heavy Sputnik' failure
12 Feb 1961	Venus lander	Venera 1 (contact lost)

Following the Venus and Mars failures of 1960–1, Korolev decided to redesign his interplanetary probes. They were standardized for Mars and Venus, and were developed in three versions:

MV-1	Mars–Venus landers;
MV-2	Mars–Venus flybys; and
Zond	Experimental spacecraft for the Moon, Mars and Venus.

Zond was intended to test the technologies for interplanetary spacecraft and iron out problems. Zond was 3.6 m high, had a mass of one tonne and contained two sealed compartments, one of which contained instruments either for a flyby or for a descent capsule. It carried a KDU 414 course-correction engine of 200 kg thrust using UDMH and nitric acid, developed by the Isayev KB. The solar panels had a span of 4 m. A 2 m highgain antenna was used for communications with Earth over the long interplanetary distances. The MV-1 and MV-2 series had similar dimensions.

FIRST COSMONAUT FATALITY

The failure of the two Vostok-B missions caused much careful redesign during the spring. By March, all was ready for the two dress rehearsals, using the Vostok-V. Spaceship 4 flew on 9 March and Spaceship 5 on 25 March, a mere two weeks apart. Spaceship 4 carried the dog Chernushka, made one orbit around the Earth and came down in the planned landing zone. Spaceship 5 had another husky aboard, Zvedochka. It was a repeat in every detail. Both carried a dummy, who even had a name: Ivan Ivanovich. On one of the missions, Ivan Ivanovich came down in the snow and was greeted by some villagers. Unsure whether the suited object was a real spaceman or not, they rushed to get help, but by the time they returned, paratroopers had surrounded the dummy and would not let them near. Eventually, a delegate from the village was allowed through to touch the cold, rubbery face of the dummy. Satisfied he was beyond help, they returned to their village through the snows. Korolev had ironed out the bugs at last. The moment of truth, of the final test, drew near. The prairie flowers were blooming on the steppe, peeping through the few patches of snow that lay round about. Warmth and life were returning to the spring earth.

Even as Spaceship 5 was being counted down, the cosmonauts received a sharp and terrible reminder of the risks they faced. On 23 March, 24-year-old Valentin Bondarenko, the very youngest of the trainees, neared the end of a three-day test in a high-altitude chamber. A piece of cotton wool caught fire on a small cooking grill. Because it was an altitude chamber, it took a full half hour to depressurize and open the door. Even knowing all along that it was hopeless, doctors struggled for eight hours to save him, giving him pain-killing injections, but burn shock overcame the youngest of the team of cosmonauts. 'I'm so sorry; no one is to blame but me', he kept repeating to the doctors. It was Yuri Gagarin who spent the last hours at Bondarenko's bedside. Bondarenko was buried in Kharkov, Ukraine, but his wife Anya and five-year- old son, Sasha, stayed on at the training centre. A small memorial was erected to him in Kharkhov, but it made no mention of his role in the first cosmonaut squad. Years later, a young officer, Alexander Bondarenko, was able to tell historians of his father's tragic part in the conquest of space; and in Kharkov, the extra words 'remembered by the cosmonauts of the USSR' were added. Garbled rumours of a cosmonaut death soon began to reach the West at this time. Identifying dead cosmonauts became an industry in parts of the Western media. An amateur radio station in Turin, Italy, used its radio apparatus to pick up signals from stranded, dying cosmonauts and in three years wiped out an entire squad of cosmonauts.[21] In fact, Bondarenko's death was the only accident concealed from the public.

Spaceship series

15 May 1960	Spaceship 1
28 July 1960	Failure (no launch)
19 Aug 1960	Spaceship 2
1 Dec 1960	Spaceship 3 (lost)
22 Dec 1960	Failure (cabin recovered)
9 Mar 1961	Spaceship 4
25 Mar 1961	Spaceship 5

THE SPHERICAL SHAPE OF THE EARTH...

So who would fly the first mission? Early in the cosmonaut training programme, Karpov had realized that it would be impractical to train all 20 to the same level of preparedness for the first mission. So in May 1960 he selected six of the 20 as a training group for the first flight (the Americans did something similar, selecting Shepard, Grissom and Glenn from the seven rivals). The six were Kartashov, Varlamov, Gagarin, Titov, Nikolayev and Popovich. When Kartashov and Varlamov were invalided out, they were replaced by Nelyubov and Bykovsky. The six were kept waiting even as the final preparations went ahead.

5 April. Final assembly of the manned spaceship in the huge 20 m high hangar at the cosmodrome. Korolev and the State Commission were present and all the cosmonauts were at the launch site. They watched the assembly process from Korolev's glass office on the second floor inside the building. Konstantin Rudnev, the chairman of the State Commission, was there; so too was Valentin Glushko.

The manned spaceship was carried by crane across the assembly hangar and placed gingerly on the third stage. Fasteners were tightened and connectors joined. The nosecone was put in position. The long grey, white and silver rocket lay on its railcar in the hangar, shining under the arc lamps, pointing towards the pad.

8 April. The last meeting between the State Commission and the cosmonaut team. Its purpose was formally to select the pilot and the backup. One of the few pieces of documentary film from the time shows the scene. Nearly twenty cosmonauts in green military suits were huddled around desks in a crowded room behind three rows of desks. Up at the front were Korolev and the State Commission.

There had never been much doubt but that Yuri Gagarin would be selected. Korolev had long identified him as the brightest and most balanced of the team. Gagarin for his own part had always made his desire to be first abundantly clear. The meeting was a short one: Gagarin thanked the Commission, addressed his colleagues, and it was all over. Gherman Titov was named the backup, and Grigori Nelyubov was put in reserve.

Yuri Gagarin (left), with Chief Designer Sergei Korolev.

10 April, 4 p.m. Final meeting of the State Commission, this time on its own. Korolev formally requested permission 'to bring the launch vehicle to the launch pad and prepare for blastoff on 12 April'.

11 April, 5 a.m. It was still dark when the hangar doors clanked back and the railcar, with the manned spaceship on its back, began the hour-long journey to the pad. The darkness, pierced by the lights of the site and the air of expectation, must have reminded the older hands of the days just before Sputnik 1.

1 p.m. Yuri Gagarin was driven to the pad. The rocket had been erected behind him. The chief of the cosmonaut squad, General Kaminin, presented Yuri Gagarin to the assembled workers on the launch pad. Applause broke out when Kaminin told them that Gagarin had been selected. Supervisors from each of the launch teams came forward to give them their good wishes.

Gagarin and Korolev took the escalator to the top of the pad. Together they spent an hour going through the final checks, the problems, the procedures. Bulky, sturdy Korolev went over his creation with the short, stocky, youthful Gagarin, a man not even half his age, trusted for the ultimate assignment. Parting advice.

For Korolev, the strain was too much. His heart, weakened by exhaustion, the frantic preparations and the worry, came close to giving out on this the threshold of his triumph. He made it back to his wooden cottage, surrounded by peaceful poplars, fifteen minutes away. He took pills; then collapsed into bed. Sleep overtook him.

When he awoke it was already dark and well into the night. It was 3 a.m. Korolev was much better now. He would live to see the great day. He opened the window. The cool night air of April caught him in the face. Six hours to go. He phoned Rudnev. He could not sleep either. They arranged to meet at the flower bed outside the cottage before heading off to the pad in Rudnev's car. The only people who did sleep that night were, ironically, Gagarin and Titov. They were in the special 'cosmonauts' cottage', a wooden building right beside Korolev.

12 April, 5.30 a.m. Gagarin and Titov were woken up by Kaminin and trainer Karpov. They were up quickly. Sensors were attached to their bodies to record their every moment. They put on woollen underwear, layer after layer. Finally, attendants helped the cosmonauts into their bright orange suits, then their gloves and boots, followed by their helmets, with the letters 'CCCP' (Russian for USSR) inscribed on top.

Dawn was coming up over the eastern horizon down at the pad. At 7 a.m, final checks were under way. The rocket was fuelled up and wisps of liquid oxygen burned off from time to time. Cold winds whipped around the cabin of the 30 m high spaceship, now named Vostok 1. Designer Konstantin Feoktistov climbed in to test the cabin, switches, lights and radio. It was warm in there. All was in order.

By 7.30 a.m the designers, engineers, and pad workers were assembled at the base of the rocket. Korolev, Glushko and Keldysh stood together chatting. The minibus arrived next from the cosmonauts' cottage, with Gagarin and Titov aboard. At this stage any hopes that Titov might have had of making the flight were evaporating fast. Gagarin was healthy and ready to go.

Yuri Gagarin stepped out, walked gingerly across the apron and took some steps up the elevator. He turned around, aware that he must address the throng of designers and pad workers. Such a contrast to Cape Canaveral. Any candidate astronaut would have exchanged a few pleasantries, even a joke and climbed aboard with a merry 'send her up!' Not so at Baikonour. All were conscious of Russia's historic destiny in space, aware of three unbroken generations of space dreaming, planning and designing; history lay heavy in the air. The world would in time come to treasure this instant. Gagarin spoke:

> Dear friends, close and unknown, fellow countrymen, people of all countries
> and continents! In a few minutes this powerful spaceship will carry me to the

far-off expanses of the universe. What am I going to say to you in these final minutes?

He paused. His voice trailed away... .

Right now, all my life seems to be one wonderful instant. Everything I have ever done, everything I have ever experienced, was for the sake of this minute.

He found it hard to continue... .

Am I happy, setting out on this space flight?

He paused again.

Of course I am. In all times and epochs the greatest happiness for man has been to take part in new discoveries.

Vostok in its cradle.

It was probably his first public speech. As he stood there about to leave the planet with all its security, warmth and life, the full enormity of what he was about to do was slowly sinking in. He was the representative of the human race. He reached out to them:

> I say to you, dear friends, goodbye, as people always say to each other when setting out on a distant journey. I would like to embrace you all, friends and strangers, distant and close! Farewell!

It was 90 minutes to blastoff. Yuri Gagarin disappeared into the lift. In minutes he had clambered into the Vostok. The hatch was closed. He was on his own.

Korolev had meanwhile disappeared into his underground concrete bunker. 'Up periscope!' he commanded. He focused his sights on the rocket. All systems were brought into line: the rocket, the pad, the tracking systems, the computer command centre in Yevpatoria. Telemetry poured in from the booster. Television screens showed Gagarin in the cabin, waiting.

One hour to go. 'Zarya, how do you read ?' called Korolev to Gagarin on the final communications run. Zarya, the Russian for 'dawn', was the code name for earth control. The cosmonaut would have little control over the flight himself: if something went wrong he would open an envelope, find the number of the combination to take manual control over the autopilot and fly Vostok himself. It was an arrangement no NASA pilot would have stood for.

Six minutes. Kaminin and Popovich gathered round Korolev at the periscope. They had gone through so many hours waiting. Now it was really going to happen. The pace quickened. Inevitability set in.

'Key to go position!'

'Air purging!'

'Idle run!'

'Ignition!'

Flames licked around the base. The rocket struggled to be free. A rumbling roar shook the bunker. And away it went!

'Polyekali!' 'Away we go!' triumphed Gagarin.

The booster rose, gathering speed every second. Eyes followed intently upwards. Gradually it bent over in its climbing, heading into the north-east. Four bright light diamonds were all that could be seen of the engine chambers as Vostok disappeared from sight.

For Korolev it was nerve-racking, for contact with Gagarin broke down during the ascent. Fears grew. Had the g forces overcome him? But it was only temporary. Off came the engine fairing as Vostok reached the airless zones. Gagarin was on his own now: ejection was no longer possible. Light flooded into his cabin and momentarily blinded his eyes.

Eight minutes. Engine cutoff. The rumble and shaking of the booster subsided abruptly. Silence, total silence, enveloped Vostok. Yuri Gagarin had reached orbit, somewhere over eastern Siberia. They had done it!

Vostok was 181 km high and its orbit was to reach as high as 327 km. As he gazed through the two portholes of his silent spaceship, Gagarin began to take in the vastness of the planet. Later, he was to describe it in his own words. They tell it best:

I saw for the first time the spherical shape of the Earth. You can see its curvature when looking to the horizon. It is unique and beautiful. The day side of the Earth was clearly visible. The coasts of continents, islands, big rivers, the surfaces of water were distinguishable. It is possible to see the remarkable colourful change from the light surface of the Earth to the completely black sky in which one can see the stars. The dividing line is very thin, just a belt of film surrounding the Earth's sphere. It is of a delicate blue colour and the transition from the blue to the dark is very gradual and lovely. When I emerged from the shadow of the Earth, the horizon looked different. There was a bright orange strip along it which again passed into a blue hue and once again into a dense black colour.

Vostok was travelling at 8 km/s. It headed across the vast blue of the Pacific. Mariners had taken months and months to cross it but Gagarin would transit in 20 minutes. Down below, tossed on the waves of the ocean, Soviet tracking ships turned their antennæ skywards to hear the signals and telemetry of Vostok and the voice of its occupant.

By now, news of the flight was out. At 9.59 a.m., 6.59 a.m. in Britain and 1.59 a.m. in America, Moscow Radio came on air with the historic announcement. Static crackled as in slow measured tones, straining with excitement, the reader began, conscious of history in the making:

Today, 12 April 1961, the first cosmic ship named Vostok, with a man on board, was orbited around the Earth from the Soviet Union.
He is an airman, Major Yuri Gagarin... .

At Cape Canaveral, America's Mercury astronauts were woken and told. It must have hit them like a cold, wet sponge. None of their names would go down in history, but instead that of a diminutive Russian major, who none had ever head of. The decision to announce the launching when Gagarin was still in space was no accident, nor an indicator of openness about space travel. Quite the opposite; it arose from the paranoia of the central committee of the CPSU, who were afraid that if Gagarin landed unannounced on foreign soil he might be seized as a spy; a pre-announcement would facilitate his release.

Gagarin hurtled on. He accustomed himself to weightlessness. He wrote notes on a pad, and when he finished, it floated free and lodged under the seat. An hour into the flight and he was over Cape Horn, South America. Night fell:

I have never forgotten it. The stars were so clearly visible—blindingly bright and full-bodied. The sky was blacker than it ever appears on earth, with the real slate blackness of space.

The automatic guidance system locked on. Gagarin's next task was to test the ability of a man to eat and drink in space. He took away some tubes from their racks, squeezed them and found no difficulty. Little water droplets floated around the cabin. Vostok flashed into daylight and the Sun marched over the eastern horizon. Gas jets hissed in the vacuum. Vostok turned around to prepare for retrofire. All this time Gagarin reported back his every move, his every sensation. His voice came through the mushy crackly short wave.

10.25 a.m. Rockets fired briefly over west Africa. They cut 500 km/h off Vostok's speed. It was just enough to send the spaceship dipping into the atmosphere. Still 600 km from home, Vostok descended in a giant arc over bodies of land and water towards its motherland. The fires of re-entry glowed red around the portholes. Was the trajectory right? Would the heat burst through?

The return to Earth was not easy. The retrorocket failed to separate, and burned away during the descent, exactly as happened to John Glenn nine months later. Out of radio contact (the heat was enough to ionize radio waves), Gagarin could only wait and hope. He was pressed into his seat ever harder as the g forces built up. But re-entry heat did not break through. The g forces eased off. The worst was over. Outside, the sky was no longer black, but blue. Gagarin was back in the atmosphere once more.

The hatch on Vostok blew away. Gagarin's ejector seat then shot him away in turn. Real air blew in Yuri Gagarin's face once more. With an enormous tug the parachutes jerked him upwards. He was floating under canopy. Where was he? Down below were ploughed fields, the squares of state farms, the springtime of April. Gagarin floated earthwards, orange-suited under a white parachute. The main Vostok capsule, much heavier, was descending some distance away at greater speed.

The scorched cabin of Vostok 1 after its return from orbit. When Gagarin himself landed, farmers ran forward with pitchforks and stakes, thinking another American spy had been shot down.

The flier was first noticed by a woman planting potatoes with her six-year-old daughter. Members of a tractor brigade had seen him descending from afar and rushed to the spot. They were the first to reach the capsule, which was blackened, giving off heat and still far too hot to touch. However, they did not come to greet Gagarin. Unaware of the flight, but very much aware of Gary Powers' spy flight the previous year, they mistook the flier for another American spy. They rushed forward with pitchforks and stakes.

'Where am I? Where's the nearest town?' Gagarin kept on asking. 'I must report my return to Earth!' he argued, as he pulled off his white helmet. But for the 'CCCP' on it and news of the flight breaking on the radio, they might never have believed him.

ALL OVER

Gagarin's flight lasted a mere 108 minutes. It was an epochal flight. No one could ever make that first flight again. Nothing would ever be the same again. Elation swept the USSR. Crowds flocked onto the streets. Millions tuned in their radios to hear more about the flight and about the man who made it. Strangers greeted each other in the street. Choirs sang in his honour. Roads were named after him. Khrushchev was alert to the advantages to himself. He phoned the cosmonaut:

> You and I together with all our people shall solemnly celebrate this great exploit. Let the whole world look and see what our great country is capable of.
> Let the capitalist countries catch up with us.

The Americans fully realized what a blow this was to their own plans. Sputnik took some days, even weeks, to sink in. Gagarin's effect was total and immediate. 'Another Pearl Harbour' was a typical American reaction. The Americans had consciously tried to beat the Russians to the goal of a man-in-space: their suborbital flight was set for 28 April. They had been beaten and roundly beaten, for Gagarin had gone for a full orbit. The Americans were still at least six months from that. Congressmen fumed. Editors railed. Two days after the Gagarin flight, Kennedy met with his senior advisers and top NASA officials, led by its director James Webb. They recall afterwards that Kennedy was agitated, irritable and impatient:

> Just tell me how to catch up. Let's find somebody. Anybody. I don't care if the janitor over there has the answer, if he knows how.

Kennedy's reaction was quite different from Eisenhower's. He made no attempt to play down Gagarin. It was one in the eye. Kennedy was reeling and there would have to be some kind of response. He was reeling three days later when his Bay of Pigs invasion of Castro's Cuba collapsed. His presidency seemed near to collapse too.

Gherman Titov was the first to greet Gagarin. He landed at the nearest airfield and rushed to congratulate him on behalf of his colleagues. For the cosmonauts and Korolev, it was their best day ever. They were swept away with unrestrained joy that obliterated all the bitter memories of past failures. It was such a monumental success that no propaganda machine could ever exaggerate. The last big psychological barrier had been smashed and manned space flight was here to stay.

At nine that night they celebrated in a *dacha* (country cottage) amidst woods on a hill overlooking the river Volga. In speeches, extravagant commitments were given about conquering the cosmos. No one minded. Gagarin rested the next day. He took Titov for a boat trip and long walks to advise him about his flight while his memory was still fresh. On the 14 April, Gagarin flew to Moscow.

The heroes' welcome in Moscow attracted world-wide attention, for it was the first time that a transnational telecast had been arranged. The European Broadcasting Union carried the whole show live—to the curious Europeans and the furious Americans. As his Il-lyushin-18 propeller plane flew in over the spires of the Kremlin, seven jets rose in escort. It landed at Vnukuvo Airport. In a military coat, Gagarin marched along a thick orange carpet to the stand. He saluted Nikita Khrushchev who was bubbling and chuckling away, and stood to attention for the Internationale; then the two men drove into the city.

Moscow had known nothing like it since Victory Day in 1945. Millions turned out, flowers were everywhere, and May Day banners were hastily put up ahead of time. Gagarin's parents turned up in their farming clothes: he in his carpenter's cap, she in her old shawl. In a curious way, they symbolized the old Russia and the new.

The crowds were so big that the cosmonaut team could not fight its way through. There was a public meeting in Red Square, a reception in the Kremlin, and speeches galore. Khrushchev had a field day. He was radiant throughout. There was a tribute to Tsiolkovsky, praise for Soviet scientists, mocking comments for America's puny efforts,

Yuri Gagarin had risen from being virtually unknown to being a world hero. Away from the limelight, he relaxes water-skiing.

and promises of more spectacular flights. Gagarin was kept in the limelight. There were two reasons for this. First, until that day Gagarin was virtually unknown and now he was a world hero. Second, almost no film of Gagarin's flight had been released. Gagarin at a reception was about as close as most people would get to his achievement for the time being.

Gagarin was soon thrust into a world tour. He was sent first throughout the socialist countries, then further abroad. His youthful looks, his broad smile, his quiet manner—all won instant appeal. He went to Europe, America and Cuba. He visited Britain in July 1961. An open Rolls Royce, registered YG 1, was provided for him. Thousands lined the route from the airport. He toured London, met the Queen and spent a day in Manchester with the Amalgamated Union of Foundry workers. By this time the Americans had emerged from their trance and put together a space plan of truly colossal proportions.

Gagarin's triumph was barely a week old when President Kennedy sent Lyndon Johnson, his Vice-President and Chairman of the Space Council, the following memorandum:

(1)   Do we have a chance of beating the Soviets by putting a laboratory in space, or by a trip around the Moon, or by a rocket to land on the Moon and back with a man? Is there any programme which promises dramatic results in which we could win?
(2)   How much additional would it cost?
(3)   Are we working 24 hours a day on existing programmes? If not, why not? If not, will you make recommendations how work can be speeded up?
(4)   Are we making maximum effort? Are we achieving necessary results?

NASA argued for a Moon landing. A crash programme could achieve that by 1967 for $34bn. It would cost $22bn for a 1969 landing date. Von Braun concurred, admitting that in order to reach these targets, nearly all other programmes would have to be left aside. Kennedy still agonized. He worried about the costs, the lack of public support. A collaborative Moon programme with the Soviet Union was even considered.[22] Kennedy cast around for more earthly alternatives, even desalting the oceans. On 20 April he again asked Johnson to explore other spaceflight options, such as space stations. He asked the right questions—but to the wrong man. Johnson, giving the matter the minimum appearance of decent consideration, wrote back on the 29 April saying that only a manned landing on the Moon would be an appropriate response. Johnson had long argued for greater space involvement and had taken the view that superiority to the Russians was not just desirable, but imperative. Being a politician, he could add the growing space industry to his burgeoning empire of influence.

The likely high costs of a Moon race became less of a problem when during April the American spy and Soviet double agent Oleg Penkovsky confirmed what American intelligence had long suspected, that the R-7 rocket was not the military threat that the Americans had imagined. Only four had been deployed, all at Plesetsk.[23] This was a different matter indeed from the hundreds, even thousands, that Kennedy had warned about during his presidential campaign. Penkovsky was later caught and shot.

In the middle of this, on 25 April, America tried again. NASA planned a full-scale demonstration of the man-in-orbit flight. The larger Atlas booster would put up a Mercury capsule, which would orbit the Earth twice and be recovered in the ocean. It would put the

United States on a par with Spaceship 5 and would mean an American in orbit in the autumn. 40 seconds into the flight at 5000 m, the Atlas booster exploded sky high. Debris rained down on frightened journalists, who huddled under their cars to avoid injury. The escape system did work though.

All this was quickly forgotten when on 5 May the Americans at last put up their own spaceman. Alan Shepard, a rugged test pilot, took his Mercury capsule up 180 km over the Florida coast, turned it round in the vacuum and brought it back into the Atlantic Ocean. Millions listened with bated breath to his crisp reports. They gasped when he read out his altitude figures and they were mightily relieved when the helicopter fished him out of the sea. Reporters gabbled away: it was Buck Rogers come true.

15-minute flight or not, America was thrilled. National honour was at least partly restored. Shepard was greeted as a hero. The nation was jubilant. As Washington partied, Johnson worked through the night drafting the Moon-landing prospectus. He knew he had to move fast before sceptics cast doubt in the President's mind. On 7 May, riding high on the wave of elation, Johnson presented his Moon plans to the President. They were countersigned by NASA administrator James Webb and Defence Secretary Robert MacNamara. They recommended a man-on-the-Moon programme as the principal American space objective. 'National prestige' was cited as the main reason. There was little or no mention of science. There was reference instead to Soviet success. It was almost admitted that the programme was unjustified by scientific, commercial or military criteria. It is worth noting that no attempt was made to assess Soviet objectives in space. They were automatically and uncritically assumed to be a man-on-the-Moon as soon as possible, perhaps in 1967, the 50th anniversary of the Bolshevik revolution.

Not for the first time, Johnson had outmanoeuvred his political foes. John F. Kennedy summoned Congress into special session, and told them:

> I believe that this nation should commit itself to achieving the goal, before the decade is out, of landing a man on the Moon and returning him safely to the Earth.

Costings put the price of the venture as $20bn. The Senate approved the proposal after a debate of only one hour. Only five Senators spoke. The initial response to the idea was less than enthusiastic: perhaps the implications had not set in. But Kennedy had, perhaps even inadvertently, captured something in the American psyche. That autumn, Kennedy made a tour of college campuses around the nation. He tried a number of themes which he thought might interest the students. He received a polite, subdued response. That changed, however, when he mentioned the journey to the Moon. On one occasion, his speech was repeatedly interrupted by applause:

> We choose to go the Moon... (applause)...
> We choose to go the Moon... (more applause)... in this decade not because it is easy but because it is hard. That goal will serve to organize and measure the best of our energies and skills. That challenge is one we are willing to accept, one we are unwilling to postpone and one we intend to win... (more applause)... .

The Americans had by contrast embarked on a man-on-the-Moon programme that was conceived, planned, announced and set in train in the period of only five weeks, motivated largely by a desire not to be beaten in technical supremacy and originating from a new President desirous to achieve something, anything. Not content with the more realistic objective of going around the Moon first, the Americans were starting a lap behind the USSR and set themselves an extra lap to run. It was by all accounts a panic decision, a gut reaction. Few people were consulted. Hardly any other options were considered. In another age, it would have been a recipe for national disaster. But any critics (if there had been any) reckoned without NASA's organizational capabilities and American industry booming in top gear.

GOOD MORNING EARTH!

As if to underline the wisdom of the new venture, NASA prepared a second mission to follow Alan Shepherd. The pilot was Virgil Grissom. Once again the scene shifted to Cape Canaveral. The excited crowds, the shimmering heat, the exasperating countdown delays. Grissom lifted off on 21 July. Up he went, 190 km high and back down into the ocean. Then suddenly all the radio commentaries were interrupted and suspended. Music played. The worst was suspected.

As his capsule bobbed in the ocean, Grissom's hatch blew off. The cabin filled rapidly with water. The astronaut scrambled out, swallowing water, and was rescued by helicopter. His helmet was being investigated by a 3 m long shark when it was found. His capsule sunk to the bottom. Could America now get a man in orbit, a proper space flight, before the Russians repeated Gagarin's flight?

The cosmonaut team—all twenty of them—had spent most of May vacationing near the Black Sea at Sochi. They were joined by Korolev, his wife and daughter and some senior trainers. It was their first rest since they were recruited. Gherman Titov was appointed to fly the next mission. The aim of the second flight was a full day in space—Korolev's original objective. Actually there was little choice about the duration of the mission. Vostok could not come down on Soviet territory once it had gone three orbits, for its flight path would have moved too far to the west. And it would not be near the landing site again till orbit 16, a day later.

Gherman Titov remembered going asleep in the cosmonauts' cottage the night before the mission. It was hot and stuffy so he had to open the windows and run fans. He fell asleep listening to the metallic sounds that came from the assembly workshop. The date was determined by Khrushchev, designed to impress people with Soviet power as tensions rose in Berlin (the Berlin wall was erected that month). But at night-time, as in any desert, the temperature fell, waking him. He turned off the fans. He must have contemplated the fact that he would be the first man to sleep in space. The following day was Sunday, 6 August, and two men, Titov and his backup Nikolayev, left for the pad in the transfer van. There was none of the tension of 12 April. The two men joked and sang.

Vostok 2 lifted off at 9 a.m. The rocket sped away rapidly from the scorched summer steppe and headed into the Sun. At one stage anyone looking upwards might imagine that there were two bright suns close together in the sky, so brightly did the rocket flames shine. Vostok 2 went into an orbit of 183 by 244 km, 65 deg, 88.4 min. As weightlessness descended on the cosmonaut, Titov floated free, upside down, and headed for the first of seventeen sunrises and sunsets that he was going to experience over the next day.

Gherman Titov scheduled an activity for each orbit. Throughout, he was observed on TV at 10 frames/second. Ground observers noted him eating the first space lunch on orbit 3. It consisted of purée, meat and liver pâtés and blackcurrant juice. Some of the juice escaped and floated off round the cabin. On orbit 4 to 5, Titov manoeuvred his spaceship manually, something Gagarin had not done. Gas jets moved it around its centre of mass. At the same time, Titov took movie pictures of the Earth out of the window, using a 'Konvass' camera. Primitive and of poor quality, the pictures conveyed something of the speed of orbital travel, as Vostok 2 soared over mountains, clouds, seas and oceans.

It was on orbit 6 that Titov came across one of the first major problems of space travel: nausea. Of all the terrible afflictions that orbital travel was predicted to bring—from madness to genetic mutation—nausea was subsequently to prove both the most mundane and the most intractable. Over the next twenty years, nausea was to afflict 50% of all travellers in space, Russian and American alike. All that Gherman Titov was trying to do was to go to sleep. Yet as he did so he got more and more disorientated and sicker, and saw his control panel floating away above him. By lying perfectly still he overcame his

Four early Soviet cosmonauts (left to right): Gherman Titov, Pavel Popovich, Alexei Leonov and Andrian Nikolayev.

vertigo and got to sleep. The reason for space sickness, it was subsequently determined, was loss of balance in the inner ear. Otoliths—tiny stones in the liquid-filled inner ear—normally signal a change of balance or position to the brain. In weightlessness the otoliths lose their reference point.

Nausea or not, Gherman Titov eventually slept soundly—indeed he overslept 35 min over the 7½ hours planned. 'Good morning, Earth!' hailed one British daily, celebrating the fact of Titov being the first man to awake to the world from orbit. The effortless ease of the second Vostok flight was one of the main features to strike Western observers. As night fell that summer evening, Vostok 2 could be seen as a bright light crossing the sky from the south-west to the north-east over a period of three or four minutes. It crossed the United States too.

The nausea passed. The cosmonaut was bright and alert come early 7 August. He wrote up his logbook and prepared for the return to Earth. The retrorockets fired on orbit 17. Titov blazed through the upper atmosphere. Outside the cabin, flames turned from pink to scarlet to purple and crimson. Titov ejected from the cabin and came down by parachute. He landed only 200 m from a railway line. He had been up there for 25 h 18 min, covering 703 143 km.

Soon after landing, he was met by Andrian Nikolayev and Yuri Gagarin, the latter just back from a triumphant tour of the United States. There was a debriefing the next day at the Zhiguli hills overlooking the Volga. A parade through Moscow followed. There was then another reception at the rocket assembly plant when a beaming, proud Titov presented Sergei Korolev with his flight logbook. For observers, Titov had confirmed Soviet space supremacy. Gagarin was not just a 'lucky first'. A full day in space was, coincidentally, the objective of the last Mercury mission —and the Americans had yet to make even one flight into orbit! What would the Russians do next?

FIRST MOONSHIP DESIGNS: THE SOYUZ COMPLEX

Korolev was already preparing plans for the next Soviet steps into space. On 10 March 1962, Sergei Korolev, as Chief Designer and Director of OKB-1, approved a document entitled 'Complex for the assembly of space vehicles in artificial satellite orbit (the Soyuz)'. This described a 3-man spacecraft which would link up in orbit with a stack of three propulsion modules which could send the manned spacecraft on a loop around the Moon.[24] On 10 May 1963, Korolev approved a second version, called 'Assembly of vehicles in Earth satellite orbit', known in shorthand as the Soyuz complex. The complex comprised a rocket block, which was launched 'dry' (not fuelled up) and which was the largest single unit. It contained automatic rendezvous and docking equipment and was labelled the 'Soyuz B' by Korolev; a space tanker, containing liquid fuel, called the Soyuz V; and a new manned spacecraft, called the Soyuz A. Initially, the Soyuz complex would enable the Soyuz to manoeuvre to high orbits and to build and refuel space stations. Soyuz A was a new generation spaceship, 7.7 m long, 2.3 m in diameter, with a mass of 5800 kg. The design was radical, to say the least. At the bottom was an equipment section with fuel, radar and rocket motor. On top of this was a cone-shaped cabin for a three-man crew. Orthodox enough so far, but on top of that was a large cylindrically shaped orbital module. This provided extra cabin space (the cabin on its own would be cramped) and room for experiments and research.

The sequence of events for a Moon flight was as follows. On day one, the rocket block, Soyuz B, would be launched into an orbit of 226 km, 65 deg. It would be tested out to see that its guidance and manoeuvring units were functioning. On day two, the first of three Soyuz V tankers would be launched. Because the fuel was volatile it would have to be transferred quickly. The rocket block would be the 'active' spacecraft and would carry out the rendezvous and docking manoeuvres normally on the first orbit. Fuel would then be transferred in pipes. After three tanker linkups, a Soyuz A manned spaceship would be launched. It would be met by the rocket block, which, using its newly transferred fuel, would blast Moonwards.

In 1961–3, when the Russians first began to consider a manned flight to the Moon, the method which the Soyuz complex outlined, Earth orbit rendezvous (EOR) was a natural proposition to a nation bred on the theories of Tsiolkovsky. The two other possible methods of going to the Moon were direct ascent and a much more obscure method called lunar orbit rendezvous. Direct ascent was the most popular one in the science fiction literature of the time. The *Stories of Tintin* cartoon depicted this type of method. A huge rocket—it really would have to be massive—would put up a Moonship which would fly direct to the Moon, slow down while coming in to land, touch down and deposit two or three astronauts directly on the surface. After a period of exploration, the cosmonauts would climb back into their mother ship and fire direct back to Earth. Another variation on this was lunar orbit rendezvous (LOR). A booster would place both command ship and lunar cabin direct into Moon orbit, cutting out the Earth orbit stage. The rest of the mission would then proceed as in the EOR method. It was a simpler method, but depended on a big, reliable booster, though nothing as big as for the direct ascent method.

The obvious follow-on to Gherman Titov's flight was simply a longer mission—perhaps three days. Sergei Korolev, however, thought ahead just one stage further. Since orbital rendezvous was so critical to the Soyuz complex, could not some early work be done on this problem? Even though Vostok was not manoeuvrable, could they not test launching accuracy by launching one Vostok into close orbit with another, seeing how close they would come?

AMERICA'S ROUTE TO THE MOON

Even as Korolev's design bureau struggled with the Soyuz complex, America's engineers laboured to put out a plan with a similar purpose in mind. The key difference between the two was that the Americans had a specific objective and a definite date to aim for.

First off the drawing board—and designed some time even before Kennedy's announcement—was the manned spacecraft. The Space Task Group at Langley, Virginia, came up with a prototype Moon craft, Apollo, as early as July 1960. The group was led by Maxime Faget, the designer of the Mercury capsule. Apollo would carry three astronauts in a shirtsleeve environment, would employ a powerful manoeuvring engine and would have the ability to navigate independently of the ground in flights lasting up to ten days. Apollo would have the ability to fly in and out of lunar orbit and would consist of a cone-shaped command module atop a service module which held the rocket engine and nozzle.

But which method would the Americans use? The von Braun team favoured EOR, like the Soyuz complex, but it was in a minority. Virtually everyone else favoured direct ascent using a massive rocket, which in time came to be called Nova. This would be a giant rocket-to-end-rockets, with a thrust of 6 million kilogrammes and able to put up 180 tonnes. It would be 7 m higher than the length of a football field. This leviathan would be in keeping with the nation that built the Empire State Building and the Hoover Dam.

Even though Nova was NASA's favourite throughout 1961, the von Braun team at Huntsville, Alabama continued to sow doubts in people's minds. Instead, they put forward a booster called Super-Saturn. Two of these, each half the size of Nova, could do the same job using EOR. The Nova people replied by pointing out that EOR had never been tried before, that orbital refuelling was an unknown quantity and potentially dangerous, and the two Super-Saturns would have to be launched with enormous accuracy. Long countdown delays were the norm in 1961. Direct ascent was a no-nonsense, straight, it'll-get-us-there approach.

Yet, on closer examination, direct ascent had its own drawbacks, quite apart form the size of Nova. The main one was: just how do you land on the Moon? The moonlander would have to be streamlined and pencil-shaped, by virtue of its position on the top of the Nova. So how do you land a pencil-shaped object on the Moon, steering from the top? How do you look down from the top? Or could you land on the side? Or would it then turn over?

With both these proposals under fire, a third emerged. Lunar Orbit Rendezvous (LOR) was the campaign of a Langley engineer called John Houbolt. He borrowed the idea from a paper by Yuri Kondratyuk of 1930. Houbolt's proposal was first made in December 1960. LOR had two advantages: it cut out the EOR stage; and the thrust required to put two spacecraft in lunar orbit was actually not that much more proportionately than that needed for EOR. The lunar cabin could be entirely purpose-built, since it did not need to return to Earth through a re-entry; and any problems about viewing the landing site could be forgotten.

All three methods were in the melting pot at NASA during the springtime of 1962, with EOR a firm favourite, having ousted direct ascent. NASA chiefs then asked the questions: Which was the most likely to succeed? Which was the safest? Which was soonest? Direct ascent faded under all three criteria, so it boiled down to a choice between EOR and LOR. The clincher came on 7 June 1962, when von Braun changed his mind. He now backed LOR. It was simpler than EOR, as safe, and by his reckoning could be accomplished six months sooner. NASA announced on 11 July 1962 that LOR would be the method. Later that summer, President Kennedy toured NASA's growing empire, and in October the contracts were set up. Russia's plans were still on the drawing board in Sergei Korolev's office. As the American Moon effort got into gear, the Soviet political leadership showed no interest in moving them out of the design bureau onto the factory floor. With the Soviet Union so far ahead in space, there seemed no need to.

SPACE TWINS

As 1962 came in, America still had not put a man into orbit. This was rectified when after months of exasperating delays John Glenn rocketed into orbit on 20 February. John Glenn seized the imagination of the American people. There was live minute-by-minute coverage from the scorching launch at Cape Canaveral to splash down in the Atlantic five hours later. His reports by radio were heard sharp and crisp as he passed over the Indian Ocean...then Australia... then California. They heard John Glenn describe the sunrises, the sunsets, his old booster tumbling below; fireflies (small particles) outside the cabin; and the oceans and landmasses below. Crisis struck on the third and last orbit when telemetry indicated that the heat shield had come loose. The whole nation prayed as he came through re-entry and the shield stayed in place. John Glenn was welcomed home as a hero no less so than Gagarin or Titov in their countries. He was feted everywhere—there were ticker-tape parades, and schools were named after him. American honour was indeed restored.

NASA ran a repeat mission in May. Aurora 7 went aloft on the 24 May, carrying Malcolm Scott Carpenter. His flight was at least as nerve-wracking as John Glenn's. By the third orbit he had run out of fuel—partly because some thrusters had been used inadvertently, and partly because he had used excessive fuel and time getting pictures of the sunsets in orbit. He had to align Aurora 7 for re-entry himself. His tiny Mercury capsule was 27 deg in yaw out of alignment by the time of retrofire. The rockets did not fire and by the time he pressed the button himself, four seconds later, Aurora 7 was way off course. He was not heard from again and radio commentators concluded that he was lost. In sepulchral terms, they prepared the nation for the worst. Two hours after the estimated splashdown time, a rescue plane spotted Carpenter in a dinghy. He had come down 330 km off course and not far from Puerto Rico. But NASA's confidence, if anything, improved. It was now a full year since Kennedy had laid down the great challenge.

IRON MAN

In the USSR the next Vostok pilots were entering the most intensive phase of training. The 'iron man', Andrian Nikolayev, took his place in Vostok 3, and Pavel Popovich was appointed to Vostok 4. The upcoming double flight was the best kept secret the Russians ever had. Normally, leaks about new missions reached the West beforehand, and on later occasions the names of the crew get out. But on this double flight, not a hint escaped. 4 August was the last night the cosmonauts had in Moscow before the flight. Andrian Nikolayev held a party in his spacious bachelor apartment accompanied by fruit and wine. In the same building, Pavel Popovich celebrated with Marina and daughter Natasha. At 11 p.m. the party was over. A final planning session was held in Star Town, and the next morning the space squad and their backups took an Illyushin 18 propeller plane for the lengthy journey across Russia down to Kazakhstan. On 6 August, Gherman Titov held a celebration to mark his own flight a year earlier. Sergei Korolev came as well. His eyes were bloodshot: the strain from preparing the new flight and designing the Soyuz complex had taken their toll.

Vostok 3 headed off at 11.30 a.m., 11 August, a Saturday. In eight minutes Andrian Nikolayev was in orbit, silent and free, and settled down for a marathon four-day journey, quadrupling the existing day-long record. His orbit was 183 by 235 km. Andrian Nikolayev became the first man to float free in his cabin out of the restraining straps. An encouraging sign was that when he tried to go to sleep some orbits later he felt none of the nausea that had afflicted Gherman Titov.

Vostok 3 commander Andrian Nikolayev (left) with Yuri Gagarın.

'Long trip likely by Soviet spaceman' was a typical Western press headline. Andrian Nikolayev was expected to fly several days. A number of radio stations on the ground in the West picked up his voice as he reported back. Moscow television showed him smiling and waving and spinning his log book and pencil around the cabin. The best known of the tracking stations was the huge 80 m dish operated by Sir Bernard Lovell from Jodrell Bank in Cheshire in England. He had become something of an expert on 'what the Russians were up to'. Any reporter wanting to get a line on the latest Vostok put a call through to Jodrell Bank.

At 11.30 a.m. on Sunday morning, 12 August, Lovell's radio technician tuned in to pick up Vostok 3 as it flew overhead. He got the fright of his life. Instead of picking up the sole voice of Andrian Nikolayev talking calmly to ground control, he got the bubbling voice of an excited new cosmonaut reporting from Vostok 4. Two cosmonauts were now circling the Earth!

As Vostok 3 passed over Baikonour on its 16th orbit it was most precisely tracked by ground radar. Vostok 4 counted down amazingly smoothly and without a hitch. Right down to liftoff, new data were fed into Vostok's computer, giving exact altitude, azimuth and orbital inclination. And accurate it was! As Pavel Popovich soared into orbit aboard Vostok 4 his entry point in orbit closed to a mere 6500 m from Vostok 3. It was a moment of triumph. Just a year and a half after Gagarin, The USSR had two cosmonauts flying in orbit within sight of each other, or, put mathematically, a mere 1/2000th of an orbital radius. Andrian Nikolayev, alone for the previous day, could see Vostok 4 gleaming in the

Examples of the food eaten by Vostok 3 and 4 cosmonauts Andrian Nikolayev and Pavel Popovich, including small pieces.

sunlight through the porthole as it rose to meet him. The two of them and Yuri Gagarin, the capsule communicator, were wild with delight.

Vostok 4's orbit measured 180 by 237 km. Lacking a manoeuvring engine, the two cosmonauts drifted gradually apart, but retained continuous radio contact. Pavel Popovich was an enthusiastic flier and kept up endless chatter with the ground. As he swept across the Pacific Ocean, he recorded:

> The spacecraft is flying at an incredible speed so the view keeps changing. Now I can see starry sky through the right view port. It is inky black. The big bright stars are visible as from Earth but they don't twinkle. The little ones look like bright pin points.
>
> The spacecraft is coming out of shadow. What a view! A person on Earth will never see anything like it. This is the cosmic dawn. Just look! The Earth's horizon is a vivid wine colour. Then a dark blue band appears. Next comes a bright blue band shading off into the blue sky. It keeps widening, glowing, spreading out and the Sun appears. The horizon turns orange and a more delicate lighter blue. Beautiful!

The launching of Vostok 4 threw the West into frenzy. For sheer nerve, daring and imagination, the double flight was overwhelming. The significance of the close approach on the first orbit was lost on no one. The Press Association's science correspondent, in a wire dispatch that was used throughout the world, was one of many to be entranced in a report that appeared in many newspapers on the morning of 13 August 1962. Although he was far from accurate in his assessment of what Vostok could actually do, the same could not be said for the implications of the close flight. One would almost think that he had seen the design of the Soyuz complex:

> At about 8.30 a.m. this morning the Russians may decide to make an attempt to send the two cosmonauts now in space on a flight to the Moon in one of two spaceships describing almost identical orbits around the Earth.
>
> They are travelling at 18 000 mph only a few miles apart. When the two astronauts are near their control base an attempt may be made to bring them together. This would be the most critical time in the history of space exploration.

Sir Bernard Lovell volunteered that the flight was 'the most remarkable development man has ever seen'. President Kennedy, holidaying in Boot Harbour, Maine, was reported to be 'severely jolted'. Nikita Khrushchev was of course having a ball and spoke repeatedly to the men by phone.

Once the first shock had passed, there was little to do but watch as the flight went into a third and then a fourth and finally a fifth day, with no signs of any difficulty. The next American flight, it was pointed out contemptuously, was to be a long one of nine hours. No linkup was of course forthcoming—a first approach was all that had been contemplated. By the 33rd orbit, the 'space twins' were 850 km apart and by the 64th, 2850 km.

Because of the length of the flight, a huge range of experiments could be conducted. Medical instruments kept a continuous watch on each cosmonaut's pulse, breathing, strain, sleep, eyes and nervous system. The two men tested how water bubbles formed in a flask in zero gravity. As they observed the Earth by night they could make out the lights of cities.

The marathon came to an end on Wednesday morning 15 August. As if to flaunt their precision, both re-entries were timed together. Andrian Nikolayev came down by parachute at 9.52 a.m. after 64 orbits, Popovich at 9.57 a.m. after 48 orbits (four and three days respectively). The following Saturday, Moscow gave the two heroes the welcome they deserved.

For Korolev's design of the Soyuz complex, now maturing, the flights of Vostoks 3 and 4 were immensely encouraging. The first orbit approach of 6500 m was better than what had been hoped and took much of the fear out of the notion of orbital rendezvous. The length of the flight, the effortless precision of launch and landing, the reliability of Vostok—these things were icing on the cake. But by the time Vostok 5 left the ground, disappointments in the unmanned programme lay ahead.

VENUS, MARS AND THE MOON

The promising start made by Venera 1 on its flight to Venus in 1961 encouraged Soviet scientists to try a major assault on Venus in the late summer of 1962. The Venera 1 experience indicated that real discoveries could be made once problems with long-distance communication were sorted out. Three probes were built. The first two were MV-1s (landers), the third a flyby.

What was to be the first probe to Venus took off on 25 August 1962. The escape stage failed to restart and the probe decayed on 28 August. A second launching met the same fate on 1 September, decaying after five days. On 12 September, the third stage of the flyby probe exploded into seven large pieces. All these launches were monitored by American radars in Turkey, although details were not released by the Pentagon until 1964.

What was basically affecting the upper stage of the Molniya rocket was the difficulty in igniting propellants in zero gravity. During the boost phase, propellants are forced by gravity into the pumps. Once in zero gravity, these conditions no longer hold true, and propellants begin to behave in peculiar ways. American space probes during the same period were not much more successful either. Of the three American space probes to the Moon of 1962, Ranger 3 missed the Moon by 37 000 km and Ranger 5 by 700 km. Ranger 4 crashed on the far side, its radio dead. Of its Venus probes, Mariner 1 crashed into the South Atlantic Ocean, though Mariner 2 was much more successful, flying by Venus in December 1962 and returning a stream of valuable data.

Similar problems plagued Soviet attempts to reach Mars in 1962. Again, three probes were prepared, the first two as flybys, the third as a lander. The first launch was on 24 October. The probe broke up while trying to struggle free of Earth's atmosphere. It broke into so many pieces that it nearly persuaded American radars that the United States was under missile attack, which was worrying timing, for the Cuban missile crisis was then at its height. The final Mars probe, the lander, on 4 November, failed to leave orbit and decayed two months later. The lander had been overweight, a problem which Korolev solved in characteristic manner. He ordered that the life-detection device be removed to the nearby desert to see if it could find life in that particular spot in the Kazakhstan desert. It couldn't, so it didn't fly to Mars either.

The only bright spot in the five out of six failure rate was when on 1 November the Mars 1 probe successfully got away. Within days it was clear that it was working well and on an accurate path to the Red Planet. Mars 1 was much more sophisticated than its Venus predecessor. It weighed more, at 894 kg, and was larger: a cylinder 3.3 m long, with solar panels giving it a wing span of 4 m and it had a huge umbrella-shaped high-gain antenna. It carried a mid-course correction engine and thermal radiators. Mars 1 was an ambitious experiment for its day. It carried television cameras, meteoroid detectors and instruments for reporting on the atmosphere, radiation fields and surface of Mars. The information collected was telemetred to Earth every five days.

At the time, Mars held out major hopes for astronomers and science fiction addicts, not to mention scientists themselves. Smaller than Earth but larger than the Moon, cooler because it was further away from the Sun, there were indications that it had an atmosphere. Its red colour was visible in telescopes; the more discerning could make out polar caps and possible waves of vegetation. Perhaps there was life. Mars 1 headed out into the raw cold of deep space. It picked up and measured the solar wind. Meteoroid matter declined the further it moved away from the Earth's orbit.

Sadly, there was to be no televisual encounter. On 21 March 1963 the orientation system broke down and as a result the transmitters no longer pointed towards Earth. Mars 1 was 106 million kilometres away at the time, which was a new record for long-distance communication. Maybe photographs were indeed taken as Mars 1 approached the planet at 197 000 km in June and were transmitted somewhere else.

Observers were nonetheless impressed. Despite America's triumph with Mariner 2, Mars 1 was seen to be more ambitious. They would have been less impressed if they knew of the failures that lay behind Mars 1.

Second round of Venus, Mars missions

25 Aug 1962	Venus lander	Failure
1 Sep 1962	Venus lander	Failure
12 Sep 1962	Venus flyby	Failure
24 Oct 1962	Mars flyby	Failure
1 Nov 1962	Mars flyby	Mars 1 (contact lost)
4 Nov 1962	Mars lander	Failure

BACK TO THE MOON

The fact that these problems with the Molniya upper stage were still not ironed out became obvious once more with the premature resumption of the Moon programme in early 1963. The objective of the three 1963 Moon probes was nothing less than a soft-landing on the Moon. A soft-landing was absolutely essential to landing cosmonauts on the Moon. Not until a probe soft-landed would it be possible to know the exact nature of the lunar soil, the dangers of rocks and craters, and the amount of radiation on the surface. These measurements were essential because they would determine, in the first two instances, the strength and size of the lunar module's landing legs.

The Moon probe had two modules. The instrument compartment, cylinder-shaped, carried a combined manoeuvring engine and retrorocket, orientation devices, transmitters and fuel. The lander, attached in a sphere on the top, was quite small, only 100 kg. It was ball-shaped, and on landing would shoot out and, once it settled on the surface, a camera would peep up to take pictures. It followed very closely the popular image of what an alien probe landing on Earth would look like. The final approach to landing would be the most difficult phase. The rocket on the 1500 kg vehicle had to fire at the correct angle about 46 s before the predicted landing: too early, and it would run out of fuel before reaching the surface, pick up speed again and crash to pieces; too late, and it would impact too fast.

Thanks to more problems with the upper stage, these issues were to remain academic throughout 1963. The first Moon probe went up on 4 January and the second on 2 February. The first failed to eject from Earth orbit, the second broke up and crashed into the Pacific near Midway Island. Again, these launches were not announced at the time.

Luna 4, launched on 2 April 1963, got off to a more promising start and first reports indicated how satisfied the controllers were with the accuracy of the flight. Tass added:

> Scientists have to clarify the physical conditions cosmonauts will meet, how they are to overcome landing difficulties and how they should prepare for a prolonged stay on the Moon. The human epoch in the Moon's history is beginning. There will be laboratories, sanatoria and observatories on the Moon.

This heady enthusiasm soon evaporated. On 4 April, the USSR announced that Luna 4 (the term 'Luna' had replaced 'Lunik', for some reason), of weight 1422 kg, would fly past the Moon at 9301 km. Contact was lost two days later as it entered solar orbit. The Russians claimed—quite unconvincingly—that a lunar flyby was all that had been intended. But they shut up about health resorts on the Moon for the time being.

1963 Moonshots

4 Jan 1963	Failure
2 Feb 1963	Failure
2 Apr 1963	Luna 4 (missed Moon)

Korolev ordered a complete redesign of the Molniya upper stage. The level of failures represented a rate of attrition that no programme could sustain. Later that year, Korolev launched the first of the Zond spacecraft, designed to test the technology required for deep space missions. The first Zond spacecraft was launched on 11 November 1963. Its purpose was to test photographic equipment for interplanetary flyby missions by taking pictures of the Moon's far side. Once again, the Molniya stage frustrated Korolev's intentions, and the mission was explained away as an Earth-orbiting satellite, Cosmos 21.

SCHIRRA AND COOPER

America's Mercury project recovered its nerve after the near-disaster on the Carpenter flight and after the double shock of the Vostok 3 and 4 joint flight. Walter Schirra was put into space on 3 October 1962. His six-orbit flight went perfectly and he rode his Mercury capsule down into the Pacific Ocean right beside a waiting carrier. On 15 May 1963 Gordon Cooper took the last Mercury capsule aloft on a day-and-a-half mission. It was much the most successful venture by NASA to date. Cooper overcame one problem after another in his tiny capsule, and flew it back through a hair-raising manual re-entry after the automatic electrical system failed.

NASA at one stage considered firing aloft a seventh Mercury capsule late in 1963 for a three-day mission, but thought otherwise. Mercury was officially closed in August 1963. The extra mission would have held things up for at least six months, achieve little more than what Gordon Cooper had done, and as NASA was learning very fast, would have cost time. And time was what it was all about now.

NASA's Moon programme was now in full swing, even if it had not produced any hardware as yet. Originally Mercury was to lead to the three-man Apollo in 1965. But the large new ship could not possibly be ready by then. An intermediate spacecraft called Gemini was commissioned. Although similar in shape to Mercury, it was significantly different in concept and performance. Gemini would carry two men and would be fully manoeuvrable. Its task would be to test the vital technique of orbital rendezvous until NASA felt that it could do it in its sleep. Gemini would test the techniques of Apollo before Apollo. It would fill a two-year gap. A new team of astronauts was recruited to fly Gemini in September 1963. The first flight was set for late 1964.

SPACEWOMAN

Similar considerations probably inspired Sergei Korolev to repeat the Vostok 3–4 flight in the summer of 1963. The Soyuz, like Apollo, would not be ready for manned tests until 1965 at the earliest. A repeat of the double flight would provide more experience of orbital rendezvous and extend duration to five days.

But then political considerations intervened. Khrushchev, it appears, had the brainwave of putting a woman into the last Vostok. This decision had political overtones. Not only could the USSR demonstrate its technological superiority to the world, but also its social advantages. The USSR made much of its claims to female social equality at the time. But Khrushchev had a point. What was unthinkable in America provoked a Soviet response of 'well, why not ?'. 400 women were in the initial selection, which was reduced to 58, then 30, then 5. One who failed the medical was ace jet pilot Marina Popovich, partner of Pavel Popovich.[25]

Selection for the first flight by a woman in space, 1962

Tanya Kuznetsova
Valentina Ponomareva
Irina Solovieva
Valentina Tereshkova
Zhanna Yorkina

The women were either fliers or parachutists, Solovieva holding several world records. Zhanna Yorkina was an English teacher; Irina Solovieva an engineer; Ponomareva a mathematician. Tatania Kuznetsova was only 20 years old, probably the youngest space flier ever selected anywhere. Valentina Tereshkova came from the ancient Russian city of Yaroslavl. Her father died fighting the Germans during the war and her youth had not been easy. She left school and found work in a textile combine as a loom operator. There she might have spent her life had she not applied to join the local flying club. She took up parachuting as her speciality and made her first jump in May 1959 when she was 22 years old. On one jump she came down in the Volga and almost drowned but, undeterred, she went on the make 126 jumps. If fearlessness and determination were qualities required for flying into orbit, then Tereshkova had plenty of both.

Valentina Tereshkova—cotton mill worker, parachutist and cosmonaut.

The male cosmonauts seem to have regarded the arrival of the women with surprise and amusement. Yuri Gagarin found it necessary to warn his male colleagues against teasing them. Tereshkova, in particular was supervised by Yuri Gagarin and Andrian Nikolayev, and she became very friendly with Nikolayev. This actually served as a useful cover, for otherwise the appearance of women in Star Town would filter out to the West and the plan would be blown. Instead, Valentina was explained away as Nikolayev's girlfriend, who was taking a close interest in his professional career.

The six cosmonauts of the Vostok series (left to right): Gherman Titov, Yuri Gagarin, Valentina Tereshkova, Valeri Bykovsky, Andrian Nikolayev, Pavel Popovich.

Although Tereshkova was favoured for the flight by Gagarin, the choice was made by Khrushchev. She was working class rather than professional, the kind of person he understood. Backups were Ponomareva and Solovieva. Preparations for the new double flight went ahead, and in May 1963 the State Commission confirmed the appointment of Valeri Bykovsky as Vostok 5 commander. Her flight was to last just one day, with the possibility of extension if it went well.

The June heat soaked the summer cosmodrome and on 14 June 1963, Valeri Bykovsky soared into space. His orbit measured 175 by 221 km, 65 deg, 88.3 min. His mission got off to a low-key start and observers expected a flight to run to about a week. Soon, however, rumours began to leak out of an impending flight of a woman cosmonaut. No attempt was made to refute them, and it might not have mattered had Vostok 6 taken off on schedule the following day. But technical problems forced a hold and the second mission was put off for 24 hours. In the meantime, viewers had to concentrate on Valeri Bykovsky. TV pictures showed him passing floating objects around the cabin and writing the log. Tass regaled listeners with details of his diet: sausage pie, roast beef and chicken fillet. From orbit, Bykovsky reported seeing rivers, lakes and seas. Roads and town were visible and their lights stood out clearly by night.

Whatever had been rumoured about the launch planned for 15 June, what happened the next day left no one in any doubt. Soon after midday, Vostok 6 soared aloft carrying white-helmeted, orange-suited Valentina Tereshkova. The USSR exulted. Excitement in the cities reached a peak unknown since the flight of Yuri Gagarin. The Russians made no effort to conceal their glee, and the effect of a female cosmonaut was felt in the West by those who would find difficulties in appreciating the technical significance of particular scientific achievements or aspects of orbital rendezvous. Telecasts were made from orbit showing a smiling, cheerful Valentina in obvious good health and in full control of her situation.

Vostok 6 entered orbit within sight of Valeri Bykovsky—a mere 5,000 m apart—achieving even greater accuracy than Nikolayev and Popovich the previous year. They quickly established good shortwave radio communication with each other though they soon began to drift apart. Vostok 6's orbit was 181 by 231 km, 65 deg, 88.3 min. Valentina Tereshkova was originally scheduled to land on orbit 17. What may have influenced the designers to keep her up longer was the fact that on the first day she overslept so long that ground control began to wonder if she was still alive. If she was able to sleep that well, so the thinking went, she would be well able to stay up there.

The rest of the flight was, after the early excitement, a comparative anticlimax. By 18 June, Tereshkova had flown in space for longer than all of America's astronauts put together. The two cosmonauts continued their observations of the Earth and the stars. The order to land came on the 19th. The simultaneous re-entry of the last flight was not repeated—Valentina Tereshkova came down at 11.20 a.m. and Valeri Bykovsky at 2.06 p.m. He had been up for a record five days and 81 orbits, and she for three days, 48 orbits. She came down by the method that she knew best—parachute. It was a contrast of the old and the new. She came down on barren steppe on the site of the old caravan routes to the East. She was spotted coming down by herdsmen on horseback minding their sheep. They galloped to her spaceship and peered in to gasp at the modern creation. She was welcomed as a hero and given the traditional meal of cheese, flatcakes and fermented mares' milk. She was still devouring it when the rescuing helicopters arrived.

Valentina Tereshkova and Valeri Bykovsky received a festive reception in Moscow the following Saturday. On 3 November 1963, she married Andrian Nikolayev. It was the romantic conclusion to the double flight and the nearest the Russians ever came to Hollywood. Valeri Bykovsky and Yuri Gagarin were the witnesses. There were endless toasts. The celebrations went on all night. Nikita Khrushchev was in his element and sang repeatedly. Russia had a leading role in space, he said, and the capitalist countries would never catch up. Khrushchev allowed a rare concession at the wedding. Cosmonauts awaiting their first flight and the Chief Designer were permitted to appear in public. Photographs taken at the ceremonies reveal both Korolev and Valentin Glushko. It was a rare and happy privilege for them.

The Nikolayev–Tereshkova marriage was, so far as could be seen, not so enduring, although a baby was born in June 1964. Valentina took the name of 'Nikolayeva-Tereshkova' but the former part was used less and less in the 1970s and eventually disappeared. The two were rarely seen together after the first two years and they divorced in 1980. It's probably not fair to suggest as some people have that the marriage was ordered up by Khrushchev. No evidence supports this. Valentina Tereshkova went on to a political career in women's and peace organizations, and by 1983 reached government rank during the brief Andropov era. She made many visits abroad. She remained the only spacewoman for 19 years. She was still in the cosmonaut squad in 1996, aged 59.

The women's group stayed together until 1969. But when the prospects of their flying diminished the group was disbanded, but not without some resentment, for they felt many years afterwards that they had been recruited for a political stunt. Zhanna Yorkina wrote a history of cosmonautics. Irina Solovieva took part in Antarctic expeditions. Valentina Ponomareva wrote a thesis on the stabilization of spacecraft during rendezvous and went on to work in the Academy of Sciences. Tanya Kuznetsova trains space crews in geophysical experiments.

Vostok series

1	12 Apr 1961	Yuri Gagarin
2	6 Aug 1961	Gherman Titov
3	11 Aug 1962	Andrian Nikolayev
4	12 Aug 1962	Pavel Popovich
5	14 Jun 1963	Valeri Bykovsky
6	16 Jun 1963	Valentina Tereshkova

VOSKHOD PROGRAMME

With the first Soyuz not due for flight until 1966, Korolev devised a programme to fill the gap. At one stage, consideration was given to flying a solo Vostok 7 for a week-long mission: a young Moscow doctor, Boris Yegorov, was even selected for the mission. But what Korolev decided on was an improved version of Vostok which took advantage of what was by American standards a large space cabin. By taking out the ejector seat system and by having the crew wear overalls, rather than bulky spacesuits, it would be possible to fit as many as three cosmonauts in the old Vostok cabin. By fitting an airlock, it would be possible to make a spacewalk that would test the spacesuit necessary for walking on the Moon. By fitting rendezvous and docking systems, it would be possible to test techniques for spaceships linking together in practice for the later Soyuz missions. The revised Vostok was initially a four-mission programme: a multi-manned flight, a spacewalk, a duration flight and a docking. There would be more missions later. The new craft would be called Voskhod, Russian for 'sunrise'. It also had the advantage that it would beat Gemini point by point over 1964–5.

Removing the ejector seats and spacesuits carried certain risks. Without ejector seats, escape would be impossible in the first 27 s of launch until the upper stage could fire: but Korolev reckoned the R-7 was reliable enough by now. Without suits, there was the danger of depressurization, but the cabin had proved itself sturdy and reliable. The conversion of Vostok into Voskhod was masterminded by Korolev design bureau engineer Konstantin Feoktistov who, with Korolev's approval, volunteered to fly in it himself to prove the safety of the new system.

SUNRISE

The R-7 booster was uprated with a more powerful upper stage, enough to enable a payload of between 5.3 tonnes and 7 tonnes to enter low earth orbit (later, this was termed the Soyuz version of the R-7). Despite the risks that were being taken with Voskhod, some safety features were added. First, a spare retrorocket was fitted on the nose: a long Voskhod flight would need a high orbit, but it would be one which would not decay naturally before the air ran out. So a spare retrorocket would ensure that no one got stranded in orbit. Second, the lack of ejectors held consequences for the landing—the crew was no longer in a position to bale out before the five-tonne cabin hit the ground. A landing in seats would make for quite a jolt, broken bones not being ruled out. Accordingly a retrorocket was fitted to the base of the capsule below the (now detachable) heat shield to cushion the impact. It would fire 1.5 s before touchdown.

The changes in the Voskhod cabin meant that there were seats not for two cosmonauts, but for, at a squeeze, three. Since only one cosmonaut was required to fly the new spacecraft, Korolev had two seats at his disposal for a new type of cosmonaut. This selection was an important decision in the Soviet space programme. From 1964, cosmonaut selection divided into two streams. The first comprised air force pilots typical of the group selected in 1960. But from this point, recruitment began of civilian engineers, designers, scientists, physicians and other specialists, principally from the design bureaux where the spacecraft were built and made, but also from medical institutes and the Academy of Sciences. The first design bureau to contribute cosmonauts was, unsurprisingly, Korolev's OKB-1, later called informally the Korolev kindergarten. By contrast, the American space programme did not recruit its first scientists until 1968, and few American scientists flew in space until the space shuttle became operational in the mid-1980s.

Tall, white-haired, and distinguished-looking, spacecraft designer Konstantin Feoktistov was quite unmistakable. Born in 1926 in Voronezh, Feoktistov was a child prodigy. He mastered maths and physics at the age of ten in order to learn Tsiolkovsky's formulæ. A scout during the war, Feoktistov was captured by the Germans, shot in the head and left for dead. He recovered, entered the Bauman Technical College in Moscow in 1943, and was awarded a degree in engineering in 1949. He was a theoretical lecturer to the cosmonaut team in 1960 and helped to design Vostok. After his flight he wrote up his doctorate.

Boris Yegorov was also intimately involved in the space programme. A short, slim, dark-haired doctor, he was one of the leading space doctors and had a key role examining cosmonauts both before and after their flights. His father was Moscow's leading brain surgeon. Young Boris had specialized in both aviation medicine and the inner ear (the location of the nausea problem). Some reports say that only six months training was given to both Feoktistov and Yegorov. The doctor was required to make eleven parachute jumps.

The choice of a mission commander was not a hard one, and it fell naturally to the most unflown backup—Vladimir Komarov. Born in 1927 he was older than the others—square-jawed, solid, firm and reliable. He had impressed all when grounded after Popovich's flight due to irregular heartbeat, and he toured all the leading heart specialists in Moscow collecting endorsements verifying that this problem would not impede a space flight. He was returned to flight status in 1963, just in time.

Preparations went ahead. A one-day test run was carried out on 7 October with Cosmos 47, which carried two dummy cosmonauts. Cosmos 47 orbited at 177–413 km, 90 min, and was recovered after 16 orbits. The mission was faultless.

Civilians selected for the Voskhod 1 mission, May 1964, from the Korolev OKB-1

Konstantin Feoktistov
Sergei Anokhin
Vladimir Bugrov
Vladislav Volkov
Georgi Grechko
Gennadi Dolgopolov
Alexei Yeliseyev
Valeri Kubasov
Oleg Makarov

Civilians selected for the Voskhod 1 mission, May 1964, from Academy of Sciences

---

Georgi Katys

Civilian selected for the Voskhod 1 mission, May 1964,
from Institute for Medical Biological Problems (IMBP)

Boris Yegorov
Boris Polyakov

BLUE JACKETS

The way was clear for Voskhod 1. The crew of three, all smiling broadly, Komarov, Feoktistov, and Yegorov, stepped out of the transfer van at the pad. They had silver-grey woollen suits with blue jackets. Up they went in the lift and the three swung into their spacious cabin, which was heavily padded with soft foam and embellished with light-blue instrumentation panels. All they needed to do was to don small white helmet headphones and they were ready to fly.

Voskhod 1 blasted into the autumn sky and settled into a safe orbit of 178 by 408 km, 65 deg, 90 min, the longest period ever. Boris Yegorov, peering out of the right porthole, at once spotted the Siberian forests and tundra. One striking impression followed another. The lights of the settlements and cities of Australia, the white icecap of Antarctica, the shimmering lights of the southern Australian auroræ. Compared to Vostok, this was real passenger service. The three men ate on Caspian roach, caviare sandwiches and vacuum-packed roast beef slices. They talked to Nikita Khrushchev by radio link. They sent greetings to North Vietnam. Vladimir Komarov guided the ship around. High-quality pictures of 25 frames/second were sent back. Boris Yegorov took blood samples. Konstantin Feoktistov photographed the stars.

In terms of the international reaction, Voskhod 1 had exactly the desired effect. 'Three men in space!' the headlines screamed, when everyone would have considered two a huge advance. American astronaut Malcolm Scott Carpenter:

> I wouldn't have been surprised if two had been sent up. But three—the Russians seem to do this, just what you don't expect them to.

The *New York Times* spoke of Russia widening its space lead and 'an air of resignation among US officials'. It was another humiliation, for the three-man Apollo would not be ready until 1966 at the earliest and the Americans had not even thought of flying doctors or scientists, even less in shirt sleeves.

The crew came down a day later, 2000 km south-east of Moscow. The descending cabin was spotted by the pilot of an Il-14 plane near Maryeva. The parachute came out at 5300 m at a speed of 240 m/s. Just as it touched down, the new soft-landing rockets blasted to ease the touchdown. It was as gentle as promised! The three cosmonauts opened the hatch and clambered out onto the flat steppe land. A helicopter crew was soon to hand. The cosmonauts had been up 24 h 17 min. They had flown 16 orbits.

Voskhod's return was swiftly eclipsed on the front pages by startling news from Moscow. After speaking to the cosmonauts from his holiday *dacha* on the Black Sea, Nikita Khrushchev resumed his autumn holiday. As he did, the plotters moved. At a special meeting, the Central Committee of the Soviet communist party voted him out of office. Late that night the CPSU was able to announce a triumvirate to take his place. The new president was Nikolai Podgorny; chairman of the Council of Ministers was Alexei Kosygin; and first secretary was Leonid Brezhnev. Western analysts perceived Kosygin to be the *primus inter pares* of the trio. Khrushchev 'retired' immediately, was occasionally seen out walking in the park, and died in 1971. It was, at least, a more civilized way to run politics than in Stalin's time. And when the three heroes of Voskhod 1 returned to Moscow on the 15th for a triumphant reception, if they had any comments on going up during one man's premiership and coming down during another's, they kept their thoughts to themselves.

Vladimir Komarov was to fly again on the first test of the new Soyuz spaceship. Konstantin Feoktistov was a prominent space designer during the 1970s and 1980s. Boris Yegorov returned to his medical work and became Head of the Biomedical Technology Institute of the Ministry of Health. Tragically, his 20-year-old son died during the shootout at the Ostankino TV centre during the fighting in Moscow in 1993 associated with the assault on the White House; Boris Yegorov himself died suddenly in September 1994 at the age of 57.

OUT INTO THE ENDLESS VOID

No sooner had the Voskhod 1 trio returned than preparations began for the second stage of the Voskhod programme in mid-March. This, by happy coincidence, was the date set for the first flight in America's much-delayed Gemini programme. The first space walk was set, early on, as the objective for the second Voskhod mission. The first spacesuit for work outside the cabin had been built in 1963. No ordinary spacesuit would do: the life-support system had to be a backpack (as would be needed on the Moon), not simply a connecting air hose (which could not be trailed around on the Moon's surface).

The problems of a moonsuit or spacesuit were not to be glossed over. Any cosmonaut venturing outside his cabin would need a huge amount of protection—from the vacuum, meteorites and the intense heat and cold. It would have to keep him at a comfortable temperature and ensure that he did not overheat. The suit would have to not balloon out and prevent him from returning. If different atmospheres and pressures were used, measures would have to be taken to prevent the 'bends' that afflicted deep-sea divers. Altogether it was a risky undertaking. Voskhod itself presented an additional problem. Because not enough air could be carried to repressurize it after a spacewalk, a separate airlock had to be carried. Once again, Korolev's genius came to the rescue.

Space limitations did not give him much to play around with, so he designed an exterior inflatable airlock which could be cast away after use. It would inflate once Voskhod reached orbit. The two-man crew would let air gush into the airlock. The one spacewalker would then climb into the airlock, a tunnel-like cylindrical tube, and close the door behind him. He would then exit from the airlock, which would be gradually depressurized. He would use the same method, in reverse, to return.

INAUSPICIOUS START

It was to be a mission fraught with danger, and there were nasty shocks ahead. First was the dry-run advance mission. Cosmos 57 was put up on 23 February into a 90 min, 195–512 km orbit. Although the hatch was deployed on schedule at the point of entry into orbit, Cosmos 57 then broke up into 180 fragments. Apparently, ground controllers had sent two commands simultaneously rather than sequentially to the Cosmos, confusing its control system and activating the destruct system. Several days later, a drop test of a Voskhod cabin ended in disaster when the parachute failed to operate and the cabin was smashed on impact.

Were corners being cut? Nervousness was so high that the Committee on State Security, the KGB, pronounced that saboteurs were at work and put all the preparatory activities under guard, which made everyone even more jittery. Despite the disastrous test record, Korolev and Keldysh still recommended that the flight should proceed. The crew continued its preparations. The prime crew comprised Pavel Belyayev and Alexei Leonov. Pavel Belyayev, the commander, was a World War fighter pilot and had fought the Japanese. He had fallen out of the 1960 class a year after joining when he smashed an ankle during a bad parachute landing. He exercised relentlessly till it healed and it was on Yuri Gagarin's insistence that he was reselected in 1963.

Alexei Leonov was to appear again, and to the West he became one of Russia's best known and most personable cosmonauts. He had a colourful personality that was to shine through the more staid biographies of his colleagues. Alexei Leonov's ambition in life was to be the first man on the Moon. He might well have been so. When selected in 1960 he was known for his enormous determination, athleticism and courage. When a boy at 15 he made himself a bicycle from spare parts and cycled endlessly each day. He went to air force school and was later a parachute instructor. A chatty, cheerful man, fair-haired, a smile never far away, he had two brushes with death in his early years in training. One night his car left the road when he was returning home and plunged through ice into a pond. He struggled out, rescuing his wife and the driver in the process. Soon after, when bailing out of an aircraft, his ejector seat jammed and he escaped only by bending the metal strap restrainers by bare force. He got free and came down safely.

While waiting for his flight, Leonov cycled 1000 km, ran 500 km, and skied 300 km, all in a year. He combined his athletic passions with art. Alexei Leonov was an enthusiastic painter, and by all accounts a good one. He focused on space themes—his own impressions from orbit, sunsets and sunrises, and futuristic drawings of spaceships landing on other worlds. He was a notorious cartoonist and sketchmaker, and for many years edited the cosmonauts' own newsletter called *Neptune*.

SNOW FLURRIES

Snow lay on the ground and there were white flurries in the air as Pavel Belyayev and Alexei Leonov, both spacesuited, took the lift to the top of Voskhod 2 on the wintry morning of 18 March 1965. In America the first Gemini launch was still five days away as

Pavel Belyayev (left) and Alexei Leonov (right) on the way to the launch of Voskhod 2 in March 1965. They are accompanied by Vladimir Komarov, commander of the previous Voskhod mission.

Virgil Grissom and John Young went methodically through their countdown drills. Voskhod 2 reached orbit safely—it was in fact the highest orbit ever at 174 by 498 km, 90 min.

Then on the second orbit, as Voskhod 2 swung over the Caspian Sea for the first time, Alexei Leonov struggled in the small cabin to put on the backpack he would need for his protection. To his suit he attached a 5.5 m lifeline to keep him connected to his spaceship. The line also carried voice communications. The backpack provided air and devices to regulate the temperature inside the suit. With a 'good luck' from Pavel Belyayev he pushed his way into the airlock and sealed the door behind him. He would be on his own now. Finally came the moment of truth, the opening of the airlock. Scorching bright sunlight flooded in, the blinding brightness of the direct rays of the Sun. Alexei Leonov felt as if he was at the bottom of a well and peering out of underneath the Earth for the first time. Looking up he could see the inky blackness of space and the unblinking light of the stars. He pulled himself gingerly out of the airlock. Television pictures captured his diver-like figure as he emerged. He gasped, contemplating the 500 km that separated him from the ground. Down below were the Black Sea and the snow-capped peaks of the Caucasus Mountains. Alexei Leonov got his breath back and finally cast himself free into the abyss of space. He soared, he swam, he turned end over end, exuberant at the new freedom conferred on him. The whole universe was before him, and below him stretched the still-frozen expanses of the Volga basin and further to the north, the Ural mountains. He disappeared from sight from the eye of the camera. Then, eerily, loops of line appeared, followed by Alexei Leonov's white suit. Marked sharply on the top of his helmet were the initials 'CCCP'. He grew in confidence, felt the lightness of the sensation of zero g and moved a full 5 m away from his ship to admire it. Voskhod was at the northernmost point of its orbit and about to track southwards again, heading for the Pacific. After 12 min, it was time to climb back in. This was where the trouble started. First of all, the movie camera which had been recording all his movements snagged. It would not go back in the airlock and instead got wedged in the entrance. By the time he had forced it in, Alexei Leonov was sweating profusely and producing more perspiration than the suit could absorb. Then, much worse, he could not get back in himself. His suit ballooned to the point he just would not fit. He pushed and pushed, all to no avail. Sweat had covered his eyes, and in a helmet he could not clear it. He was using up air fast. His heart was pounding madly.

Alexei Leonov reduced his suit pressure from 0.4 atmospheres (ats) to 0.3. It was no good. Down to 0.27, the permissible limit. Still it would not fit. He faced disaster. Still, this was the kind of thing that he had trained for five years for. He eased it down still further, to 0.25 ats. With a heave of desperation as much as personal strength, he finally went through. Alive! He clambered back in, to be greeted by Pavel Belyayev, who was just as relieved himself. The airlock was then cast free. Leonov had been in open space for 12 min and took 10 min struggling to get back in. Not that this was known at the time—such difficulties were glossed over. As a result, the Americans underestimated the problems of spacewalking, and in orbit a year later Gemini 9's Eugene Cernan nearly came to grief when he overheated and his helmet fogged up from overexertion.

The next orbits were mundane by comparison. The two men rested, ate, and talked to the ground. They passed outside the range of ground stations from orbits 8 to 13—so they slept. At 5.12 a.m. the following day they actually passed quite close to another orbiting sputnik, circling the Earth about a kilometre away, though they could not identify it. The world below applauded their feat. Even *The Times* of London described it as 'fantastic history' in its opening account. The London *Evening Standard* showed American astronauts about to follow in pursuit, captioned 'follow that cab!'. Virgil Grissom and John Young went glumly through their tasks. They had been left at the starting post—again. At least so it seemed until the very next day, 19 March. Most people expected the Voskhod to return on its 16th orbit. There was silence. There were no reports all morning, none in the afternoon either. Then, later on, came a report that the crew was down and being picked up. In fact nothing of the sort was happening. They were down, and alive, but in a north Russian forest, surrounded by a pack of hungry wolves.

As Voskhod 2 reached retrofire point on orbit 16, the rocket should have fired for 56 s to brake it out of orbit. Nothing happened at all. Belyayev could have then pressed the manual button himself, but he held off. Wisely, in the event, Voskhod 2 had strayed out of attitude and this had alerted the computer, automatically preventing a retrofire. Belyayev and ground control argued over what to do next and a manual return was agreed, to take place on orbit 17. Alexei Leonov had been put to the test the previous day and now it was his commander's turn. Pavel Belyayev had to get the orientation right manually or they would never return. At 11.30 a.m. he pressed the switch and wham! off it went.

It was accurate enough to get them home—but only just. It was a hot and scary re-entry, so hot that the capsule was enveloped in flames and all the communications aerials burned off. As a result, they had no means of telling anyone where they were. They were in fact over a thousand miles off course by now. As they drifted in to land, they were not greeted by the flat steppe that they had hoped for, but mountains and forests, clad in winter snow. Voskhod 2 crashed into big fir trees and the parachutes snarled high up in the trees.

The two men were out in five minutes and it was bitterly cold. It was well over half way through the day and darkness was only four hours away. There was silence all about. They realized that no one would know where to look for them. They did not know themselves where they were though they surmised (correctly) that they were down in the Ural mountains. The rescue and welcome team was a full 1300 km away, and the pressmen with them realized that something was wrong when they were sent home empty-handed. Ground control at once summoned aircraft to search for the missing cosmonauts. The worst was feared. Korolev wept openly, convinced they were lost.

But Leonov and Belyayev had been trained for this kind of situation. They set up a radio beacon and collected wood to start a fire. And waited. Three hours later the drone of a searching plane could be heard in the distance. It came closer, flew overhead and circled—and flew away again. Help was coming. Not long after, a helicopter arrived, but the ground was too rough to land, and after dropping supplies it too flew away. They had come down near the city of Perm. By now night was falling and the cosmonauts faced a night in the snow and the forest. The cold was bitter indeed and they huddled around their fire for warmth. The baying of wolves could be heard. They grew closer and the frosty breath of their shadows could be made out lurking behind the pine trees. More rescuers arrived at daybreak and the crew was airlifted out safely. The full extent of their campfire ordeal did not come out for many years.

2000 correspondents gathered at the post-flight press conference on 26 March. Mstislav Keldysh proclaimed:

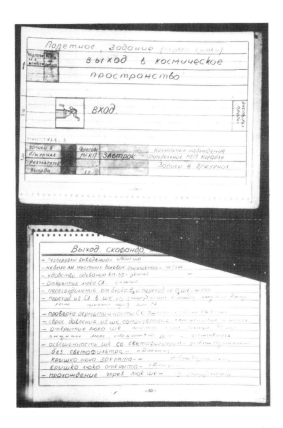

This is the log book in which Alexei Leonov described his spacewalk.

Voskhod 2 opens up prospects for the establishment of orbital stations, the linkup of spaceships in orbit and the carrying out of astronomical and geophysical explorations. It would be possible in the near future to place in Earth orbit a space research institute in which scientists specializing in the most diverse fields would work. The results of Voskhod are extremely important for flights to the Moon.

As for the Voskhod programme, Belyayev revealed at the press conference that a two-man Voskhod could orbit the Earth for a month. It could also manoeuvre in space and change orbit. Although this was not realized at the time, Belyayev was in fact describing the next two Voskhod missions.

Voskhod 3 was planned as a two-week to month-long, two-man flight to coincide with the party congress scheduled for March 1966. A crew was trained to fly it: Boris Volynov and Georgi Shonin. The Voskhod 4 rocket, which was designed for space rendezvous, would have linked up with another unmanned spaceship. Also in the pipeline was a second biomedical flight of two weeks, in which physician cosmonauts would study animals; a spacewalk by a woman; and a spaceflight that would carry a journalist.

For the spacewalk by a woman, Valentina Tereshkova's companions, Tanya Kuznetsova and Zhanna Yorkina, began training. For the biomedical mission and the flight by journalists, new cosmonauts were recruited. Korolev had expressed his dissatisfaction at the quality of reporting back by the cosmonauts, and came up with the idea to fly a journalist in space.

Civilians selected for medical Voskhod mission, 1965

Yevgeni Illyin
Alexander Kiselev
Yuri Senkevich

Journalist selection, February 1965

Yaroslav Golovanov
Yuri Letunov
Mikhail Rebrov

To prepare for the Voskhod 3 mission, there was a duration flight by dogs, Veterok and Ugolyok, each in separate containers. The mission was called Cosmos 110 and took the two dogs right into the Van Allen radiation belt. It flew at 51 deg and out as far as 900 km. The launch date was 22 February 1966. There was a thorough test of the circulatory system in the space environment. Both dogs were clad in spacesuits. Full data on how they reacted were telemetred back each day. Eventually their capsule came down intact and was recovered on 16 March, after 22 days. The dogs survived and were in good condition. Dr Boris Yegorov was the medical expert in charge.

There were repeated delays in trying to organize Voskhod 3. Eventually, within weeks of its liftoff in May 1966, it was cancelled. The decision was most unpopular among the cosmonauts. To save time and to prepare for the first flights of the Soyuz spaceship, the rest of the Voskhod programme was terminated. The journalist group was disbanded.[26] Golovanov later became one of the historians of the Soviet space programme, Mikhail Rebrov of *Krasnaya Zvezda* one of the first writers about its hidden pages. Letunov was a television newscaster, who died in 1983.

By this stage, the Soviet Union at last had a Moon programme.

Voskhod series

7 Oct 1964	Cosmos 47
12 Oct 1964	Voskhod 1 (Vladimir Komarov, Konstantin Feoktistov, Boris Yegorov)
23 Feb 1965	Cosmos 57 (failure)
18 Mar 1965	Voskhod 2 (Pavel Belyayev, Alexei Leonov)

ASSESSMENT

This period was later known as the golden years of Soviet rocketry. The Russians beat the Americans to every major space objective during this time. Even if the individual missions were opportunist, they were not lacking in imagination by their designers nor courage by their cosmonauts. The interplanetary missions were ambitious. Whereas the Americans did not attempt to land probes on the planets until the mid-1970s, the Russians attempted to do so at the very first chance. However, two worrying problems nagged at the successes of these years. First, the Russians had still failed to master the problems of rocket upper stages. Second, the hectic activity belied the absence, until August 1964, of any long-term plan.

3

Moon race

Would they do all this, if they realize what really lies ahead? The first inevitable failures will discourage the faint-hearted and undermine the confidence of the public.

Konstantin Tsiolkovsky, 1929.

A central assumption in NASA, in the American political community and in the Western media was that the Soviet Union had a long-term plan to send a man to the Moon. All Soviet missions were explained in the context of this presumed, methodical master plan.

Nothing could have been further from the reality. It was certainly true that design bureaux presented the Soviet leadership with short, medium and long-term plans and projects, but these were approved on a short-term, *ad hoc* basis. In the autumn of 1963, Nikita Khrushchev volunteered that the Soviet Union was not in a Moon race and had no plans to send men to the Moon. On 26 October, he declared:

> The Soviet Union is not at present planning flights of cosmonauts to the Moon. Soviet scientists are studying it as a scientific problem.
>
> The Americans want to land a man on the Moon by 1970. We wish them luck and we will watch to see how they fly there and how they will return. I wish them success. Competition would not bring any good but might to the contrary cause harm because it might lead to the death of people.

No one believed him, and his remarks were interpreted as a trick. In fact, he was telling the truth. At the same time, during the 1963 conference of the International Astronautical Federation in Paris, Yuri Gagarin told the assembled delegates:

> A flight to the Moon requires a space vehicle of tens of tonnes and it is no secret that such large rockets are not yet available. One technique is the assembly of parts of spaceships in near-Earth orbit. Once in orbit the components could be collected together, joined up and supplied with propellant. The flight could then begin.

Again, Gagarin was outlining the true Soviet position. Design studies were under way (he was describing the Soyuz complex), but no decisions had been taken and certainly no man-on-the-Moon programme had been adopted.

SOVIET DECISION TO GO TO THE MOON

The situation changed the following year, though the precise reasons and circumstances remain in the archives in the Kremlin. The Soviet lunar programme was formally established on 3 August 1964 when a joint resolution of the Council of Ministers and the central committee of the Communist Party of the Soviet Union, called 'On work involving the study of the Moon and outer space' was passed. The resolution, number 655/268, aimed to land a single cosmonaut on the Moon in 1967–8, though the resolution did not include the key phrase of making such a landing to be an 'objective of national importance'. One may speculate that the Soviet leadership now appreciated the full significance of the Johnson–Kennedy decision of May 1961, and decided to match it. How the Soviet Union managed to misjudge the significance of Kennedy's decision to go to the Moon is difficult to fathom, for it was hardly a secret. It may have been interpreted as a plan or a design study, like many of their own. Overestimation of their own space capabilities and contempt for the Americans may also have played their part. Whatever the reasons, the Soviet Union had, by summer 1964, found itself three years behind. Equally important, the key questions of *how* to get there, which NASA had resolved in 1962, had yet to be taken. The resolution of 3 August 1964 led to three proposals from three design bureaux.

Acting on the resolution, Korolev prepared a proposal which he completed on 25 December 1964, the N-1 ('N' stands for 'nositel', or 'carrier'). Two other design bureaux also prepared proposals for a manned landing on the Moon: the Chelomei design bureau (OKB-52), whose project was called the UR-700 (UR stands for Universalnaya Raketa, or universal rocket), and Mikhail Yangel's design bureau in Ukraine, whose project was called the R-56.[27]

Rival moon projects, 1964–7

Korolev design bureau (OKB-1)   N-1
Chelomei design bureau (OKB-52) UR-700
Yangel design bureau (OKB-586)   R-56

Korolev had originally planned the N-1 as a rocket which would send large spaceships unmanned, then manned, on a flyby of Mars. The original concept of the N-1 dated to the period 1956–7 and was refined over the next few years by Mikhail Tikhonravov, Yuri Maksimov and Konstantin Feoktistov. They designed a Heavy Interplanetary Spacecraft (HIS), like a daisy stem (nuclear power plant at one end, crew quarters at the opposite), which would fly past Mars and return within a year. In 1967–8, three volunteers—G Manovtsev, Y Ulybyshev and A Boshko—spent a year in a HIS cabin testing a closed-loop life-support system. N-1 was now adapted for a manned flight to the Moon.

The full designs of the UR-700 and the R-56 have not been fully revealed, though it is now possible to speculate with accuracy what they may have been like.[28] Large rocket engines were designed and built for the UK-700 and the R-56 between 1962 and 1971 by Valentin Glushko's Gas Dynamic Laboratory. Called the RD-270, the engines used UDMH and nitrogen tetroxide, producing a vacuum thrust of 685 tonnes, a specific impulse of 322 s and had a pressure of 266 ats in its combustion chamber. The RD-270 weighed 4.7 tonnes, was 4.8 m high and could be gimballed. The American equivalent was the F-1 engine, used on the Saturn V. Nine would have been used on the first stage of Chelomei's UR-700. The R-56, Yangel design, was also intended to use the RD-270 on a cluster of long, pencil-like first-stage engines (this concept was to re-emerge as the Zenith rocket in the 1980s). In the event, the R-56 did not turn out to be a serious competitor. Yangel's R-56, like Korolev's N-1, had been a paper study since April 1962, but it seems to have dropped out of the contest in 1964.

Contrary to Western impressions that the Soviet space programme was centralized, in fact it operated in a decentralized, competitive way. Thus, in the period after the government decision of 1964, three design bureaux were at work not only designing but building rival Moon projects. Again, this marked a key difference from the American programme. In the United States, rival corporations submitted proposals and bids, but only one was chosen to develop the project and build the hardware (the company concerned was called the prime contractor). In the Soviet Union, by contrast, rival design institutes not only designed but built hardware. Decisions about which would fly were taken much later. As a result, the Soviet Moon programme, and indeed other key programmes, contained several rival, parallel projects. This was something not appreciated in the West at the time.

A further, most significant, complication was that at the same time the Soviet Union adopted an important, secondary objective for its Moon programme. Vladimir Chelomei was given the explicit authorization to prepare for a round-the-Moon mission using a new rocket system, the UR-500K, which he had in design. A round-the-Moon mission had long been part of Soviet space thinking, for Mikhail Tikhonravov had sketched such a mission as far back as 1951.

Chelomei proceeded to design a new, three-stage booster carrying nitrogen tetroxide and unsymmetrical dimethylmethylhydrazine (UDMH). The engines of the first stage were built by Valentin Glushko and became the famous RD-253 engine. The second and third stage engines (RD-465 and RD-473) were built by the Kosberg design bureau. Vladimir Chelomei's rocket became known as the UR-500K project and more widely—and publicly—as the Proton. His design seemed a more straightforward one than the Soyuz complex as put forward by Korolev in 1962 and 1963, and so Earth orbit rendezvous as a means of going around the Moon was quietly dropped.

To fly around the Moon, Chelomei devised a Mooncraft to fly atop his UR-500K. It resembled a scaled-down Apollo-type command and service module, 5.2 m long with 7.27 m wide solar panels. The small, 2.7 m long cabin would have carried one man around the Moon. The first spacecraft were constructed by September 1965. When fitted to the top of the UR-500K, the entire space vehicle would have been 46.7 m high.

The Proton had the most advanced rocket engines in the world for 20 years. Valentin Glushko's RD-253 engines recycled their exhaust gases to create a closed-circuit turbine system. Pressures of hundreds of atmospheres were obtained on delivery. Each engine

Vladimir Chelomei's UR-500K Proton rocket on its side in the assembly hall.

weighed a modest 1280 kg. The turbines went round at a fantastic 13 800 revolutions a minute, or 18.74 MW. Temperatures reached 3127°C in the engine chambers and the walls were plated with zirconium. Specific impulse was 2795 m/s at sea level and 3100 m/s in vacuum.

The idea that the Soviet Union might attempt to send a man around the Moon first was one familiar to Western analysts. The around-the-Moon mission required much less rocket power, hardware and testing than a landing. The psychological effect of going around the Moon, the excited commentaries, in Russian, of the lunar surface at first hand, would have a considerable effect on world public opinion. In 1965, Gherman Titov wrote in *Na Zhdiot Luna* (*The Moon awaits us*), published in Moscow in 1965:

> I myself dream of flying around the Moon. Practical considerations dictate that
> a flight to the Moon be preceded by a flight around it. Today's cosmonauts
> have a good chance of getting a close look at the Moon.

DESIGNERS FALL OUT

The competitive nature of the programme within the Soviet Union led to an early clash between Korolev and Glushko. Korolev asked Glushko to design the engines for his N-1 rocket, asking him to use either liquid oxygen and liquid hydrogen, or liquid oxygen and kerosene. Glushko refused, preferring new, storable chemicals such as UDMH. Korolev regarded them as toxic and dangerous (following the Nedelin disaster, one can see why). In the end, Korolev had to turn to the aircraft engine designer Nikolai Kuznetsov, whose bureau was located in Kyubyshev (now Samara). Because of his inexperience in space rocket engines, Kuznetsov opted for kerosene rather than the more powerful but more difficult hydrogen, and a large number of engines of modest thrust.

The consequence of this feud was that the N-1 design was difficult. The first stage had no fewer than 30 engines. The piping was a plumber's nightmare. The launch mass was an enormous 2700 tonnes. Even though the N-1 was to be the same size as America's Saturn V, its less efficient fuels produced a smaller payload. Even though the N-1 would follow a profile identical to Saturn V and Apollo, N-1 had the capacity to send only two cosmonauts into lunar orbit and only one down to the surface.

This was not the only quarrel. On Christmas day, 1965, Korolev managed to wrest an important part of the round-the-Moon project away from Chelomei. Although Chalomei's UR-500K rocket would continue to be used, it would fly Korolev's round-the-Moon spacecraft, called L-1, a Soyuz derivative, capable of carrying two men rather than one, even though examples of Chalomei's Mooncraft had already been built. The increased weight of the Zond cabin extended the height of the UR-500K stack to 63 m. The UR-500K would also have a new fourth stage, called the block D, designed by the Korolev bureau.

RACE TO THE PLANETS

Even as the Soviet Union's Moon plans unravelled, further missions to the planets went ahead. All the Venus launches of 1964 were intended flybys. The outcome was disappointing. Four spacecraft were prepared, the first two failing on 19 February and 1 March (neither reached orbit). The third was launched on 27 March, but failed to leave Earth orbit and was named Cosmos 27. More successful was the second attempt on 2 April. It was the first probe to carry the Zond designation and was described by the Russians as a 'deep space engineering test'. Indeed, the Russians persisted merely in describing its position in the sky, without mentioning the word Venus. It successfully altered its course twice, once at 563 780 km and again later. Its purpose was to take photographs of Venus, and it managed to place itself onto an encounter course of 99 780 km for 19 July 1964. But the radio was long since dead by that date.

In order to test the technology for the next Mars missions that autumn, a demonstration model was prepared. This Zond was meant to take pictures of the far side of the Moon en route to solar orbit. In the event, it never reached Earth orbit (4 June 1964).

Two probes were prepared for the next Mars window, which opened in November 1964. Only one, Zond 2, was actually launched, and it was a very low-key affair. The reasons for this became apparent when the Russians admitted that the probe had lost one of its solar panels. As a result, it had to manage on only 50% of its expected power supply. After a mid-course correction, its signals failed.

Zond 2 carried a descent craft. Western observers noted Zond 2's phenomenally accurate course to the red planet and put it down to good tracking and navigation devices. Zond 2 took a high energy but long, slow, and curving trajectory—one which minimized its speed at Mars arrival. Zond 2 shot past Mars on 6 August 1965 within a mere 1500 km at 5.62 km/s, which was accurate, but not accurate enough for the intended landing. Whether the approach speed would have been sufficiently slow and the parachutes large enough to have lowered the Zond 2 cabin on Mars is uncertain.[29] In the event, the Martian atmosphere turned out to be very thin (8 mb, instead of the then fashionable estimates of 80 mb). Zond 2 was also worth remarking insofar as it tested low-thrust ion plasma engines. Six such thrusters were carried, and they were fired during the period 8–18 December.

Four probes were once more prepared for Venus in 1965. A lander failed to get away on 23 November and became known as Cosmos 96. Another flyby failed on 26 November. Of the two that did leave Earth, one was a flyby probe, Venera 2: an accurate launch put it on a flyby course of 24 000 km with arrival due in February 1966. A television system was set up to broadcast the flyby. Venera 3 was wasp-shaped with solar panels, umbrella antenna, cylinder and motor. One end held a bucket-shaped descent capsule, 90 cm across. It was to be released as Venera 3 approached Venus: parachutes would open and it would descend into the raging hot atmosphere. Originally Venera 3 would have missed Venus by 60 550 km, but in the first month after its 15 November launch no fewer than 13 300 measurements were taken of its course before a correction on 26 December. It was aimed at the dead centre of Venus. Later, it became known that contact with Venera 3 had been lost during the first half of its journey to the planet. Its 'impact' was announced on the basis of mathematical calculations that it *would* hit the planet.

By 1 March 1966, when Venera 1 crashed into Venus—it was the first probe to reach another world—not one Soviet interplanetary mission had carried out its full and intended mission. The Americans had made four attempts, and two, Mariner 2 and 4, had been spectacular successes. Mariner 4 flew past Mars in July 1965 and sent back, laboriously slowly, 22 pictures. There were no canals, but craters galore. In 1965, owing to the pressures of the Moon race, the design of interplanetary probes was transferred from Korolev to the Babakin design bureau in the Moscow suburb of Khimsky.

Venus and Mars missions, 1963–5

19 Feb 1964	Venus flyby	Failure
1 Mar 1964	Venus flyby	Failure
27 Mar 1964	Venus flyby	Failure (Cosmos 27)
12 Nov 1965	Venus flyby	Venera 2 (contact lost)
16 Nov 1965	Venus lander	Venera 3 (contact lost)
23 Nov 1965	Venus lander	Failure (Cosmos 96)
26 Nov 1965	Venus flyby	Failure

PREPARING FOR THE MOON

As the design institutes competed for their different Moon plans, new groups of cosmonauts were recruited to fly the Soyuz spacecraft and, ultimately, the Moon missions. The 1963 air force group consisted of test pilots, much older and more experienced than the first, 1960 selection. The 1965 selection, called the Young Guards on account of their youth, comprised young pilots who, it was expected, would stay in the programme for some time and provide continuity well into the 1970s.

Air Force pilots selected, January 1963

Georgi Dobrovolski
Anatoli Filipchenko
Alexei Gubarev
Anatoli Kuklin
Vladimir Shatalov
Lev Vorobyov
Yuri Artyukhin
Eduard Buinovski
Lev Demin
Vladislav Gulyayev
Pyotr Kolodin
Eduard Kugno
Alexander Matinchenko
Anatoli Voronov
Vitaly Zholobov
Georgi Beregovoi (1964)

Young Guards, October 1965

Leonid Kizim
Alexander Kramarenko
Alexander Petrushenko
Gennadiy Sarafanov
Vasili Shcheglov
Ansar Sharafotdinov
Alexander Skvortsov
Valeri Voloshin
Oleg Yakovlev
Vyacheslav Zudov
Boris Belousov
Vladimir Degtyaryov (replaced by Vasili Lazarev)
Pyotr Klimuk
Anatoli Fyodorov
Yuri Glazhkov
Vitaly Grishenko
Yevgeni Khludeyev
Gennadiy Kolesnikov
Mikhail Lisun
Vladimir Preobrazhensky
Valeri Rozhdestvensky
Eduard Stepanov

Air Force selection, April 1967

Valeri Beloborodov
Sergei Gaidukov
Vladimir Kovalyonok
Vladimir Kozelsky
Vladimir Lyakhov
Yuri Malashev
Viktor Pisarev
Mikhail Sologub
Vladimir Alekseyev
Mikhail Burdayev
Vladimir Isakov
Nikolai Porvatkin

Civilian selected from Academy of Sciences, 1967

Valentin Yershov

Civilians selected from the Korolev OKB in January 1967

Nikolai Rukavishnikov
Vitaly Sevastianov

Civilians selected from the Korolev OKB in May 1968

Viktor Patsayev
Vladimir Fartushny (Paton Institute)
Valeri Yazdovski

ASSAULT ON THE MOON

As the new cosmonauts arrived for their training, the unmanned probes that would herald their arrival on the Moon were prepared for launch. The new soft landing probes had designs very similar to Luna 4. But the elimination of faults which had plagued the 1963 missions was easier said than done and when the first of the new probes took to the skies in 1965, it too became stranded in Earth orbit. The 1470 kg probe, later called Cosmos 60, was put up on 12 March 1965.

The next spacecraft did improve on Luna 4's record. Luna 5 got away on 9 May 1965, and set off in good working order. It carried out a mid-course manoeuvre and headed straight for the Sea of Clouds. But when the time came to fire the retrorockets for touchdown, nothing happened! The rockets just did not come on and Soviet scientists in the control room listened helplessly to Luna 5's signals as it crashed unaided into the Moon at great speed. Its equipment exploded and sent up a cloud of dust 80 km wide and 225 km long.

Luna 6 was a disaster. Put up flawlessly on 8 June, the time came two days later to make a mid-course manoeuvre. Although the rocket switched on correctly, it would not turn off! The engine continued to blast away remorselessly, sending Luna 6 away in the opposite direction. It missed the Moon by no less than 161 000 km, a record.

The only lunar success for the Soviet Union that summer was Zond 3, which was, ironically, flown as part of the interplanetary programme to test equipment for use on Mars and Venus probes. It took off on 18 July 1965; nothing further was heard of it until 15 August, when a new space success was revealed. Zond 3, a 950 kg probe, had shot past the Moon at a distance of 10 000 km, some 33 h after launch en route to a deep space trajectory in the direction of Mars. Its f106 mm camera blinked away for 68 min at 1/100th and 1/300th of a second. 25 pictures were taken.

The details shown were excellent and were on 1100 lines (the American Ranger cameras of the same time were half that). Soviet scientists waited till Zond 3 was 1.25 million kilometres away before commanding the signals to be transmitted again by remote control. They were rebroadcast several times and Zond 3 was still functioning on 16 September.

Zond 3 sweeps past the western limb of the Moon, July 1965.

There was grandeur in the photographs as Zond swung around the Moon's leading edge—whole new mountain ranges, continents and hundreds of craters swept into view. Zond 3's ultimate fate as a Mars probe is not clear.

Zond 3 may have encouraged the designers to believe that in their next soft-landing mission, Luna 7, they would at last meet with success. The space probe, launched on the Sputnik anniversary of 4 October 1965, went through all stages flawlessly right up to retrofire. After the predicted touchdown, scientists tried to contact the capsule, which should have been deployed. Hours passed—silence. Luna 7 was down in the Ocean of Storms near the crater Kepler, but no response.

Eventually the scientists gave up. 13 h after touchdown, they admitted that Luna 7 had failed. 'Most operations necessary for a soft-landing were carried out', the Soviet news agency said. The conclusion: the retrorockets had fired too early, had slowed the capsule down to zero, but with fuel exhausted, it fell the rest of the way unaided and was irreparably damaged. But they had nearly done it.

Two months later, Luna 8 followed the same path, lifting off on 3 December. 83 h into the mission, the rockets switched on. They were too late, it transpired, and the probe was destroyed. A soft-landing was proving an elusive target—more so than any previously attempted. Yet another probe was prepared. But tragedy lay ahead.

Zond interplanetary series for technology testing

11 Nov 1963	Lunar flyby	Failure (Cosmos 21)
2 Apr 1964	Venus flyby	Zond 1
4 June 1964	Lunar flyby	Failure
30 Nov 1964	Mars lander	Zond 2 (contact lost)
18 Jul 1965	Lunar flyby	Zond 3

DEATH OF A DREAMER

Luna 8 was the last probe that Sergei Korolev witnessed. He was dead a month later. He was admitted to hospital on 13 January 1966, for the removal of colon tumours. No less a person than the Minister for Health, Dr Boris Petrovsky, carried out the operation—at Korolev's request. Mid-way through, a more serious tumour was discovered. The operation continued. A large blood vessel burst; haemorrhaging began; and Sergei Korolev's heart—weakened as it had been from the toil of the labour camps—collapsed. Frantic efforts were made to revive him but on 14 January he was pronounced dead. Once dead, his identity and importance could safely be revealed, and indeed they were, following burial in the Kremlin wall on 16 January 1966. A flood of Korolev literature followed. No efforts were spared in telling of his boundless energy, iron will, limitless imagination and engineering genius.

This could have been mistaken for nostalgia, but it was not. With Korolev's death, the Soviet space programme was never the same again. The driving force went out of it, and with it that unique ability to command, inspire, bargain, lead, design and attend to detail. After 1966 the programme had many excellent designers, planners, politicians, adminis-

Memorial to Sergei Korolev in Moscow.

trators and prophets, but never in one person all together. Not that this was immediately obvious. The programme carried on much as before. Design and testing of the upcoming Soyuz proceeded apace—indeed it was a tribute to Korolev that thirty years later it was still carrying cosmonauts into space. But the sense of direction slackened. Indeed the absence of Korolev may have made the critical difference to the climax of the Moon race in 1968–9. He was replaced by his deputy, Vasili Mishin, who had worked alongside him since 1945. Mishin was not confirmed in his position until May 1967; nor was he automatically made a senior member of the Academy of Sciences.

AHEAD AGAIN

Luna 9, 1583 kg, got away on 31 January 1966. It may actually have been the last one manufactured in this phase of soft-landing spacecraft. It did not disappoint. On 3 February, 46 s before impact, the retrorocket fired, exactly on schedule. It halted Luna 9 direct in its tracks. The little 99.8 kg capsule separated and bounced along the rocky dusty lunar surface like a heavy-bottomed toy. It settled. On the top part, four petal-like wings un-folded. Four minutes later, four 75 cm aerials poked their way out of the dome, slowly extending.

Luna 9 was down in the Ocean of Storms between the craters of Reiner and Maria. On Earth, ground controllers gathered that winter night, in a moment of expectation. The descent module's signals had died as it crashed. Ground controllers had to wait 4 min to know if the capsule had survived, if its instruments were still functioning, and whether they would get usable information. Or would they be robbed of victory yet again?

They were not. It was an agonizing wait. Exactly on schedule, from the walls of the control room where loudspeakers had been installed, flooded in the beeps, pips and hum-ming squeal of the signals of Luna 9, direct from the surface of the Moon! It was a sweet moment. For the first time a spacecraft was transmitting directly to Earth from another world! It was an historic moment and Radio Moscow lost no time in assessing its signifi-cance:

> A soft-landing was one of the most difficult scientific and technical problems in space research. It's a major step towards a manned landing on the Moon and other planets.

Its importance was not lost on the West. 'New space lead for Russia' and 'Russians move ahead again' were typical headlines. Once again, America's equivalent project called Surveyor had managed to get itself a year or two behind schedule. American engi-neers were quick to point out that their craft was much more sophisticated than Luna 9. Surveyor planned a real parachutist-type landing, with no rough-landing capsules, and would do a more detailed job. But, so what? people asked. It was still in the shed.

For the next few days the eyes of the world focused on the Moon. At 4.50 a.m. on 4 February the television camera was switched on. It was a tiny thing weighing only 159 g. It was a mere 60 cm above the surface. It began to scan the lunar surface, a process which took 100 min through the full 360 degrees. The camera was in fact the main instrument on board: the other was a radiation recorder. A series of communication sessions was held between Earth and Moon over the next three days, which was as long as the batteries permitted. Some sessions lasted over an hour. The principal one was held on 4 February from 6.30 p.m. to 7.55 p.m. Moscow time, and it sparked off a diplomatic incident. This relay was the big one—the one with the pictures.

The ever-present British radio dish at Jodrell Bank had been listening in to the Luna 9 signals all during the flight. That evening as the communications session began it was realized that what was coming in was a broadcast of television pictures and that they were not in code. On an inspiration and a hunch, a car was speedily despatched to Manchester to pick up the *Daily Express* TV fax machine. The car collected it, dashed back, and the fax machine was at once linked up to the radio receiver. Reporters were breathless as the fax at once began converting the signals into standard newspaper photographs.

The print was passed round to observatory director Sir Bernard Lovell and the ani-mated reporters. They could only gasp. The tall authoritative Sir Bernard drew a deep breath and could only utter 'amazing!' There it was—the face of the Moon. The camera's eye stretched to a sloping horizon and there loomed rocks, pebbles, stones and boulders, eye stretched to a sloping horizon and there loomed rocks, pebbles, stones and boulders, scattered randomly across a porous rocky surface. In the far distance was a crater dipping down. Long shadows accentuated the contrasts of the other-worldly glimpses of the Moon's stark surface.

In minutes, the world had seen the photographs. The Russians were furious at the West scooping 'their' pictures. Sir Bernard was accused of sensationalism and irresponsibility. In fact he had his scales slightly wrong and the real pictures were flatter. But from then on picture transmissions from Russian space probes were always coded and the Russians were much smarter off their marks in releasing data anyway. Transmissions were to continue for several days. More photographs were picked up—eight in all—showing the lunar horizon stretching to the far distance and Luna 9 obviously settled into a boulder field. It was eerie, but reassuring. If Luna 9 could soft land, then so too could a manned spacecraft: it would not suffocate in a field of dust as some had feared.

Its battery exhausted, Luna 9 finally went off the air for ever on 6 February after transmitting 8 hr 5 min of data over seven communication sessions. The Ocean of Storms returned to its customary silence and desolation. Luna 9 had done all that was asked of it: it had survived, transmitted and photographed, and its timer had ensured regular broadcasts from the Moon to the Earth. Another barrier was down and the Americans had been beaten once again.

LUNAR INTERNATIONALE

Booster problems returned to haunt the onward Moon effort. On 1 March 1966, Cosmos 111 failed to leave Earth orbit for the Moon. Luna 10 eventually got away on 31 March 1966. No sooner was it streaking towards the Moon than it was announced that it was directed towards an entirely new objective—Moon orbit. Again, this was essential for manned lunar flight, as arriving manned spacecraft would have to learn how to enter Moon orbit. Again, the American equivalent lunar programme called Lunar Orbiter was still months away.

8000 km from the Moon, Luna 10 was turned around in its path and its rockets blazed briefly but effectively. They knocked 0.64 km/s off its speed, just enough to let the Moon's gravity field capture it. Luna 10 had the same base as Luna 9 but with a 245 kg scientific cabin on top. The boiler-shaped instrument cabin separated on schedule. Luna 10 was pulled into an orbit of 349 by 1017 km, 71.9 dg, 178.3 min. It was designed to answer the key questions: would cosmonauts survive the radiation levels of near-Moon space? How would the Moon's magnetic field affect the orbital paths of spacecraft circling it?

But first things first: Luna 10 celebrated the latest Russian achievement in style. Celestial mechanics meant that Luna 10 would enter the first of its lunar orbits just as the Communist Party was assembling in Moscow for its congress—the first congress of Brezhnev and Kosygin. As it rounded the eastern edge of the Moon, Luna 10's transmitter went full on and relayed the bars of the 'Internationale'—in turn broadcast by loudspeaker direct to the party congress over the static of deep space. It was a triumphant moment and the 5000 delegates had good reason to stand and cheer wildly.

Luna 9 may have surprised people by its early closedown, but Luna 10 performed much longer. Its mission lasted way into the summer and did not end till 30 May, after 460 lunar

revolutions and 219 communication sessions. A stream of data was sent back by its magnetometer, gamma ray detector, infrared radiometer, cosmic ray detector and meteoroid
counter. Cosmonauts would be able to survive in near-Moon space.

One by one the last impediments to a manned lunar landing were being ticked off. The
Moon was safe to land on. The radiation levels were acceptable. But the Moon's gravitational field had proven more complex than anticipated, because of the presence under the
lunar seas of heavier material which distorted lunar orbits—and which could have a disastrous effect on a poorly planned lunar profile.They were an unwelcome development
because precise accuracy was required if an accurate lunar landing were to be achieved.
Errors of only 3, 4 or 5 km in orbit could bring a landing spaceship down in crater fields
instead of a flat patch by mistake. The mass concentrations—the Americans called them
mascons—had to be understood and mapped.

Luna 11 was fitted out for this purpose. Instead of detaching a separate cabin into lunar
orbit, the instrumentation cabin remained attached to the main spacecraft and retrorocket,
enabling more equipment to be carried. It left Earth on 24 August and entered Moon orbit
of 159 by 1200 km, 27 deg, 178 mins. Its 27 deg low-inclination orbit was perfect for the
accurate measurement of the lunar gravitational field in those equatorial areas between
27N and 27S where the manned lander was most likely to touch down.

Luna 12 (22 October) entered into an orbit of 100 by 1737 km, 205 min, 15 deg and
carried a full-scale television observation unit with onboard devices to scan the photographs and transmit them to Earth. A series of 1100 pictures was taken, scanning the
surface in blocks of 52 km^2 from a height of 100 km (in fact the same height as America's
later Apollo), sufficient to pick out craters 15 m to 20 m in diameter. The mission lasted
three months and ended on 19 January 1967 after 602 orbits. A Soviet photograph released late in 1966 showed cosmonauts Yuri Gagarin, Alexei Leonov, Vladimir Komarov
and Yevgeni Khrunov pouring excitedly over its pictures—looking for landing sites?

Lunar soft-landers and orbiters

12 Mar 1965	Failure (Cosmos 60)
9 May 1965	Luna 5
8 June 1965	Luna 6
4 Oct 1965	Luna 7
3 Dec 1965	Luna 8
31 Jan 1966	Luna 9
1 Mar 1966	Failure (Cosmos 111)
31 Mar 1966	Luna 10
24 Aug 1966	Luna 11
22 Oct 1966	Luna 12
21 Dec 1966	Luna 13
7 Apr 1968	Luna 14

Luna 13 went aloft on 21 December 1966, and made two course corrections en route to
the Moon. Retrorockets fired at a distance of 69 km and Luna 13 bumped down onto the
surface of the Moon in the Ocean of Storms between the craters Craft and Selenus. True

to earlier traditions of economy and not repeating its predecessor, Luna 13 was more advanced than its soft-landing precursor, Luna 9. It had an upgraded TV camera. For six days, till 30 December, it sent back a series of panoramic sweeps of surrounding craters, stones and rocks. Sun angles were low and the shadows of Luna 13's antennæ stood out against the ghostly lunarscape. Luna 13 represented a significant advance in that it carried two extensible arms which folded down like ladders onto the lunar surface. At the end of one was a mechanical soil meter with a thumper which tested the density of the soil. At the end of the other was a radiation density meter. Their conclusion was that Moonrock was similar to medium-density Earth soil. To conclude the series, Luna 14 was flown out to the Moon on 7 April 1968 to carry out additional work on mascons. Modelled on Luna 11, it entered into a lunar orbit of 160 by 870 km, 42 deg, 160 min. Little information about its activities were released.[30]

AMERICA'S RECOVERY

By this stage, the significant investment in the American Moon effort after May 1961 had begun to show impressive, visible results, even if in the public mind, the Soviet Union was still perceived to be in the lead. Gemini turned out to be a spectacular success. Gemini 4 was America's first spacewalk. Gemini 5 was an eight-day endurance test. Gemini 6 and 7 rendezvoused in space in a marvellous aerial ballet high over the blues of the Pacific Ocean. Gemini 7 pushed the endurance record to 14 days and Gemini 8 achieved the first space docking in March 1966. The last four Geminis were put up only two months apart. Gemini 9 refined spacewalking. Gemini 10 docked with no less than two targets. It then used the Agena target to boost the combined assembly to 800 km over Arabia. Gemini 11 achieved first orbit docking. Gemini 12 went through all the manoeuvres again. During this period, not a single cosmonaut left the ground.

The American unmanned lunar programme had two elements: a soft-lander, Surveyor, of which seven were built; and a Lunar Orbiter, of which five were built, and called simply Lunar Orbiter. Both were preceded by Luna 9 and 10 respectively, but between them they represented engineering advances. Of the seven Surveyors, all but two succeeded. They soft landed very gently and had proper landing legs. Several survived into the lunar night, and Surveyor 1 returned no fewer than 11 000 pictures over six weeks. Surveyor 7 returned 21 000 pictures from the crater Tycho. One Surveyor relighted its engine and took off, albeit briefly, from the lunar surface. The last three analysed the soil and had mechanical shovels. Surveyor ended in early 1968. The Lunar Orbiter series ran from August 1966 to August 1967. All went correctly into lunar orbit. Each returned about 200 pictures, and by late 1967, 99% of the lunar surface had been mapped, in some places better than some regions of Earth.

The third component, Saturn/Apollo, was proceeding quietly but relentlessly. The first Apollo capsule arrived at Cape Canaveral in August 1966, and Virgil Grissom, Edward White and Roger Chaffee were nominated to take it through its paces in early 1967. In the final stages of development were the lunar module and the rocket which would send it and Apollo to the Moon.

Von Braun's Saturn V was like the Pyramids of Egypt in scale. At 109 m it was higher than a cathedral. The bottom was so huge that it had to come by barge to the launch site, as no other Earthly means of communication could carry it. A tall man could be swallowed up in just one of its nozzles. It would gulp fuel at 15 tonnes a second. The Saturn V was then put together in a slab-like Vehicle Assembly Building (VAB), a structure so enormous that special air conditioning had to be designed to prevent thunder clouds from forming near the roof.

RUSSIA DECIDES

The Soviet Union was now in a position to make final decisions about how it would send men to the Moon. The progress of the Soviet Moon effort was reviewed on 16 November 1966 under a Commission of Experts headed by Mstislav Keldysh. In its early years, at least, the Brezhnev government consulted with expert commissions on a number of occasions, partly in reaction to the adventurism of the Khrushchev period. Korolev's plan for the N-1 was approved, though of course Mishin was now responsible. Chelomei and Glushko made a last effort to replace it with their UR-700 design, but to no avail. However, Chelomei still hoped that his UR-500K would still circle the Moon. The first mission of the basic model, the UR-500, or Proton booster, was a splendid success. On 16 July 1965, it climbed into space and injected into low orbit a 12.2 tonne space observatory called Proton 1. It unfurled gigantic solar panels and at once set to work observing gamma rays, cosmic rays and electrons.

The Commission's report, approving the N-1 and the UR-500K, was ratified by the government in a joint resolution on 4 February 1967 ('About the course of work in the creation of the UR-500K-L-1'), which specified test flights later that year and a landing on the Moon in 1968. The joint resolution reinforced the August 1964 resolution and upgraded the landing on the Moon to 'an objective of national significance'. This meant that it was a priority of priorities, enabling design bureaux to command resources at will. The real problem was that the Americans had decided on their method of going to the Moon five years earlier, and Apollo had been an objective of national importance for six years.

Key government and party decisions in the Moon race

3 Aug 1964	'On work involving the study of the Moon and outer space'
25 Dec 1965	Around-the-Moon cabin to be based on Soyuz design
4 Feb 1967	'About the course of work in the creation of the UR-500K-L-1'

Comparison of the key decisions between the United States and Soviet Union

Key point	United States	Soviet Union
Decision to go the Moon	May 1961	August 1964
Decision on method	July 1962	February 1967

PREPARING SOYUZ

By spring 1967, the Soyuz spacecraft, on which the Moon effort hinged, was almost ready for its first test. Variants of Soyuz would be used to fly around the Moon (the L-1) and to be the mother craft for the lunar lander (LOK). The basic Soyuz was 7.13 m long, 2.72 m wide, with a habitable volume of 10.5 m^3, a launch weight of up to 6800 kg, and a descent capsule weight of 2800 kg.

Soyuz consisted of three modules: equipment, descent and orbital. The equipment module contained retrorockets and manoeuvring engines, fuel, solar wings and supplies. The acorn-shaped descent module was the home of the cosmonauts during ascent and descent, which one entered through the top. There were portholes, a parachute section, and three contour seats. The orbital module, attached on the front, was circular, with spacewalk hatch, lockers for food, equipment and experiments. Having more space, the cosmonauts lived there rather than the cramped descent module. On top of the Soyuz was an escape tower. Normally jettisoned at 2 min 40 s into the flight, the purpose of the escape tower was to fire the Soyuz free of a rogue rocket. A solid rocket motor, with 12 angled nozzles of 80 000 kg thrust, would fire for 5 s. From the Soyuz protruded a periscope for dockings, two seagull-like solar panels, aerials, docking probe on the front, and flashing lights and beacons.

The initial tests of Soyuz were not auspicious. The first test of Soyuz was Cosmos 133 on 28 November 1966. It could not be positioned properly for re-entry and was destroyed deliberately for fear that it would land in China. A second test on 14 December ended with an on-the-pad explosion, the Soyuz cabin being safely dragged away by the emergency escape system. The third test, Cosmos 140 on 7 February 1967, followed the test profile up to re-entry when a maintenance plug in the heatshield burned through and caused structural damage. Worse followed: the cabin came down in the Aral sea, crashed through ice and sank (divers later retrieved the cabin from 10 m down).

'FIRE IN THE SPACECRAFT!'

Even as these two Cosmos missions were taking place, the American space programme was paralysed and enduring the most traumatic period since its establishment. On a windy day at Cape Canaveral, NASA lost three of its best astronauts in a ground test in horrific circumstances.

Soyuz' competitor, Apollo, had arrived at the Cape on 19 August 1966, and on 6 January 1967 had been placed atop the Saturn IB rocket that was to take it into orbit for three weeks of tests after a launching due on 21 February. It would put America into the final stretch of the Moon race. A last countdown test had been scheduled for 27 January and at 1 p.m. Virgil Grissom, Edward White and Roger Chaffee boarded Apollo 1 for the last on-the-pad checkout. It was a long procedure, which had reached T minus 10 minutes at 6.31 p.m., when a voice was heard to shout over the intercom:

'Fire in the spacecraft!'

Chaffee could then be heard calling 'we've got a bad fire!—get us out!'. He went on: 'Open up here!' There was a last scream. Outside Apollo 1 the leader of the pad technicians tried to get them out but was only able to watch helplessly as the spacecraft burst into flames. A wave of heat blew him in the face and thick smoke gushed out. Grissom, White and Chaffee died almost immediately. The fire was both lethal and rapid, and thrived on the high-pressure oxygen pumped in at 16.7 psi instead of the normal 14.7 psi (pounds per square inch). All that was left of Apollo 1 was a blackened shell.

NASA and America were shocked. Nothing had ever prepared the American people for this kind of disaster. People might have been psychologically more accepting of a disaster on a mission, at a moment of exposure to greatest danger. But out of the blue, and on the ground, and in a fire, of all things. It was not long before questions were being asked.

NASA set up a review board within hours. It had reported by the end of April. What it came up with was a mixture of the honest, reassuring, and the disconcerting. Honest, because it revealed serious flaws in Apollo's design; reassuring, because of the refusal to cover up a multiple story of negligence: disconcerting, because some of the mistakes made should not have been made by a competent household electrician. The review board listed pages and pages of wrong-doing. These included flammable fire-hazardous material in the cabin; a hatch that took at least 90 s to open; lack of firefighting equipment; poorly insulated wires which could easily fray and set off a spark that could begin a fire. That was probably what had happened.

But the review board dealt only with the more immediate aspects of the cause of the fire. It did not ask the more basic question of whether safety corners were being cut in order to win the space race. It did not suggest that complacency might have set in after six accident-free years. A whole angle to the fire—the running battle between NASA and the prime contractor—North American Rockwell, about schedules, standards, costs and safety did not come out at all.[31]

FIRST FLIGHT OF SOYUZ[32]

As April drew near, so too did rumours of an impending Russian space flight. March marked the second anniversary of the last manned flight—that of Voskhod 2. General Kaminin announced that a new flight was coming up soon. By 15 April, no Western correspondent in Moscow could be unaware of a big mission in the offing. By 22 April, rumours were flying thick and fast. At 11.45 p.m. that evening, RTE Radio News (Dublin) was able to announce that a single-man flight was on the pad and ready to go. The next day was the anniversary of Lenin's birth.

The rumours were accurate. A big shot was planned. Soyuz 1 would go first, with a single cosmonaut on board. Vladimir Komarov, 40, Voskhod 1 veteran, was the appropriate choice for this first and most challenging mission. 24 h into the flight, Soyuz 2 would follow, commanded by Vostok 5 veteran, Valeri Bykovsky. Two newcomers, Yevgeni Khrunov and Alexei Yeliseyev, would fly with him. The rendezvous would simulate the Moon linkup. Soyuz 1 would be the active craft and would rendezvous on orbit 1. Then the show would really begin. Khrunov and Yeliseyev would don suits, leave Soyuz 2 and transfer into Soyuz 1 to join Komarov. The two ships would then separate after about four hours. Komarov, now accompanied by Khrunov and Yeliseyev, would be back on the ground by the end of day 2, Bykovsky following on the 26th. The transfer would test the new Moonsuit, which, compared to Leonov's 1965 suit, had a bending capability, a high-position backpack, and thick soles and boots. So in 72 breathtaking hours the Soyuz craft

Valeri Bykovsky, ready to fly Soyuz 2 to link with Komarov.

would demonstrate Earth orbit rendezvous on the first orbit, transfer, spacewalking, a primitive space station, and put the USSR back out in front.

Meanwhile, at the cosmodrome, what was actually happening? As the launch date drew near, there were a record 203 faults in Soyuz which required correction. The pre-test flights had been disconcerting. An atmosphere of foreboding prevailed at the cosmodrome. As Vladimir Komarov climbed into the transfer van to take the ride down to the pad, he had an air of fatalistic resignation about him. His fellow cosmonauts joshed him, trying to cheer him and get a smile. They started singing, encouraging him to join in. By the time they reached the pad some minutes later, he was singing with them too and the mood of pessimism had lifted somewhat.

At 3.35 a.m. Moscow time (not quite sunrise local time) the R-7 rocket lit the sky up all about and headed off in the direction of the growing embers of the onrushing dawn. Eight minutes later Vladimir Komarov was back in orbit testing out the most sophisticated spacecraft ever launched.

The trouble started at once when one of Soyuz' two solar panels failed to deploy, starving the craft of electrical power. Other glitches developed as the day went on. The first attempt to change the craft's orbit was unsatisfactory. The ship began to rotate around its axis and only spun more when Komarov tried to correct the problem. The thermal control system degenerated, communications with the ground became irregular and lack of electricity prevented the astro-orientation system from operating. The ion system had to be used instead. The decision was taken to abandon the Soyuz 2 launch and bring Komarov home at the first available opportunity, on orbit 16 the next morning.

Even then, there was more trouble. Just as the attitude control system was lining up the Soyuz for re-entry, the craft passed into darkness and it lost orientation. The decision was made to try again on orbit 17, just as on the last mission, even though it too would bring Soyuz far away from the normal landing site. Komarov had to use the Moon to align the craft and fire the retrorockets himself. As the cabin descended through the atmosphere, the main parachute remained stubbornly in its container. When the reserve chute was popped out, it tangled in the lines of the drag chute of the main parachute. Soyuz 1 crashed at great speed into the steppe at Orenberg at 7a.m. The cabin exploded on impact and when air force recovery teams arrived all they found was burning metal, the rim of the top of Soyuz being the only hardware they could identify. They piled on the soil to extinguish the flames.

The control centre knew nothing of what had happened. As they closed in on the wreckage, the recovery team sent a garbled message to the effect that the cosmonaut needed 'urgent medical attention', but the local air force commander closed off all communications. Defence minister Ustinov was informed of the true outcome at 11a.m. and Leonid Brezhnev an hour later in Karlovy Vary, Czechoslovakia. The Soviet people were officially informed later in the day.

Vladimir Komarov, who crashed at Orenberg, 24 April 1967, the first man to die during a space mission.

Gagarin himself removed Komarov's body from the wreckage. Some days later, some young Pioneers found some further remains of Vladimir Komarov on the steppe. They buried them and made a small memorial for him of their own.

Even today, the doomed flight of cosmonaut Komarov occasions rumour and speculation. Almost thirty years later, a newspaper article alleged that the cosmonaut died in orbit when the air run out. Before this happened, Komarov had liberally cursed the organizers of the flight and Brezhnev personally, explaining why the government never erected a proper memorial to him, so it is said.[33] The Soyuz 1 disaster halted the Soviet programme in its tracks just as effectively as the Apollo fire did the American one only four months earlier. Both disasters raised the same questions of each side cutting corners or being careless in its desire to win the Moon race.

Vladimir Komarov's loyal comrades laid his remains to rest in the Kremlin wall two days later. It was a sombre and chilling occasion, an unwelcome reminder of the real costs of the Moon race. As the bands played the haunting Chopin funeral march, the grim-faced and tight-lipped cosmonaut corps, now diminished to nine men and one woman, swore that the programme must go on relentlessly. There could be no turning back.

Start of the Soyuz programme

28 Nov 1966	Cosmos 133 (failure)
14 Dec 1966	Pad explosion
7 Feb 1967	Cosmos 140 (failure)
23 Apr 1967	Soyuz 1

AROUND THE MOON

The preparations for the flight of Soyuz 1 coincided with those of Korolev's Soyuz-derived, L-1 cabin, which would fly a cosmonaut around the Moon. The L-1 cabin was called Zond, thus creating confusion with the engineering tests developed by Korolev as part of the interplanetary programme.

Zond was a stripped-down version of Soyuz. Its weight was 5400 kg, length 5 m, span across its two 2 m by 3 m solar arrays 9 m, diameter 2.72 m and a habitable volume of 3.5 m³. It could take a crew of either one or two cosmonauts. The sole engine was the 400 kg Soyuz KDU-35, but it fired more thrusters than Soyuz. Its heat shield was thicker than that on Soyuz in order to withstand the high friction on lunar re-entry at 11 km/s. It carried an umbrella-like long-distance high-gain antenna, and on the top a support cone where the cosmonauts would enter the cabin on the pad and to which the escape tower was attached. Designer was Yuri Semeonov.

When wheeled out for its first test—Cosmos 146, set for 10 March 1967—the three-stage UR-500K Proton stood 44.3 m high. Six fuel tanks surrounded the central core, which carried oxidizer. The first stage would burn for two minutes with 894 tonnes of thrust. The second stage, with three Kosberg RD-465 and one Kosberg RD-468 engines with a thrust of 245 tonnes, would burn for 215 s. The third stage, with a single RD-473 of 64 tonnes thrust, would place the Zond or L-1 in low Earth orbit in a 255 s burn. Finally, the Korolev block D fourth stage would fire for 100 s to achieve full orbit. One hour after liftoff, the fourth stage, block D, would relight on the first northbound pass over the equator to send Zond to the Moon. Its single 58M engine had 8.7 tonnes of thrust, and burned for 600 s, enough to accelerate the payload to 11 km/s.

Six fuel tanks surround the central core of the UR-500K rocket.

Two initial Zond tests were carried out around the same time as the Soyuz 1 disaster. These were Cosmos 146 (March 1967) and Cosmos 154 (April 1967). If the Cosmos 146 test and a second mission went well, it had been hoped to fly a man around the Moon as early as June 1967 (though many thought this schedule unrealistic). Cosmos 146 was essentially a test of the fourth stage of the Proton, and an engineering model of Zond was used. The block D successfully accelerated the cabin to near-escape velocity, 146 ending up in a high orbit. Cosmos 154 was a similar test but, frustratingly, the block D fourth stage did not fire.

ANNIVERSARY OF THE BOLSHEVIK REVOLUTION

October marked the 50th anniversary of the Bolshevik Revolution. It was a date too important to go unmarked by some kind of space achievement. The real question was not if it would be marked, but how. The Soyuz disaster meant that the chances of flying a man around the Moon for the anniversary were nil. Zond and Soyuz were too closely related and there was no way that Soyuz could be brought up to standard in time, regardless of how well Zond went. So the best that could be hoped for was an unmanned flyby, paving the way for a manned one in 1968. The failure of the block D on Cosmos 154 had already required months of checking and redesign.

Working overtime, the designers and launch teams got the first unmanned round-the-Moon Zond out to the pad by mid-September 1967. The countdown began for a launch on 28 September. The huge red-and-white Proton booster, 82 m high, weighing 1 028 500 kg, Zond cabin atop, tipped by a pencil spear of an escape tower, was taking with it Russia's Moon hopes. It sat squat on its giant pad, shrouded by its gantry, as engineers fussed with one technical problem after another. Yet it all went wrong. One of the six engines in the first stage of the Proton failed to operate when a rubber plug was dislodged into the fuel line. At 60s the rocket veered off course and impacted 65 km downrange, but the Zond cabin was dragged free by the escape system.

The best the Russians could do to celebrate the anniversary was to carry out the Soyuz 1 mission, but without cosmonauts abroad. Cosmos 186 was the first to appear, beginning a series of flights that would requalify Soyuz for manned flight once more. It went up on 27 October and was followed three days later by Cosmos 188.

Using totally automatic radar, direction-finding and sounding devices, Cosmos 186 at once closed in on 188 in the manoeuvre that Komarov was to have carried out in April. Whatever the past difficulties, the manoeuvres that followed went with astonishing accuracy and precision. At orbital insertion, 188 was only 24 km away. 186 closed rapidly, within two-thirds of an orbit. One hour later over the South Pacific, they clunked together to form an automatic orbiting complex. 3.5 h later, they separated. 186 was down the next day, 188 two days later. It was a flawless display of advanced robotics. It proved the feasibility of first-orbit rendezvous, the viability of Soyuz-style docking, and took some of the fears out of lunar orbit rendezvous when all this would have to be done a third of a million kilometres away.

However, the elation surrounding the Cosmos 186–188 mission was followed by a disheartening experience three weeks later. On the next attempt to launch Zond, very early on 23 November local time, one of the four engines in the second stage of the Proton failed to operate. The automatic control system closed down the other three engines, and the emergency system was activated. The landing rockets fired prematurely during the descent but the cabin was recovered. The Proton itself crashed 300 km from where it took off.

AMERICA MOVES AHEAD

Spring 1968. Rather than run the embarrassment of trying to reach a real Moon the next time and fail again, it was decided that the next Zond would aim towards a simulated Moon . It would involve the same type of return trajectory as a real Moon flight. But time was pressing even more now, for the Americans were nearly back on their feet again.

Virtually unaffected by the Apollo fire, the enormous Saturn V booster was nearing completion under the direction of Peenemünde veteran Wernher von Braun. It was the German's last and most brilliant achievement, the climax of his engineering career. Von Braun had been working on Saturn V since 1962, and his ultimate project was now reaching the moment of truth. It is a tribute to his genius that this giant creation, five times larger than anything ever before flown, was to take to the skies, eleven times, and complete every assignment.

In von Braun the Russian rocket engineers at last met their match. His Saturn V was not merely a giant—height 110.6 m, launch weight 27.7 million kilograms, thrust 3.4 million kilograms—it was a miracle of efficiency and precision. It used, for the first time, the supercold, ultrapowerful and extremely difficult fuel of liquid hydrogen. And after the fire, ground testing ensured that the words 'fanatically thorough' were an understatement of the engineers' approach. The Saturn V arrived at the pad in late August 1967 for its first, unmanned test.

After three days' counting down, the first Saturn V at last reached the magical moment of zero, during the winter darkness of 9 November 1967. The five monstrous engines belched and roared for nine full seconds before generating enough thrust for liftoff. Night turned to day. Pillars of smoke bellowed into the night sky. In the midst, the Saturn V rose. The roar of the engines knocked people over three miles away as Saturn bent over towards the Atlantic Ocean. At 58 km, travelling at 9658 km/h, the main engines cut off, the bottom stage separated, and there was a sharp flash as the second stage lit up. Its blue flames pushed Saturn out of sight into the night sky and it was lost to view. Saturn V put an unmanned capsule, Apollo 4, into orbit atop its third stage. After two revolutions, that third stage was restarted. Then Apollo fired its own motor to push its orbit out to 40 000 km, before blasting it back into the atmosphere to simulate a lunar return at high speed. After an eight-hour flight the blackened and charred capsule was fished out of the sea.

This morale-boosting success was underscored when on 22 January 1968, NASA put its lunar module aloft for the first time. It was designated Apollo 5. The bug-shaped, spidery lunar module was put through its paces in six revolutions during which all its major stages were tested. The flight went so well that a second orbital test planned for June 1968 was cancelled. With the successful missions of Apollo 4 and 5, NASA was now moving well ahead. The USSR had failed to produce its equivalent pieces of hardware—its own lunar module, large booster or demonstrate high-speed lunar re-entry return. In fact it was nowhere near doing so.

So seriously did NASA take the Soviet challenge that in the spring of 1968 it was decided to fly men aboard the next lunar module and to man-rate the third Saturn V assuming that the second test was successful. Originally, ten unmanned Saturn V tests had been planned. The long-term NASA plans had suggested a manned Moonlanding on the seventh Apollo flight, but these plans were rapidly telescoped. So NASA was, for the first time in its history, upping the ante and advancing its schedules to beat anticipated Soviet targets. It had never done this before.

RUSSIA'S MOON TEAM

In anticipation of manned flights to the Moon, on 13 March 1968, the cosmonaut training centre, TsPK, set up a training group of cosmonauts to fly to the Moon. Their members were:

Andrian Nikolayev	Pavel Popovich	Alexei Leonov
Valeri Bykovsky	Yevgeni Khrunov	Viktor Gorbatko
Boris Volynov	Georgi Shonin	Pyotr Klimuk
Yuri Artyukhin	Anatoli Voronov	Valeri Voroshin

Anatoli Kuklin	Konstantin Feoktistov	Alexei Yeliseyev
Valeri Kubasov	Vladislav Volkov	Oleg Makarov
Vitaly Sevastianov	Nikolai Rukavishnikov	Georgi Grechko
Valeri Yazdovski	Vladimir Bugrov	Valentin Yershov

Several members of the group had already been practising lunar landings with helicopters. The accelerated training group for the L-3 lunar landing programme comprised Alexei Leonov, Nikolai Rukavishnikov, Valeri Bykovsky and Valeri Kubasov.

The next Zond got away successfully on 2 March 1968. This time the UR-500K Proton main stages and the block D worked perfectly. Zond 4 was fired 300 000 km out to the distance of the Moon, but in exactly the opposite direction of the Moon, where its orbit would be minimally distorted by the Moon's gravitational field. Cosmonaut Vitaly Sevastianov and Pavel Popovich used a relay on Zond 4 to speak to ground control in Yevpatoria, Crimea. The problems developed on the return. Instead of making a skip re-entry into the atmosphere, an attitude control error led to a rapid 20 g ballistic re-entry over west Africa. Ground controllers quarrelled about what to do: some favoured the landing to go ahead, others feared that the Zond would fall into foreign hands, spilling the secrets of its intended mission. Dmitri Ustinov insisted that ground control set off the self-destruct system: Zond 4 was blown apart 10 km over the Gulf of Guinea.

But NASA was on the march again and on 4 April 1968, Apollo 6 went up on the second Saturn V. It was intended that it would repeat the dazzling success of Apollo 4. But now it was NASA's turn to gasp as one thing went wrong after another. Two minutes into the mission the red lights flashed as the whole Saturn V structure went into a wild pogo effect—shaking up and down violently. Soon after, some parts of the lunar module adaptor section shook free. This was the least the pogo effect would do. Worse vibration, and the astronauts could not read their instruments. Worse, the rocket would break up. That stopped, but more trouble started. On the second stage, two engines shut down for no evident reason. Apollo 6 went into an orbit of 172 by 395 km, instead of one circular at 175 km. Then the third stage refused to ignite. Apollo 6's motor had to do its re-entry manoeuvres itself instead of the Saturn third stage. This it did, and the capsule was recovered after a re-entry at a much lower speed than planned.

Undaunted by this flirtation with disaster four times over, NASA then announced that its Saturn V was man-rated as from 29 April, and it was now happy to fly astronauts on top. The faults had been ironed out, NASA assured everyone. It revealed its new plan: a three-man Apollo in the autumn in Earth orbit; then an Earth orbit test out to 6000 km before the New Year; and a lunar module test in the spring. A lunar orbit next, a final test, and then a landing. The investigations of the Apollo 6 difficulties were indeed thorough and exhaustive. Still, the NASA decision so soon afterwards was open to the accusation of haste. It is unlikely if such swift man-rating standards would ever have been used before or since. James Webb's decision must have shocked and exasperated the Soviet space planners, whose two goals of Moon landing and around-the-Moon flight were now slipping from their grasp.

Some consolation could be drawn from a repeat of the Cosmos linkup of the previous winter. On 15 April 1968, Cosmos 212 (the active ship) linked to Cosmos 213, this time in a record 47 min, easily beating America's Gemini 11 (94 min). Television showed the last 400 m of the docking manoeuvre as they aligned their wing-like panels one to another. Millions saw the separation 3 h 50 min later over the blue void of the Pacific. The way was now clear for the first Soviet manned mission for a year.

By the end of April 1968, the problems experienced by Zond 4 had been cured and the time was ready to try the first circumlunar flight to a 'real' Moon this time. Launch took place on 23 April. Unfortunately, about a minute into the mission, the escape system triggered accidentally, shutting down all the Proton engines and flinging the Zond capsule clear, needlessly saving the cabin and thereby wrecking the mission in the process. A replacement mission was planned for 22 July, but in a pad accident, the block D and L-1 toppled over onto the launch tower. The L-1 was salvaged for a future Zond mission.

FAREWELL TO GAGARIN

Sadly the pilot assigned the first new Soyuz mission was dead. Early on the morning of 29 March 1968, and not long after his 34th birthday, Yuri Gagarin had taken off with flying instructor Vladimir Seryogin on a routine flight test aboard a MiG-15Uti aircraft from a flying field northeast of Moscow. It was part of his regular flight training. As the training plane was coming in to land, a MiG-21 passed close to their plane. Although the MiG-21 pilot was probably never aware of it, he had caused such a jetwash as to put Gagarin's plane into a spin. The MiG crashed into a forest near the airfield and burned.

His wife Valentina was in hospital at the time having an operation for a stomach ulcer. She was able to get up and walk on the 28th, and the following evening phoned home to check whether Yuri had returned from his day's flying. She called for an hour and a half and was eventually told the line was out of order. Something began to nag at her that things were wrong. Then the following morning, quite unexpectedly she said later, Valentina Tereshkova, Pavel Popovich and Andrian Nikolayev appeared. She recalled:

As soon as I saw them, my heart was gripped with fear.

'Has anything happened?' I asked them.

'Yes', they said 'yesterday morning ... '.

It could not have come at a worse time. Always popular, accepted as a leader, Gagarin had taken upon himself the task of solving the problems that had killed his friend Vladimir Komarov. Now he too was gone. His nine comrades bore his body through the streets of Moscow two days later amidst black scenes of great grief. It was a further blow that the great adventure could ill afford.

Almost as if to take advantage of the USSR's sagging position in the space stakes, NASA Apollo programme manager George Low began to advance the notion of an even earlier Apollo flight to the Moon. Until the summer of 1968, NASA planned three earth orbital flights before going anywhere near the Moon. Sorting out the problems in the lunar module (LM), were, despite the success of the January flight, taking longer than expected, and the next LM might not be ready to fly until some time into 1969. Why not, argued Low, do a lunar flight first, using the Apollo command cabin only, and then test out the LM later? He put forward an ambitious—or looked at another way, reckless—plan: if the first Apollo Earth orbital flight were successful in October, Apollo 8 could go around the Moon two or three months later. Apollo 9 could do the LM tests in Earth orbit, and Apollo 10 could do the LM tests in lunar orbit.

Low's scheme was logical enough—testing what was available when it was available rather than waiting. As for the gamble of the first Moon flight, it had to be done sooner or later, so why not sooner? It would be just as dangerous one flight later, just as psychologically challenging. But there were some negative sides to the plan. Apollo 8 would be only the second Apollo to fly. And it would be only the third flight of the Saturn V. Unlike their rivals, NASA had absolutely no means of testing out Apollo on a round-the-Moon trip unmanned and automatically before putting humans on board. So the proposal was not without risks. Indeed, throughout this period, Soviet scientists repeatedly expressed their concerns to Western colleagues that the Americans were taking unjustifiable risks.

George Low's proposal was quickly accepted at senior management level within NASA, including von Braun. Administrator Webb and President Johnson took several weeks to agree. They must have been sceptical about flying around the Moon a spacecraft that had not yet flown and which had already incinerated its first crew. But agree they did—on the strict condition that the first Apollo, named Apollo 7, was entirely successful. And Apollo 6-style faults would not qualify.

So it was on 19 August 1968, that NASA announced a revised Apollo schedule. Apollo 7, crewed by astronauts Schirra, Eisele and Cunningham, would test out Apollo in a ten-day Earth orbit shakedown cruise starting 11 October; Apollo 8 (Borman, Lovell, Anders) would go to the Moon (lunar orbit or figure-of-eight flyby) in December; and Apollo 9 (McDivitt, Scott, Schweickart) would test out the LM back in Earth orbit when it was ready. That was expected to be March 1969.

Surprisingly little public notice was taken of this announcement in the West. This was partly because it was during the summer break, partly because it was in disbelief that the USSR was still racing. Another factor was that Apollo 7 had yet to fly, and even thinking of doing anything beyond that could be written off as either daydreaming or wishful thinking.

THE RIPOSTE

But the announcement must have put the wind up the planners in Moscow and Baikonour, who almost certainly considered the Americans to be out of their minds to man-rate a spacecraft for Moon flight on only its second mission and before the first flight had even taken off. Based on the more conservative safety considerations in Soviet thinking, such a proposal in the USSR would have always been a non-starter. The step-by-step Soviet plan of the time called for two Zonds around the Moon, with simultaneous Soyuz requalification. Only if this went properly would they contemplate a manned Zond-around-the-Moon, probably in January 1969 at the earliest. So the NASA announcement hurried this up out of all proportion. The manned Zond—Zond 7—would now have to be ready at least a month earlier to beat Apollo 8. The heat was on. As luck would have it, the same launch window that might take Apollo 8 to the Moon opened for America on 21 December but much earlier in the USSR—in fact 7–9 December. This was entirely due to the celestial mechanics of the optimum launching and landing opportunities.

Autumn was well in the air and the night-time temperatures were cool once more, when at midnight on 15 September 1968, Zond 5 rose off the pad at Baikonour and its Proton launch vehicle silhouetted the gantries, masts and assembly buildings for miles around. It all went effortlessly well, all the more remarkable after the frustrating 18 months that had passed since Cosmos 154 had triggered off so many frustrations. 67 minutes later, Zond 5 was Moonbound, right on course. Its cabin contained small turtles, fruit flies and other living organisms. The spacecraft weighed 5500 kg.

On 17 September at 6.11 a.m. Moscow time, Zond 5 successfully corrected its course. Only then did Moscow reveal the craft's existence. This semi-secret approach only excited the interest of Jodrell Bank Observatory where Sir Bernard Lovell quickly pointed his radio dish to track the enigmatic Zond 5. He picked up strong signals at once. On 19 September he was able to reveal that he thought the spacecraft had been around the Moon at a distance of around 1950 km and was on its way back. This information was based on the signals that he had received. But nobody really knew. Moscow categorically denied that Zond 5 had been anywhere near the Moon.

If the mission planners had been as inept as the Soviet news service, the flight would have failed at this stage. As it was, Zond 5 had seen the Earth disappear to the size of a small blue ball in the distance. Any cosmonaut then on board would have been treated to the fantastic spectacle of the Moon's craters, deserts and rugged highlands sweep below him in stark profusion. Zond soared around the Moon's far side and then, nearing its eastern limb, the full Earth rose gently over the horizon, a welcoming beacon to guide the three-day flight home. Would a cosmonaut soon see and feel this breathtaking vista?

20 September. A belated Russian admission that Zond 5 had indeed been 'in the vicinity of the Moon' (as if any spacecraft happens to find itself in the vicinity of the Moon) was eclipsed by new, even more startling news from Jodrell Bank. A human voice had been picked up from Zond 5! Was this a secret breakthrough? Had a man been aboard all along and would the Russians then announce an historic first? Not likely, said Sir Bernard Lovell. It was a tape-recorded voice, designed to test voice transmissions across deep space. He expected that the next flight would have a cosmonaut aboard. Jodrell Bank continued to track the probe till it was 80 000 km from the Earth and picking up speed rapidly.

Zond 5 was indeed returning to the Earth. 143 000 km from Earth, Zond manoeuvred a second time to refine its trajectory. At 5.30 p.m. Moscow time, 21 September, it reached the limb of the Earth's atmosphere over springtime Antarctica, met its 10 km by 13 km re-entry frame dead on, slammed into the atmosphere at 11 km/s and burned red-hot to a temperature of 13 000°C. To minimize g forces, Zond was designed to skip like a stone over the atmosphere, dissipate energy, soar back into space, and come back a second time, but gentler, and land in the Soviet Union. Instead, an operator error caused an attitude control error and no skip manoeuvre was followed. G forces built up to 16 g. Soon the ordeal was over. A double sonic boom, audible over the Indian Ocean, signified survival. Still glowing, the simmering Zond 5 was lowered by its parachute into the Indian Ocean at 7.08 p.m. Beacons popped out to mark the location of the bobbing capsule. A ship from the Soviet Navy moved in the next day, took Zond out of the water, and hoist it aboard: in no time it was transferred to a cargo ship en route to Bombay, where it was brought to a large Antonov air transport and flown back to the USSR.

The capsule was intact; the turtles had survived. In one sweet week, all the reverses of the past 18 months had been wiped out. Two tests—a repeat mission and a Soyuz test—and the Moon could be Terra Sovietica. The first glimpse out of the porthole, the historic descriptions, the joy of rounding the corner of the Moon—these could yet be Soviet achievements.

All NASA could do now was to keep its fingers crossed and hope against hope that the Russians would not somehow do it first. They now knew they could. Before long the Russians released information which confirmed NASA's worst fears. They announced that Zond was identical to Soyuz, but without the orbital compartment. It had air for one man for six days. It carried an escape tower. The Soviet encyclopedia of spaceflight, (1968), rubbed it in: 'Zond flights are launched for testing and development of an automatic version of a manned lunar spaceship'.

SOYUZ FLIES AGAIN

No sooner had Zond and its precious cargo reached Baikonour at the end of September than the three-week countdown began for the next Soyuz, designed to put right the faults that had plagued Soyuz 1 and 2 in 1967. There would be no ambitious crew transfer this time, just a four-day solo test of rendezvous performance. There would be a one-man crew, to simulate the Zond flight. The pilot would be Georgi Beregovoi, 47, then the oldest man to fly in space, and he was standing in for the late Yuri Gagarin. His wartime experience, his age, and his courage equipped him superbly to fly such a dangerous mission. Georgi Beregovoi was a veteran of 185 combat missions in the war. Everything depended on him. The test was critical. And the portents were not good. Georgi Beregovoi had already tried to fly the mission before, that August. An unmanned Soyuz 2 had gone into orbit, and he was all ready to fly Soyuz 3 up to it the next morning. Soyuz 2 developed trouble and was hastily renamed Cosmos 238 before people could suspect something was amiss. His own flight was stood down.

Evaluating the performance of Zond 5 in preparation for Soyuz took several weeks, and Soyuz was not ready to go until 25 October. So close were the American and Soviet programmes to each other at this stage that Soyuz 2 flew only three days after the first test of America's new Apollo. It was uncanny. It needed such close parallels to persuade many Western observers that there was indeed a race at all.

11 October. Four years less one day after Russia's three-man spaceship, the Americans were airborne with Apollo. A bright start, with the red, orange and yellow flame of the Saturn IB propelling Apollo 7 into a safe orbit, set the tone for the rest of the mission. Twice-veteran Walter Schirra, with novices Walter Cunningham and Don Eisele, put Apollo through its paces. The main service engine fired exactly as the engineers wanted, a full eight times. The three astronauts sent back repeated telecasts from their roomy cabin with its rows of switches and nooks and crannies. They were clearly delighted, confident and fully at ease. The astronauts caught colds and had a few rows with ground control but that was all that could be reported on since the flight was otherwise going so well. No one remembered the fire any more and it almost seemed that it was because they had nothing left to test that Schirra, Eisele and Cunningham dropped out of Earth orbit on 22 October and splashed down in the Atlantic.

Nothing now stood in the way of an Apollo 8 Moon flight in December. On 11 November, NASA's new Administrator, Tom Paine, confirmed that Apollo 8 would fly to the Moon, would make ten lunar orbits and would be launched on 21 December. He may well

Soyuz spacecraft being raised to the launching position.

have doubted if his team of Frank Borman, Jim Lovell and Bill Anders would be the first to report back from deep space, for by 11 November there were two good reasons to think they would not be.

Even as Apollo 7 floated in the Caribbean swell, Soyuz 2 and 3 were trundling down to their pads, flat on the backs of their railway launchers. On the 25th, Soyuz 2 went aloft into an orbit of 185 by 224 km, 51.7 deg. A new procedure was followed for this mission. Rather than launch the active craft first and risk the non-launch of a passive craft second, leaving Beregovoi in orbit with only half a mission to perform and some explaining to be done, they would put up the passive craft first and fly the normal profile from the moment of insertion. As for the problem of a Soyuz 2 announcement provoking speculation of an imminent Soyuz 3 launch (and suggestions of failure if none took place), the Soyuz 2 launching was simply not announced for 24 hours!

At 12.34 p.m. on the 26 October, the swing arms fell back and Soyuz 3 roared off the pad at Baikonour into the misty, drizzling midday sky. A smiling Georgi Beregovoi had boarded his craft only an hour before. Eight minutes later he was in orbit and the mission began immediately. He turned his spacecraft around and orientated it towards Soyuz 2. Radars began their search. Direction-finders 'pinged' their target. Figures flowed into the computers. Within a revolution, automatic systems had brought Soyuz 3 to within 200 m of Soyuz 2. Beregovoi resumed manual control and kept station with it for some time.

Then he pulled away to a distance of 565 km. 'This is Argon ... this is Argon ...': his voice and his call-sign could be heard repeatedly in ground control in Yevpatoria. He rested and transmitted an orbital telecast from his spacecraft, bringing viewers around his spacious home and pointing the camera out the window. Then a second rendezvous: Soyuz 3 began the chase once more, closing in from a distance of 500 kilometres. Once at 200 m, Beregovoi took up manual control. On 28 October, Soyuz 2 returned to Earth and was

With Soyuz 3, the Russians released, for the first time, pictures of the Soyuz spacecraft and the rocket which sent it into space.

recovered in Kazakhstan. Docking had been planned but did not take place (Beregovoi apparently brought his craft in the wrong way up.)

The main part of his mission over, Georgi Beregovoi spent 29 October observing the Earth and its weather, typhoons and forest fires, and the stars, the Moon and the planets. The next day, 30 October, was the moment of truth. On its 61st orbit, Soyuz 3 fired its retrorocket for 145 s over Africa. At mission control, memories of the last flight were uppermost in people's minds, but they need not have worried. At 9000 m the parachute blossomed out.

Thick, early snow lay on the ground and the temperature was 12°C below zero. Helicopters were in the air looking for Beregovoi, and villagers were outside their houses on the lookout too. Strong winds blew the capsule sideways into a snowdrift, and the impact was so gentle that Georgi Beregovoi barely noticed it. Villagers waded through the snowdrifts and amidst flecks of snow the grinning flier had his picture taken before being whisked away for debriefing. Beregovoi later became a leading director of cosmonaut training. He died in July 1995.

LAST TRY: ZOND 6

Less than a week later, Zond 6 headed away from Earth onto a Moon trajectory (10 November). Two days later it adjusted its path and on 14 November rounded the Moon at a close point of 2418 km, with its automatic camera clicking away and taking metres and metres of photographs of the Moon's surface.

Zond 6 was returning to Earth. Its jets fired briefly on 15 November, 251 900 km out, and again a day later, a mere eight hours before re-entry. It was on pin-point course for home. NASA was in a dry sweat. If this worked, only a cosmonaut could take the place of the cameras and the test animals. It was not the kind of mission that needed a third rehearsal. On 18 November, a British newspaper reported:

> The spherical cabin of Zond 6 splashed down south-east of Madagascar. Then the capsule was bobbing in the ocean for about eight hours before Russian ships recovered it.

It could not have been more wrong. Zond 6 was nowhere near the Indian Ocean. Instead, Zond 6 had re-entered over the Indian Ocean at 45 km altitude but had pointed its heat shield at 90 deg to the flight path. This generated a cushion of lift underneath the Zond, pushing it back into space. It was skipping across the atmosphere like a stone skipping across water, its speed now down from 11 km/s to 7.6 km/s. Zond 6 soared back into space in an arc and several minutes later began its second re-entry. At this stage, things began to go badly wrong. First, a gasket blew, depressurizing the cabin while it was still in space—which would have been fatal had unsuited cosmonauts been on board. Second, the parachutes deployed prematurely and the cabin crashed with such violence that a human crew would have died outright. Instead, the film was salvaged and exhibited to the world as proof of a completely successful mission.

With the flight of Zond 6, the Western press rediscovered the Moon race. *Time* magazine ran a cover of an American and a Russian in spacesuits elbowing each other out of the way as each raced Moonbound. Newspapers printed cutaway drawings of 'The Zond plan' and 'The Apollo plan'.

CLIMAX

NASA kept its fingers crossed. The Apollo 8 plan now included ten lunar orbits, which they knew was more than what Zond was capable of doing. Astronauts Borman, Lovell and Anders were right in the middle of their pre-flight checks. Their Saturn V was already on the pad. In London, Independent Television prepared to go on air with special news features the moment Zond went up. Models and spacesuits decorated the studio. The whole world was waiting ... .

Two weeks later, Frank Borman, James Lovell and William Anders burned their Apollo motor for four minutes on the far side of the Moon and slid into Moon orbit. 'The Moon is essentially grey ... no colour ... looks like plaster of Paris ...' echoed Jim Lovell's prosaic voice as he described what he saw. With the quality of a 1930s black-and-white movie, crater after crater rolled by, then lunar sea, then upland, then more craters. Quality or not, it was the Moon, and there were three Americans circling it. On Christmas morning they fired their motor again and blasted back to the little ball of Earth they had proudly displayed on their cameras. And on 27 December they were fished out of the Pacific Ocean, tired, unshaven, but alive.

It was an epic flight and there could never be anything like it again. The sheer bravery of the adventure, voyaging out a quarter of a million miles from the refuge of our planet to the harshness of the tempting Moon. The grandeur of the lunar craters. Three days' travel away. The Earth, a small blue jewel in the black sky. The five or six danger points where a wrong fraction in the computer could bring instant (or even a slow) death. All these things impressed people deeply. Suddenly the spectacle of men walking on the Moon within the year became something real and John Kennedy's historic challenge something feasible after all. The psychological barriers that stood in the way of the Moon landing were coming down.

Despite Western speculation, there had been no serious prospect of a Soviet lunar flight in the first week of December 1968. Six cosmonauts wrote to the politburo offering to undertake the mission, despite the risks involved. Zond 5's faulty re-entry and the catastrophic return of Zond 6 put paid to that. But the shortcomings of both missions were not made known to the West, which only saw two successful dress rehearsals for a manned attempt around the Moon. Film of the shattered wreckage of Zond 6 was not released from the archives until 1995. The Zond programme was not abandoned at this point. To the contrary, it was kept alive in the expectation that the Soviet Union would still fly men to the Moon, and, possibly, in the hope that Apollo would at some stage falter.

NEW JOINT RESOLUTION

A new joint resolution of the party and the Council of Ministers was passed on 1 January 1969. It authorized the manned Moon programme to continue, ordered the urgent construction of an unmanned soil sample return mission to beat an American manned landing on the Moon, and confirmed the development of a manned space station programme by Vladimir Chelomei's design bureau.

Lined up next was a double manned linkup. A rendezvous of Soyuz 4 and 5 was a natural progression from Soyuz 2 and 3 the previous October, and indeed the roots of the mission went back to the ill-fated Komarov flight of 1967. This time, both ships would be manned and the crews would transfer. It was a mission absolutely essential for the manned Moon landing, and that was why it was in the programme. However, mindful of the additional new objectives of the space programme, the mission would now be hailed in terms of an essential step towards an orbital station. It was a convincing explanation for Soyuz 4 and 5 and it took everyone else in at the time—except for the chiefs of NASA and one of the populist British dailies, the *Daily Express*. Appearance triumphed over reality again.

The New Year was only two weeks old when Soyuz 4 stood ready on its pad. The temperature was 22°C. Pressmen were invited to inspect the 45 m high rocket: the night was clear and starry and the snow crunched crisply under their boots. Warm air had to be pumped ceaselessly to the pad just to keep the machinery from freezing solid. Clad only in blue coveralls, Vladimir Shatalov arrived at the pad at 8.30a.m. the following morning, the 14th. He was a flight instructor, then a regimental commander and then an air force inspector. He wasted little time talking to people on the ground and straightaway took the lift up to the warm cabin awaiting him. It swayed gently in the breeze as the count continued. At 10.38 a.m. the gantries fell away and amidst sheets of steam and vapour, Soyuz 4 climbed skywards. A bright diamond of flame was all that could be made of it as it bent over in its climb. Georgi Beregovoi was the ground controller and his comforting voice could be heard reassuring Shatalov throughout the ascent.

This time Tass, the Soviet news agency, showed some signs of learning from the Apollo experience. Within an hour it had released a full set of video pictures of the launching and

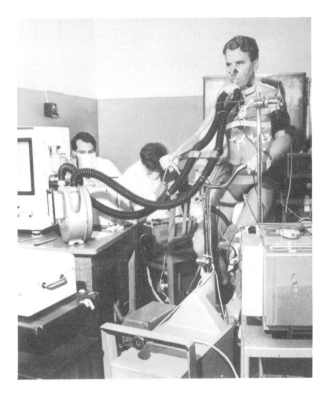

Commander of the linkup, Vladimir Shatalov (Soyuz 4) in training.

showed Shatalov reporting back from orbit. Once on his own the lone cosmonaut settled down quickly into the routine of flight. The solar wings were sprung free, he manoeuvred his spaceship from one orbit to another, took pictures of the Earth from the cabin, and squeezed blackberry juice out of toothpaste-like tubes for his dinner.

Mid-morning on the 15th, Vladimir Shatalov turned his Soyuz 4 towards the launch site to try to spot Soyuz 5 rising to reach him. At 10.14 a.m exactly, it blasted aloft with its full complement of three men aboard: Boris Volynov, Yevgeni Khrunov and engineer Alexei Yeliseyev. They quickly opened up the tunnel into the orbital module and began experiments. It was the first time that three Russians had flown together since Voskhod 1 back in 1964.

Boris Volynov's first duty was to establish radio control with Soyuz 4, which he did by using ultra-short wave channels. But at this stage the mission took on a new aspect and perhaps its main technical innovation. Instead of going for first-orbit docking, as the Moon plan required, the rendezvous was spread out over a full day—as it would be on a space station run, with the Soyuz chasing the larger target of a space station. So Soyuz 5 went ahead of Soyuz 4 and orbited at 88.92 min, with 4 in pursuit at 88.85 min.

LIKE THE WINGS OF A SEAGULL

So by 10.37 the following morning, they were only 100 m apart. Tension rose:

> Shatalov: Baikal clearly on the periscope. Speed 0.25, distance 30 m, all normal.
> Ground: All right.
> Shatalov: Distance 20 m, speed 0.25.
> Ground: See you well.
> Shatalov: Distance 10, speed 0.25.
> Ground: Perfect.
> Volynov: Just waiting for contact.
> Shatalov: Final approach. Normal. Contact! Linkup. Full docking ... no relative movement of the spacecraft.

Approaching each other, like seagulls with wings outstretched as they escort a ship at sea, 4 had inserted its pointed probe into 5's drogue. Latches clawed at the probe, grabbed it tight, and sealed the system for manoeuvring, power and telephone. Moment of contact was 11.20 a.m. over Soviet territory. Ground controllers listened with anxiety as the two ships high above came together and met. Soyuz 4 was on its 34th circuit and Soyuz 5 on its 18th. The complex of the two ships was orbiting at 209 by 250 km, 51.40 deg, 88.85 min.

The docking—smooth and flawless though it was—was only part of a more ambitious experiment. No sooner had the cosmonauts settled down after their triumph than Khrunov and Yeliseyev struggled into their spacesuits. It was a slow process that could not be rushed. There was layer upon layer to put on, inner garments, outer garments, heating systems, coolant, helmets, vizors. Finally, an autonomous backpack. Valves were checked through, seals examined. It was not that they had not practised it enough, but it had to be right this time of all times.

Khrunov pulled a lever and the air poured out of the orbital compartment. Vladimir Shatalov had already done the same in his orbital compartment, from the safe refuge of his command cabin. The pressure gauge fell rapidly and evened off to zero. Khrunov described what happened next:

> The hatch opened and a stream of sunlight burst in. The Sun was unbearably bright and scorching. Only the thick filtering vizor saved my eyes. I saw the Earth and the black sky and had the same feeling I had experienced before my first parachute jumps.

The spectacle of the two docked craft was breathtaking, he recalled. He emerged, Yeliseyev following gingerly behind, moving one hand over another on the handrails. They filmed each other, inspected the craft for damage and watched the Earth roll past below. Within a half an hour they were inside Soyuz 4. They closed the hatch and repressurized. They had done it. The hatch into the Soyuz 4 command cabin opened, turned like a ship's handle on a bulkhead. Vladimir Shatalov floated through, and it was hugs and kisses all round. The only thing that went wrong was a bottle to toast their success. It burst and the contents went all over the wall of the cabin. Khrunov and Yeliseyev also became the first space postmen. They brought Vladimir Shatalov some letters and copies of

Pravda of the 15th—so that he could read about his own launching. After 4 h 35 min, the ships uncoupled and went their separate ways, drifting apart into separate orbits. Boris Volynov, alone now in Soyuz 5, fired his craft out of 4's way and at 6.40 p.m., in a state of exhaustion, radioed good night to 4 and anyone else who was listening, and fell into a sound sleep.

The linkup was a neat exercise, the spacewalk difficult and potentially dangerous. Factories ground to a halt throughout the Soviet Union as one telecast from orbit followed another. Tass announced formally the 'establishment of the world's first experimental orbital station'. Considering it ran for only two orbits and there was no interconnecting tunnel, this was an overstatement. But it is easy to understand the Soviet exuberance. There were several firsts: they were all new cosmonauts; and they had done it all in the middle of winter. If this was what orbital stations were all about, this was a flying start. Academician Anatoli Blagonravov:

> The time is not far off when a permanent space laboratory will be circling the Earth. Scientists will go there for a tour of duty working in comfortable surroundings and return to Earth when necessary.

Getting the four men back down was almost an anticlimax. Soyuz 4, with Shatalov and now Khrunov and Yeliseyev aboard, came down the following morning and in conditions even worse than when they had left. They impacted on hard snow and winds were whistling across the snowscape blowing up fine icy particles. Temperatures plunged to -35°C. Soyuz 4 was spotted as it came in: helicopters landed beside the craft and hustled the three men into warm coats even before giving them welcoming bearhugs, which was extremely un-Russian. Boris Volynov was probably glad to be where he was in the relative warmth of Soyuz 5. He asked for an extra day aloft so as to avoid the snow storms. This was refused, but he was granted an extra orbit so as to come down in calmer conditions, near Kustanai.

Early Soyuz missions after Soyuz 1

27 Oct 1967	Cosmos 186
30 Oct 1967	Cosmos 188
14 Apr 1968	Cosmos 212
15 Apr 1968	Cosmos 213
28 Aug 1968	Cosmos 238 (failure)
25 Oct 1968	Soyuz 2
26 Oct 1968	Soyuz 3 (Georgi Beregovoi)
14 Jan 1969	Soyuz 4 (Vladimir Shatalov)
15 Jan 1969	Soyuz 5 (Boris Volynov, Yevgeni Khrunov, Alexei Yeliseyev)

All four men returned to Moscow on 24 January. It had been Russia's best week in space since Alexei Leonov or the Luna 9. But the reception in Moscow turned into a nightmare. As the motorcade headed from the airport to the Kremlin reception it passed the Borovitsky gate. Gunfire erupted as a young lieutenant in uniform brandishing a gun started firing wildly at the cavalcade. He was aiming at Leonid Brezhnev but so wildly was he firing that he got the cosmonauts' limousine instead. Its driver slumped over his wheel, dead, bleeding profusely. Beregovoi's face was splattered with blood and glass. Nikolayev and Leonov pushed Valentina Tereshkova down onto the floor to protect her. The lieutenant was grabbed by the militia and taken off to an asylum, and that was the last that was heard of him.

The awards ceremony went ahead as planned. Putting the memory of the afternoon behind them, Russia's scientists bathed in the glow of their achievement. Mstislav Keldysh promised:

> The assembly of big, constantly operating orbital stations, interplanetary flights, and advances in radio, television, and other branches of the national economy lie ahead.

A few Western reporters still needled Keldysh about the Moon race. There was no plan to go to the Moon at the moment, he said, but when asked to confirm that Russia had abandoned plans to go the Moon altogether, he would not.

A new Zond was readied to fly the Zond 5–6 profile again in January and left the pad on 20 January 1969. The second stage shut down 25 s early, triggering an abort, the emergency system lifting the Zond cabin to safety.

N-1 ON THE PAD

By the time of their return, the N-1 rocket was at last almost ready for launch. When rolled out in February, it was the largest rocket ever built by the Soviet Union, 100 m high and weighing 2700 tonnes. The first stage, block A, which was designed to burn for two minutes, had two spherical tanks fitting into a tapering stage 17 m wide at the base, with thirty Kuznetsov NK-33 rocket engines. The second stage, block B, with eight Kuznetsov NK-43 engines, would burn for 130 s and bring the N-1 to altitude. The third stage, block V, which would bring the payload into 200 km low Earth orbit with four Kuznetsov NK-39 engines, was able to burn for 400 s. The use of so many engines raised serious questions about reliability. Accordingly, Mishin designed an Engine Operation Control System, called KORD in Russian, which would shut down any badly performing engine automatically and a good engine immediately opposite, so as to preserve the symmetry of the vehicle's thrust. Atop this monster was the fourth stage (block G), designed to fire the lunar complex to the Moon. Block G had just one Kuznetsov NK-31 engine, which would burn for 480 s to send the payload to the Moon. But in the haste to construct the N-1, Mishin was forced to take the decision not to do all-up testing of the engines. They were tested individually, but never, with the KORD system, on a test stand together.

N-1's payload consisted of a rocket motor (block D) whose first function was to brake the manned lunar orbiter and lander into Moon orbit. Block D would first slip the orbiter and lander into a lunar orbit of 110 km and then lower it to 16 km, a procedure not dissimilar to Apollo. The two cosmonauts would fly out to the Moon and back, and spend the early hours of Moon orbit in the lunar orbiter, which was known as the Luna Orbitalny Korabl, or LOK. LOK was an adapted Soyuz, fitted with fuel cells rather than solar panels and an engine identical to the one carried by the lunar lander. The fuel cells, called Volna, weighed 70 kg and could generate 1.5 kW at 27 V for 500 h. At the front of the LOK was a hatch for the crucial spacewalks for the cosmonaut to leave to reach the lunar module and to return. For manoeuvres in lunar orbit, LOK had a restartable, single-chamber 417 kg thrust engine; for the crucial trans-Earth injection, LOK had a two-nozzle engine able to generate 3.3 tonnes of thrust.

Once in lunar orbit, one of the two cosmonauts would transfer from the lunar orbiter, spacewalking along the hull, to the lunar lander, a manoeuvre which explains much of the significance of the Soyuz 4–5 linkup. The next hours were the most crucial of all. The lunar orbiter, with one cosmonaut on board, would separate from the block D and lunar lander, to orbit the Moon alone for up to four days. The block D, with the lunar lander on top, would fire for the final time, braking the assembly toward the lunar surface. Its job done, block D would be jettisoned about 2000 m above the lunar surface. The lunar cabin, guided by the single cosmonaut, would descend gently to land on the lunar surface.

The Soviet lunar lander, called the L-3, was different from the Apollo Lunar Module (LM) in a number of respects. First, it was much smaller, being only 5.5 m high and 5 tonnes weight (the LM was, by contrast, 7 m high and weighed 16 tonnes). It had room for only one cosmonaut standing and the lower stage would have no room for the extensive range of scientific instruments, not to mention lunar rovers, carried by Apollo. Second, the L-3 had a single 2050 kg thrust engine which was used for both descent and take-off (Apollo's LM had a descent motor and a separate one for the small upper stage). Like the LM, the L-3 would use the descent stage as a take-off frame.[34]

The descent and take-off engine was a throttleable, 2.5 tonne rocket burning nitrogen tetroxide and UDMH. A back-up engine was also available should the motor fail to light for the critical liftoff from the Moon. The engine was designed by the Mikhail Yangel OKB. For attitude control during the nerve-wracking descent to the Moon, eight low-thrust engines designed by the Stepanov aviation bureau fed off a common 100 kg propellant reserve. The system was both safe—it ran off two independent circuits—and sensitive, for thrust impulses could last as little as 9 ms.

The L-3 lunar lander, like Apollo, had four legs and was built for three days of independent flight, of which up to two could be spent on the Moon, though the first Soviet Moon-landing was planned to last only a few hours. During the descent, the standing cosmonaut, watching through his window, guided the L-3 lander with a control stick for attitude and rate of descent. As the L-3 came in to land, four tiny solid rocket motors would fire downward to plant it on the lunar surface. The cosmonaut would exit through the lander's hatch, erect a Soviet flag, collect soil samples, take pictures and deploy some instruments. The spacesuit, first worn by Alexei Leonov, permitted an excursion of 1.5 h. As a precaution, the suit carried a small hoop which would enable the cosmonaut to stand up again should he fall over.

After several hours on the surface, the cosmonaut would lift off from the Moon in the upper stage of the L-3, and conduct the type of rendezvous pattern tested by Cosmos 186–188, 212–3 and Soyuz 2–3 and 4–5, in which the LOK orbiter performed the active role. Once re-docked in lunar orbit, the cosmonaut would have to make his third spacewalk of the day to transfer along the outside of the L-3 into the lunar orbiter, with, of course, the precious samples and film. The rest of the mission would be similar to Apollo:

the lander would be jettisoned, the orbiter would leave lunar orbit for the three-day coast to Earth, and recovery would take place in Kazakhstan after a skip re-entry.

N-1'S FIRST FLIGHT

For the first-ever test of the N-1, a dummy L-3 had been placed on top and a simplified Zond instead of the LOK. Called the L-3S ('S' for simplified), the intention was to place the L-1S in lunar orbit. It was a freezing night; the temperature dipped to -41°C. At 12.18 on 21 February the countdown of the N-1 reached its climax, the engines roared to life and the rocket began to move, ever so slowly, skyward. Seconds later, two engines were shut down by the KORD system, but the flight was able to continue normally, as the system anticipated. However at 66 s, vibration caused a 2 mm diameter oxidizer pipe to burst, causing a fire at the rear of the first stage, which was then just over half way through its burn. Four seconds later, KORD shut down all the remaining engines, and the escape system fired the Zond capsule free. The N-1 was destroyed, though the cosmonauts would have survived the failure. Some of the debris fell 50 km downrange.

Several cosmonauts trained for the Moon missions. Slated to fly the L-1 Zond around-the-Moon missions were two teams: Valeri Bykovsky and Nikolai Rukavishnikov; and for the second, Pavel Popovich and Vitaly Sevastianov. For the landing on the Moon, the first team consisted of Alexei Leonov (who would make the landing) and Oleg Makarov. The second crew was Valeri Bykovsky and Nikolai Rukavishnikov. The third was Pavel Popovich and Georgi Grechko.

MOONSCOOPER

Following the government decision of 1 January, work proceeded at a rapid pace in the Babakin bureau to prepare the unmanned mission to recover soil samples from the Moon. Early in 1969, rumours reached the West that such a Moonscooper was in existence. It was ready for launch on 15 April 1969, just one month after America's Apollo 9 had tested out the lunar module in the relative safety of Earth orbit. The Moonscooper was technically very complex.

The base was a set of landing engines, fuel tanks and instrumentation—the same base as the manned lunar cabin then being designed, 3.96 m. On top sat the cylindrical instrumentation unit, the spherical return capsule atop it in turn, and underneath, the ascent stage. A long robot arm, not unlike a dentist's drill, swung out from the descent stage and swivelled round into a small hatch in the return cabin. The Moonscooper's height was 3.96 m, weight 1880 kg. The plan was for a four-day coast to the Moon, the upper stage lifting off from the Moon for the return flight to Earth. Such a mission required extreme accuracy. If Russia could get Moonrocks back before Apollo by automatic spacecraft and without risking human life, it was at least a respectable second best.

The first such Moonscooper prepared for launch failed. The second, on 14 June 1969, did not do any better. Both coincided with the worst phase in the development of the Proton booster. At the time of the second attempt there were floods of rumours of a planned Moon attempt. The previous month, May 1969, had seen the triumph of Apollo 10: Tom Stafford, Eugene Cernan and John Young had flown out to the Moon, and Cernan and Stafford had brought the LM down to less than 14 400 m over the lunar surface in a dress rehearsal for the Moon landing itself. Apollo 11 had been set for 16 July, and the Americans had tested about all they reasonably could before actually touching down.

LAST DESPERATE THROW: SECOND FLIGHT OF THE N-1

Time was running out for the Soviet challenge—whatever that was. In the West, observers realized that there would be some challenge, though no one seemed sure exactly what. As July opened, the eyes of the world began to turn to Cape Canaveral and focused on the personalities of the three courageous Americans selected for the historic journey of Apollo 11—Neil Armstrong, Michael Collins and Edwin Aldrin.

At this very time, Mishin's crews wheeled out the second N-1. An engineering model was also at the second N-1 pad at the time, and spectacular pictures show the two giants standing side by side just as the Moon race entered its final days. Impressive though the two N-1s must have been to the Russians gathered there, photographs of them snapped by prying American spy satellites must have created near apoplexy in Washington, where they panicked some American analysts to speculate on a last, desperate Russian effort to beat Apollo with a man on the Moon. As in February, the second N-1 carried an L-1S for insertion into lunar orbit.

But it was not to be. The second N-1 lifted off very late on the night of 3 July, at 11.18 p.m. Moscow time. The bottom skirt of the N-1 was just about to clear the tower when a steel diaphragm from a pulse sensor broke, entered the pump of engine no.8, which exploded, disabling engines nearby. KORD, once again, shut the entire system down. N-1 began to sink back on the pad. As it did so, the top of the rocket came alight, the escape system whooshing the Zond cabin free just before the collapsing N-1 crashed into the base of its stand, utterly destroying the launch pad and causing devastation throughout the surrounding area. It took 18 months to identify the fault.

To Soviet space planners it was clear that the game was nearly up. Foiled by the Apollo 8 success, frustrated by one pad failure after another, the past two years had been marked by one misfortune after another. Nothing seemed to go right. It was a dramatic contrast to the early days when they could do no wrong and the Americans could do no right. It was the other way round now, and Apollo steamed on from one brilliant achievement to another, dazzling the world like an acrobat who has practised a million times: except that as everyone knew, NASA had not.

MOONSCOOPER CHALLENGE

One last desperate throw of the dice remained. A third Moonscooper was prepared and hustled to the pad in early July. The scientists may well have expected that the Proton booster would let them down again. It was probably to their surprise that it did not. As if to scorn the earlier run of failures, it hurtled Luna 15 Moonwards on 13 July 1969. If all went well, its tiny recovery capsule would be back on Earth on the morning of 24 July. The Apollo 11 capsule was not expected back until later in the same day. The Americans could still be beaten, by just a few hours. It was like Scott and Amundsen racing to the South Pole in 1912.

Luna 15 produced the expected level of consternation in the West. The press, perhaps bored with Apollo's ability to do everything, however difficult, exactly on schedule, thrived on this competition. Most observers thought that Luna 15 could be a scooper, but doubted whether the USSR had the technological ability to pull it off. A typical view was the following in the British *Daily Telegraph*:

> While the moonshot is regarded as a last-minute attempt to detract from the American effort, it is not thought the Russians can land and bring back samples. The technical complexities are thought to be too great.

But as the Apollo 11 launching drew near—it was now only three days away—one absurd idea rivalled another. Luna 15 would jam Apollo 11's frequencies. It was there to 'spy' on Apollo 11—like the Russian trawlers during a NATO naval exercise presumably. It was there to report back on how the Americans did it. It was a rescue craft to bring back Armstrong and Aldrin if they got stranded.

15 July. Luna 15 is exactly half way to the Moon. Jodrell Bank—invariably tracking it—said it was on a slow course to save fuel. It was right. So there was more speculation as to the ulterior motives of choosing a slow course to the Moon to save fuel. Sinister implications were read into the tiniest details.

16 July. At 2.32 p.m. Apollo 11 blasts skywards from Cape Canaveral. It is a beautiful launch, and soon the astronauts are gazing out at the blue globe of our planet as they shoot away from it at 36 000 km/h. They send back pictures showing their own relaxed humour. The hours of danger lie ahead.

17 July. Luna 15 breaks into lunar orbit. Its exact path is closely watched. Its path measures 133 by 286 km, 2 h 30 min, 45 deg. Scientists, experts, engineers, anyone short of a clairvoyant, are called into the television studios to comment on every change of path or signal. Jodrell Bank reports back that its signals are of an entirely new type never heard before. Georgi Beregovoi, who could always be counted on to be indiscreet, lets it be known that 'Luna 15 may try to take samples of lunar soil or it may try to solve the problem of a return from the Moon's surface'.

18 July. Jodrell Bank expects a soft-landing by Luna 15. But it does not materialize. The bets are still on it being a Moonscooper. But instead of landing, the probe changes orbit. Each revolution now lasts 2 h 35 min, 94 by 220 km, 126 deg, bringing it closer to the Moon.

19 July. The cool-as-cucumber crew of Apollo 11 slips silently into lunar orbit after three days of flight. It goes through the final checks of the lunar module, Eagle. They are in the Moon's shadow: back on Earth, excitement and apprehension mount as the full enormity of the undertaking begins to sink in. Tomorrow, after two million years on the planet Earth, *Homo Sapiens* prepares to set foot on another world. Luna 15 continues to circle, descending on its 25th orbit to 85 km. It does not appear to be in any hurry to land. One source from Moscow says that it is selecting landing sites.

20 July. The big day. Neil Armstrong and Edwin Aldrin move into the LM, Eagle. Late that afternoon, they cast their spider-like cabin free from Michael Collins orbiting solo in the Command and Service Module (CSM), called Columbia. 'The Eagle has wings!' the excited astronauts exult. For a full orbit they fly side-by-side. Back at mission control the visitor gallery is filling with administrators, politicians and astronauts. The voices are

hushed, the tension mounting. The night will end either in miraculous triumph or terrible disaster.

Flash from Jodrell Bank. On orbit 29, Luna 15 fires its motor behind the Moon on the instructions of ground control. Its new orbit brings it still closer to the surface. The perigee dips to 16 km, with an apogee of 85 km, period 114 min, 127 deg. The perigee is just over the Apollo landing site in the Sea of Tranquillity. The plot thickens.

Soon after 9 p.m., Eagle starts its powered descent. It is the point of no return. Down, down and down descends the LM. The craters and rock fields are coming closer every minute. Five minutes into the descent the alarms flash: the computer is overloaded! Hasty advice from ground control: press on! Ten minutes into the descent and the Eagle should be just over the right landing spot on the lunar surface. Instead, Neil Armstrong, peering through the window, finds a crater the size of a football field and filled with rocks the size of cars.He's way off course. He takes over manual control and flies the LM like a heli-copter to find the right place. Eleven minutes into the descent. Skimming over crater fields, Armstrong rejects one site after another as too rough. The fuel warning light comes on. He's 25 m high above the surface and out of fuel.

21 July. Armstrong landed with just 20s of fuel to spare and on the only flat site in the area. The Eagle was down, and they had done it! It was a brilliant piece of flying. Six hours later Neil Armstrong was down on the lunar surface and soon Edwin Aldrin was down there with him. They walked, jumped and hopped across the surface, took pictures, picked up Moon rocks, unfolded experiments and laid out a scientific station. In the West-ern world, 600 million people stayed up through the long late summer night and celebrated with them, watching the ghostly and jerky TV images, the first ever of men on another world.

To such glassy-eyed and jaded watchers, Luna 15 became an irrelevance. Machines could not add to two brave men actually out there and as recognizable as you or me. Late on the 20th, Jodrell Bank reported that Luna 15 was still in low lunar orbit, so low down that if it did not soon alter its path it would crash into a lunar peak. It is doubtful if many people cared, so overwhelming was the Apollo experience. It was nearly an annoyance.

Time for liftoff from the lunar surface. It was another critical phase. If the motor, which was no larger than an automatic dishwasher, did not fire, then they would be there for all eternity. The air in the LM might last another day, but Michael Collins would have to return home on his own. Just as they went through this last phase a final newsflash came from Jodrell Bank. It was to serve as Luna 15's epitaph:

> Signals ceased at 4.50 p.m. this evening. They have not yet returned. The retrorockets were fired at 4.46 p.m. on the 52nd orbit and after burning for 4 minutes the craft was on or near the lunar surface. The approach velocity was 480 km/h and it is unlikely if anything could have survived.

The venue was the Sea of Crisis, and it marked the graveyard of the Russian ambitions to somehow beat the Americans to the Moon. Luna 15 was smashed to tiny pieces. Later, the Russians blamed this on their still incomplete understanding of lunar mascons.

It is worth making passing mention of how the American triumph was explained by the Russians to their own people. Prior to the Apollo landing, reports of the mission had been meagre, but once Armstrong and Aldrin were on the Moon, news coverage was more generous. At the main 5 p.m. evening news on the 21st, half an hour was devoted to the landing, most of it showing pictures of the Moon walk. The commentator described the landing as the 'realization of a dream'. Georgi Petrov, then Director of the Soviet Institute of Space Research, made no effort to conceal his admiration, nor even to trot out the new official line that 'automatic probes were better'. Wistfully he remarked:

> Maybe for the same expense automatic stations might have done more. But the fact of a man being on the Moon is great in itself and this represents the self-assertion of mankind.

EPILOGUE TO THE JULY MOON

The luck of Neil Armstrong, Edwin Aldrin and Michael Collins held, and they were back on Earth on 24 July. For the Russian space planners it marked —or so it seemed at the time—the ultimate humiliation. Beaten in the round-the-Moon race, beaten in the on-the-Moon race, and beaten decisively too: even the Moonscooper, which could have saved at least some honour, had flopped. Defeat had been snatched from the jaws of victory.

Some strangely unconvincing reasons were advanced to explain away Luna 15. One publication even had the nerve to claim that 'if it hadn't happened to coincide with the dramatic Apollo lunar flight, it would hardly have received a mention at all'. So what was Luna 15 then? Just a new Moon probe. A survey ship that was highly manoeuvrable. Indeed, it had a flexibility that the American Moonship did not have because it could manoeuvre freely, unlike Apollo, which was stuck in narrow equatorial orbit. One wonders if the author —one 'Pyotr Petrov'—even believed this himself.

MOON FLIGHT SET FOR 1970 LENIN CENTENARY

The Soviet Moon programme was not abandoned at this stage. It was decided to continue tests, not with a view to an early landing on the Moon but with verifying the hardware that had been developed, like the N-1, the L-1, the L-3 and the LOK. So much investment had gone into these programmes that it was better to test out the technical concepts involved than write them off altogether and deny oneself the benefits of the design work. If these tests went well, a manned Moon landing could still be kept open as an option. The Moonscooper flights would be followed through, along with related programmes, and presented to the public as an inexpensive, safer 'alternative' to Apollo. Indeed, with some of the political pressure lifted, designers looked forward to testing their equipment without the enforced haste required by American deadlines. At governmental level, no one was yet prepared to admit failure or to take responsibility for what had gone wrong. The resolutions of August 1964 and February 1967 remained in effect, unrepealed.

Zond 7 left Baikonour on 8 August 1969, only two weeks after Luna 15's demise and at about the same time as the Apollo 11 astronauts were emerging from their biological isolation after their Moon flight, isolation designed to prevent them bringing back evil bugs. It was then a new Moon and a full Earth and striking and beautiful pictures were taken of the Earth's full globe over the Moon's surface en route to and from the Moon. Movie cameras whirred as Zond skimmed round the lunar far side at 2000 km.

Zond 7 headed back to Earth, skipped like a pebble across the atmosphere to soft-land in the summer fields of Kustanai in Kazakhstan. How easy it all seemed now. After the success of Zond 7, plans for a manned circumlunar mission were revived. The decision was taken to fly Zond 8 as a final rehearsal around the Moon in December 1969, with a manned mission to mark the Lenin centenary in April 1970. Zond 8 was brought out to the pad for this mission in November, but the Lenin anniversary plan was abandoned.

Zond 8 was eventually flown (20–7 October 1970). It carried tortoises, flies, onions, wheat, barley and microbes, and was the subject of new navigation tests. Astronomical telescopes photographed the Zond as far as 300 000 km out from Earth to check its trajectory. Zond 8 came as close as 1200 km to the lunar surface. Like Zond 5, an attitude error brought Zond 8 down in the Indian Ocean, where it was found by the oceanographic vessel *Taman*. Thus of nine Zond missions, and of six attempts to fly to the Moon, only Zond 7 was wholly successful. The last two production Zonds were never used.

L-1, Zond series

10 Mar 1967	Cosmos 146
8 Apr 1967	Cosmos 154
28 Sep 1967	Launch failure
23 Nov 1967	Launch failure
2 Mar 1968	Zond 4
23 Apr 1968	Launch failure
22 Jul 1968	Pad accident
15 Sep 1968	Zond 5
10 Nov 1968	Zond 6
20 Jan 1969	Launch failure
8 Aug 1969	Zond 7
20 Oct 1970	Zond 8

TESTING LUNAR EQUIPMENT

Tests continued of the other equipment designed to support the Soviet man-on-the-Moon programme. Chief Designer Mishin continued to enjoy support at the highest level in the Politburo, especially from Andrei Kirilenko. Testing of the N-1 continued with a view to its completing its original purpose, or, alternately, to carry large payloads to low Earth orbit. After the two disasters in 1969, the KORD was redesigned. A fire-extinguishing system, using freon gas, was installed. The NK-33 engines were tested rigorously. The launch pads were rebuilt. The hardware designed to support the lunar landing, the L-3 and the LOK, was tested secretly under the Cosmos label (in the event, the tests were not so secret after all, for Western observers who monitored them suspected a link to the manned space programme).

These tests took place in the course of 1970–1. The lunar lander, the L-3, was first tested without its landing legs, launched on a sunny morning, 24 November 1970, under the designation Cosmos 379, witnessed by its designers. On 27 November, after simulating the three-day coast to the Moon, the L-3 fired its variable-throttle motor to simulate the lunar landing, descent and hovering over the Moon's surface. On the 28th, after a day on the surface of the Moon as it were, the L-3 fired its engine again to model the lunar ascent. Everything went perfectly. Cosmos 379 ended up in a 14 035 km high orbit, eventually burning up in September 1983. Further tests of the L-3 Moon cabin were made by Cosmos 398 (26 February 1971) and Cosmos 434 (12 August 1971). The true nature of these tests was not revealed until *glasnost*, though, by accident, word of the nature of Cosmos 434 came out much sooner. In 1978, a nuclear-powered Soviet spy satellite, Cosmos 954, went out of control and eventually crashed in Canada. Not long after, in August 1981, another Cosmos, Cosmos 434, began to spiral down to Earth. One Soviet spokesperson insisted that there was no need to worry because it was (in his words) 'a prototype lunar cabin' and had no nuclear fuel and therefore posed no danger.

Tests essential for lunar orbit manoeuvres were conducted. The L-1 was adapted for tests of the block D, which would be used during lunar orbit insertion and the descent toward the surface. Two L-1 spacecraft were adapted for these tests and named the K-L-1E ('E' for experimental). The first, on 28 November 1969, failed. The second was Cosmos 382, sent aloft on 2 December 1970, which successfully carried out the necessary block D engine firings. By the end of the summer of 1971, the hardware that the cosmonauts would fly for a Soviet manned landing on the Moon had been successfully tested. Mikhail Yangel, who had designed the L-3, died two months after its last test.

Moonship tests, 1969–71

18 Nov 1969	KL1E	Failure
24 Nov 1970	L-3	Cosmos 379
2 Dec 1970	KL1E	Cosmos 382
26 Feb 1971	L-3	Cosmos 398
12 Aug 1971	L-3	Cosmos 434

At the same time, a manned Earth orbital test of the lunar orbit rendezvous maneouvre was planned, similar to that which the United States carried out on Apollo 9. This was called the 'Kontakt' mission, and its purpose was to test the rendezvous mechanisms of the LOK and the L-3 lunar lander. Two Soyuz were specially adapted (the version was called the 7K-OK): one active, one passive. The active crew was Anatoli Filipchenko and Georgi Grechko; the crew for the passive Soyuz was Georgi Dobrovolski and Vitaly Sevastianov. However, at around this time, the decision was taken to replace the 'kontakt' rendezvous system with a new one, called 'igla', and in January 1971 the mission was cancelled.[35]

Even as these tests were taking place, Vasili Mishin devised a Moon plan even more ambitious than that of Apollo. The limit of Apollo's capability was three days on the Moon—this was the profile flown by the advanced Apollo missions, Apollo 15, 16 and 17 in 1971–2. The new Mishin plan, called the L-3M ('M' for 'modified'), envisaged a manned lunar mission of two N-1 rockets. The first N-1 would place a large 24-tonne lunar lander descent stage, the GB-1, in lunar orbit. Independently, a second N-1 would deliver a three-man lunar lander and return spacecraft, GB-2, to link up with the descent stage. Together they would descend to the lunar surface. Initially, two cosmonauts would work on the Moon for a full lunar day (14 Earth days) but this would later be extended to a month or longer. The Americans might be first to the Moon, but the Soviet Union would build the first Moon base. Mishin envisaged the dual N-1 mission taking place in the late 1970s. Mishin's new plan was formally approved in the spring of 1972, just as the Apollo programme was entering its final phase. It even won the approval of long-time N-1 opponent, Valentin Glushko.

THIRD AND FOURTH FLIGHTS OF THE N-1

The third N-1 was ready to fly again two years later. Unlike its two predecessors, it was not aimed at the Moon, carrying only a dummy LOK. Launching took place on 27 June 1971, while, incidentally, three cosmonauts flew overhead in the Salyut 1 space station. Half a minute into the mission the vehicle started to roll and at 51 s, the new KORD system shut the whole rocket down. It crashed to destruction, gouging out a 30 m crater 20 km downrange.

Almost 18 months later, it was time for the fourth full test of the N-1. A new roll control system had been installed. Take-off took place on 23 November 1972 in a launch directed by Boris Chertok, Mishin's deputy (the Chief Designer was in hospital at the time). This N-1 carried a real LOK, which was intended to be put in lunar orbit and return to Earth. 107 s into the mission, there was a failure on a 250 mm line from the liquid oxygen tank; pressures overloaded, a fire broke out, and the first stage exploded, the emergency system extracting the LOK descent module just in time.

Flights of the N-1

21 Feb 1969	Failed after 66 s
3 Jul 1969	Failed after 6 s
27 Jun 1971	Failed after 51 s
23 Nov 1972	Failed after 107 s

END OF THE ROAD

The engineers again set to work to tame the difficult beast, installing new propellant lines and computer control systems. Two new N-1s were built, the first set for launch in August 1974 and the second later that year, with the intention of making the N-1 operational by 1976 and then proceeding to the L-3M plan. At this stage, political events conspired to frustrate the programme. Mishin had come increasingly under fire not only for the failures of the N-1 programme but also for the difficulties being experienced by the manned space station programme. In May 1974, his enemies persuaded Leonid Brezhnev to remove Vasili Mishin from his post as Chief Designer. He was dismissed and replaced at once by Valentin Glushko, who was shortly elevated to membership of the Central Committee of the Communist Party, the apex of political power. Within days, Glushko suspended the N-1 programme. Two years later, the order was given to destroy all the N-1 hardware.

The only items to survive were the NK-33 rocket engines, which were stored away in a shed in the Kuznetsov plant in Kyubyshev; four lunar landers, now to be found in various museums; and half an N-1 fuel tank, which was converted to a bandstand shelter in a park in Leninsk. Mishin was sent to lecture at the Moscow Aviation Institute and, when *glasnost* broke, emerged to break the story of the N-1. Korolev's OKB-1 was renamed the Energiya NPO (NPO means Scientific and Technical Association).

Writing about these events years later, Mishin blamed underinvestment, lack of financial control, the dispersal of effort between design bureaux, and poor management of the 26 government departments and 500 enterprises involved. The investment was only $4.5bn compared to Apollo's $24bn. They underestimated the technical difficulties and should have done ground testing.

Kuznetsov continued work on his NK-33 engine at his own expense. He decided on a duration test of 20 360 s on a test stand. It ran perfectly. 14 engines logged up to 14 000 s in other tests. Chief Designer Mishin considered it to be the best rocket engine ever made.

Instead, Valentin Glushko presented his own plans for a lunar colony. In the course of 1974–6, he redesigned his old UR-700K plan as Vulkan, proposing it lift to the Moon the components of a lunar base. Drawings were made of a large Moonrover, or lunokhod, which would carry men across the surface of the Moon. In an extraordinary *volte-face*, he proposed that Vulkan should fly on oxygen and hydrogen. When his proposals went before an expert commission of the Academy of Sciences, it came under criticism for its expense and prematurity. Keldysh's scepticism was a telling factor in convincing the government not to proceed. More important, Glushko could not interest the military in the project, who became more and more concerned with countering the American shuttle.

Winding down the Moon race

1 Jan 1969	Party and government resolution to continue the Moon programme, develop an unmanned alternative programme and develop space stations
May 1974	Mishin deposed; Glushko becomes Chief Designer; N-1 cancelled
1976	Failure of Glushko's Vulkan lunar colony project to win support.

ASSESSMENT

In assessing the N-1 programme and the associated efforts by the Soviet Union to beat the United States to the Moon, some final conclusions may be drawn. The failure of the Soviet Union to reach the Moon was, at its heart, a political and organizational failure, not a technical one. During the 1970s and 1980s, most Western observers took the view that the Soviet Union never had the technical capacity to send men to the Moon or land them on it. This is not the case. The Soviet Union proved its capacity to send men around the Moon (Zond 7) and could have done so had it later wished (certainly the cosmonauts were willing enough to fly the mission). Contrary to Western notions about Soviet recklessness with human lives, the Moon programme erred on the side of caution throughout. Zond 7 was an impressive demonstration of automatic engineering and high-speed skip re-entry. The Proton rocket later became one of the most reliable in the world. The hardware for a manned lunar orbit and landing, the LOK and the L-3, performed flawlessly in Earth orbit during 1970–1 in the course of several exhaustive tests. The launch escape system, designed to save cosmonauts in the event of a Proton or N-1 failure, worked each time. A credible unmanned programme for the exploration of the Moon was later developed for 1970–6. The subsequent tests of the NK-33 suggest that it is more than likely that the N-1 would have flown eventually successfully. Chalomei and Glushko between them developed large Saturn V class rocket engines for the UR-700K and the R-56.

At the end of the day, the failure of the Russians to win the Moon race, after the great years of success, was not the outcome of a single failure of the N-1, or the Moonscooper, or Zond, or the temperamental Proton. There were two principal reasons. First, the Russians entered the Moon race far too late. The two key commitments—the decisions to go and the method of getting there—were made three and five years after the comparable American ones. It was ironic that the Russians, who had provoked the Americans to competing in a Moon race, realized too late that there was a real race under way. Second, the Russian efforts were divided between rival design teams, competing programmes and non-cooperation between the leading personalities. The dispersal and duplication of energies was something which the Soviet economy could afford even less than the American. Contrary to Western impressions, the command economy was unable to overcome these problems and command its participants to work effectively together. At its heart, the Soviet Union lost the Moon race because it misjudged American intentions and resources, mobilized its resources too late, and failed to control its competing schools of designers and rocket-builders.

Part 2: The programme

4

Behind the scenes

What we need for success is above all a reliable and high performance rocket engine. The crux of the matter is the rocket engine.

Chief Designer, Sergei Korolev, 1934.

The Soviet and Russian space programmes required a huge organizational effort. This has involved the construction of cosmodromes, the building of design bureaux, the development of a range of launchers, and the creation of other support facilities. This chapter reviews the organizational background to the Soviet and Russian space programmes.

Russia makes between 30 and 50 rocket launchings a year, down from a high point of 110 in 1982. Between 1957 and 1995, the Soviet Union and Russia launched 2656 rockets which put 2976 satellites into orbit.[36] 55% were from Plesetsk, 40% from Baikonour and less than 5% from Kapustin Yar.

Russia's space programme has always been the world's busiest. In 1994, Russia launched 46 rockets, compared to 26 by the United States, six by Europe, five by China, two by India and two by Japan. Even this total, at a time of financial difficulty, understates earlier levels of space activity. In the 1970s and 1980s, up to a hundred Soviet rocket launchings a year were by no means unusual.

COSMODROMES

The heart of Russia's space effort is its two cosmodromes—although the best known is not on Russian territory but leased from the Republic of Kazakhstan. At one stage, up to 100 000 people worked in the Soviet Union's three cosmodromes, though that number has now fallen. The first cosmodrome, Kapustin Yar, is no longer used for launching space rockets and now serves as a military test centre.

VOLGOGRAD STATION - KAPUSTIN YAR

It was on the banks of the Volga river in 1942 that Hitler's invasion was stopped at Volgograd and turned back. All the more ironic, for in 1947 German rockets were first fired

The cabin of the Vertikal sounding rocket, launched in an experiment from Kapustin Yar. The flags of participating socialist countries are marked on the side.

from east of the Volga river to rebuild Russia's post-war rocket programme. Somewhere between Volgograd and where the Volga flows into the Caspian Sea was designated as the site for testing the old German A-4 rocket.

This became Russia's first rocket base. It was constructed beside a river and built around two towns—Kapustin Yar (by which the base is known) and Akhubinsk. The towns lay on the main railway line between Astrakhan and Volgograd. Both towns had an airport. The land was dead flat. The rocket pads were built up on a triangular rail network which had Kapustin Yar and Akhubinsk as its base and the pads as the apex.

Kapustin Yar—its name means 'little cabbage patch'—was used extensively for A-4 tests in 1947–9 and its more advanced successors. The first space rabbits and dogs flew on their suborbital hops from Kapustin Yar. Once they were over, Kapustin Yar retreated into silence, and the winds, desert, and weeds began to claim it back.

There the story might have ended but for the start of the manned space programme in 1961 and the extensive range of lunar and interplanetary missions. The space planners realized that Baikonour would be working flat out for many years and that at least some diversification was needed to prevent the overloading of the Baikonour launch and tracking teams.

In 1962, Kapustin Yar was used as the launch site for the small scientific satellites in the Cosmos series, using Mikhail Yangel's small Cosmos rocket, the R-12. Kapustin Yar became the site for seven or eight small satellite launches a year. In addition, some pads were built in the late 1960s for a new series of sounding rockets—the original function of Kapustin Yar. Called V-14 or 'Vertikal' these 29 m high rockets brought small scientific packages to altitudes of about 1500 km before they parachuted back for recovery. An atmospheric probe was dropped off at 500 km, and an astrophysical probe at 1500 km. Occasional such launches were made throughout the 1970s and they filled a gap by flying short-duration missions for which a satellite would be too expensive. The last Vertikal mission was in 1983.

The R-12 rocket, associated mainly with Kapustin Yar, was retired in 1977 after 144 launches. Kapustin Yar continued its minor role with occasional spaceshots of small scientific payloads. In 1982 it became the base for the first orbital tests of Soviet spaceplanes and shuttles. A total of 83 orbital space launches took place in Kapustin Yar from 1962 to 1987 and it has returned to being a military test facility.

PLESETSK, RUSSIA'S BUSIEST COSMODROME

In the 1960s, the town of Kettering in Northamptonshire, England, was blessed with a grammar school which emphasized science in its upper classes, with a strong practical bent. The science teacher, Geoffrey Perry, was keenly interested in electronics, radios and space research: he involved his class in the building of radio-tracking devices. Whether by accident or design—history does not record—he and his students found that their radio trackers could be tuned into Soviet Cosmos and other transmitters. It was a combination of practical electronics, learning and current affairs.

It was not long before Kettering Grammar School (or the Kettering group as they later came to be called) began to build up expertise in following the Soviet space programme. They were soon able to classify all the different programmes by their signals and find out when satellites were recovered. At one stage they picked up manned spacecraft telemetry long before the launches were officially announced. The teacher and his students built up a world-wide reputation, and the American media began to depend on Kettering for interpretation of obscurer missions.

Cosmos 112 on 17 March 1966 was at first sight just another Cosmos mission until Kettering took a look at its orbital path, high point and low point, and tracked it back to somewhere northeast of Leningrad, nearly inside the Arctic Circle! It could not be! Check again. Sure enough: check after check brought the launch point back to the same place. Cosmos 114 on 6 April repeated the pattern. So they had discovered a secret and hitherto unknown cosmodrome!

The reasons for Plesetsk soon became clear. The USSR needed a northerly launch site to get satellites into Polar orbit. Such orbits are perfect for ground surveillance because a Polar orbiting satellite covers the planet every 24 h. It is also suitable for weather satellites which must cover the same ground path. Second, the northwestern USSR was the part best developed for communications. Building it further east, say in northern Siberia, would have presented even greater difficulties of access.

The cosmodrome is located around the towns of Mirny and Kochmas on the banks of the Emtsa river. Construction of Plesetsk began in 1957 as the USSR's ICBM base.[37] Construction workers erected a block of two-floor wooden huts near the tiny village of Plesetsk. The main city was built on the banks of the lily-covered shallow lake Plestsy. It was eventually named Mirny, which covered 2000 km^2 and at its peak housed 40 000 people in Khrushchev-style nine-floor apartments. The nearest big city is Archangel, 180 km to the north. From 1960 to 1966, Plesetsk served as the base for Russia's ICBM nuclear strike force. To the original R-7 pads were added R-16 rockets from 1961 onward. In 1963, the government decided to use Plesetsk as a satellite-launching base, and construction work began the following year.

Plesetsk is at 63°N, near the Arctic Circle. The summer nights are long and it never really gets dark. In winter there are only a few hours greyness at midday amidst remorseless night. The average temperature is +1°C; the lowest recorded is -46°C. It is near enough to Sweden for observers there to see the occasional launch in the far eastern sky arcing into the distance. Plesetsk is much more compact than either Baikonour or Kapustin Yar and because it is military it is heavily protected by surface-to-air missiles. There are four R-7 pads, two R-36 Tsyklon and two R-14 Cosmos pads. The small R-12 Cosmos rocket also used Plesetsk until 1977. Plesetsk has the largest oxygen and nitrogen plant in Europe and has seven assembly shops and integration halls. The road network was in such an atrocious condition by April 1992 that it nearly broke the chassis of Boris Yeltsin's limousine when he visited the site. A presidential decree soon led to improvements.

The existence of Plesetsk was not formally acknowledged until 1983. It is the equivalent of the Vandenberg Air Force Base in California. There have been two disasters there. In June 1973, an R-12 rocket exploded there, killing nine technicians and soldiers. An R-7 rocket exploded there two hours before liftoff on 18 March 1980, killing 51. They were buried on the wooded shores of a lake near Mirny, and a memorial to them now stands there. 18 March is effectively a memorial day at Plesetsk, and no launchings are ever carried out on this day.

In March 1995, construction began of the first Zenith pad in Plesetsk, the ninth at the site, due for completion in 1996–7, also capable of taking the new Angara rocket. There were 14 launches from Plesetsk in 1995.

BAIKONOUR—TYURATAM

Baikonour cosmodrome is on the railway line between Moscow and the historic city of Tashkent. Heading northwest out of Tashkent, the train crosses the Kyzylumkum desert. It is endless, flat and arid. For most of the journey, the train runs parallel to the river Syr Darya. After 600 km the train reaches the town of Dzhusaly, a mining town, and after that there is a bend in the river. The train enters a much larger builtup area: it is Tyuratam old town and the adjacent modern city of Leninsk. If our train traveller carried on, he would skirt around the north of the Aral Sea and eventually reach Samara on the Volga before pulling into Moscow a day later. Nowadays, the establishment of Baikonour is 35 000 people (mainly military) and 95 000 civilians (spouses and children). The area of the cosmodrome is 6717 km^2 and the downrange area is 104 305 km^2.[38] In December 1995, Leninsk was eventually renamed, as most place names associated with the discredited leader already have been in the new Russia, with the title 'Baikonour', even though the real Baikonour is far away.

Baikonour differs in several major respects from its American equivalent, the Kennedy Space Center at Cape Canaveral. The first is that rail is the principal mode of transport—the cosmodrome had 470 km of track—not road, although there is a poorly maintained road network (1281 km). Second, rockets are carried flat on their back on railcars from the assembly hangars to the pad where they are then raised to a vertical position. It is a system made easier by the fact that the gauge of the Russian railway is the widest in the world. By contrast, the Americans bring their rockets to the pad on giant road crawlers. The third is that the rocket launchings are handled by military officers and personnel, members of the rocket troops, rather than contracted civilian companies, as is American practice.

DEVELOPING THE COSMODROME

The R-7 pad, completed in mid-1957, is Baikonour's most famous pad. From it rose Sputnik, the first Lunas, Vostok, Voskhod, Soyuz 1–8, Soyuz 19 and 25. It is still used for Soyuz and Progress missions to the Mir space station. Any spaceship about to depart is first of all tested out rigorously in the Space Vehicle Assembly Building or the MIKKO. All the telemetry is checked through and satellites may be immersed in a vacuum chamber. It is then moved along rails formatting with the upper and lower stages of the booster. This process is completed a day before launching. By Western standards, MIKKO is an old building with very outdated equipment with standards far short of Western clean rooms.

On the big day, the entire structure, 50 m long, trundles down to the pad at a cautious 3 km/h. The transport reaches the pad, which is a concrete platform on heavy cement legs. Around it is a giant flame trench, looking like a reservoir empty of water. Once at the pad the transporter arm lifts the rocket up to the vertical. It is a delicate operation requiring extreme care. The booster is held up to the vertical while clamps rise up like a bear trap to grasp it so that engineers may inspect it at all levels. An hour before liftoff the high gantries are lowered. Any cosmonaut on board will now feel the Soyuz gently rocking in the wind. New fuel still has to be pumped on board till the very end. Liquid oxygen boils at −190°C and wisps of it always surround a rocket's stages. The fuel hoses are pulled away at 60 s before liftoff. With 20 s to go, the electrical lines are removed. The rocket's electrical systems must use their own batteries now. The ignition command is sent and flames roar out into the trenches. When the thrust exceeds the rocket's own weight, the four lower arms still restraining it fall back like petals on a flower and let the rocket free.

So busy was the first historic pad that a second one was constructed to share some of the launch load. Pad B, as it has been called, was built 30 km away, far to the northeast. It is basically the same although there are differences in detail in the position of local buildings, railway tracks and lightning towers. Work on the pad began in 1964 and it was completed in 1966. The first launch from there took place in October 1966, and Soyuz 9 was the first manned craft to use it. Most Soyuz and the later Progress craft have gone from there, though not Soyuz 11, 16, 19 and 25. Pad A was overhauled and modernized

This is an R-7 rocket, Soyuz variant, being prepared for launch. Clearly visible are the railway tracks which bring the rocket to the pad, the swing arms which clamp the rocket to the pad, and the blast pit.

as soon as pad B was available. Launches of Vostok-type missions (e.g. Resurs) and Molniya missions are made from here.

Sometime in 1965 work began on a new series of pads to the northwest near some salt lakes. About twenty—perhaps as many as thirty—were constructed and were military in nature. They were built for the R-16 military rocket, the Tsyklon and its successors. They were completed in 1967 and for a while they were the basis for the USSR's satellite-killer programme, though since then the Tsyklon developed a range of civilian applications.

The third main area of development came in the early 1960s, about 35 km northwest of the original Sputnik pad. Here the designers chose to locate two pads to support the UR-500K Proton booster built for the man-around-the-Moon programme. En route and beside the railway tracks lay an assembly area laid out like an industrial estate. Each pad was flanked by two 110 m high towers which combined the functions of lightning conductor, TV camera point and floodlamp location. There are now four Proton pads in two neighbouring complexes. The first pads, launch complex 81, were built in the 1960s and served until 1988, when a refurbishment programme began. The second set of pads, launch complex 200, built in the 1970s, lies to the east, the two pads being 600 m apart. They are all some distance from Leninsk town—a full hour-and-a-half on the train. Protons are assembled in a large horizontal assembly and integration facility which can hold up to six full Protons at a time. The assembled rocket is moved by diesel railcar to the pad about five days before liftoff. Because the Proton uses storable fuels, there are no telltale signs of valving cool fuels to herald an imminent launch. There is a single, dull thud, the Proton lifting off in 2.2 s and clearing the tower in 6 s. Riding a pillar of blue flame, Proton pitches over in 18 s. A sonic boom is heard a minute into flight. On a clear day, Proton may be followed 5.5 min into the flight to second and even third-stage ignition.

Proton launch pad, Baikonour.

The fourth area of development, in the mid-to-late 1960s, was for the N pads, set up to support the man-on-the-Moon effort. They are located a mere 3.5 km from the first R-7 pad. Work began in 1963 and was completed in 1968. The completed N pads were impressive: the two enormous pads, matched by 183 m high towers, were fed rockets from a 250 m long assembly hangar, about the same size as the old Zeppelin airship sheds. They would almost certainly have seen their first successful launch in August 1974, had not the N-1 programme been cancelled that May.

Engineers then began reconstructing their structures into a pad for the N booster's replacement—Energiya. Huge, white-painted facilities were built to support Energiya and the Buran space shuttle it was designed to fly: a Buran integration hall, an Energiya integration hall, test facilities, two parallel launch pads for Energiya–Buran (built on the exact site of the N-1 pads), one of which was used to launch Buran in 1988. A third, quite different, adjacent pad was used to fly Energiya on its first, Polyus SK1F-DM, mission in 1987. The Energiya area comprises an Energiya integration building, a shuttle integration building, a shuttle/Energiya checkout building and a vibration check facility. The Energiya integration building is rectangular shaped, 274 m long, 160 m wide and 40 m high, and is the largest single building in Baikonour. Stages were flown there by Myasishchev M-3MT aircraft and, later, the Antonov 225 aircraft. The shuttle integration building is

300 m long, 240 m wide and 37 m high, and is based on the facilities used for the N-1 programme (the outside is in poor condition). The shuttle/Energiya checkout building is similar to the Vehicle Assembly Building at Cape Canaveral, 240 m long and 60 m high. Integration is carried out by cranes and work platforms operating over two railway tracks 18 m apart. The vibration test facility is 100 m high and compares to the Dynamic Test Stand at the NASA Marshall Space Flight Center. The Energiya integration hall has four parallel integration halls. At one stage, 4000 technicians worked there, but they are now

Facilities built to support the Energiya–Buran project in the mid-1980s.

staffed by a small core of patrolling security personnel. In summer 1995, the decision was taken to modify the Energiya–Buran facilities for use as integration halls for Western commercial payloads and equipment for the International Space Station.[39]

The shuttle runway lies to the north of these pads and east of the Proton pads. Called Anniversary airfield, it is 4500 m long and 84 m wide and runs from SW to NE. Landings are controlled by a six-floor-high Command Post Direction and Dispatch Building, OKPD. In 1995, repair work began on the runway, which was designated the principal airfield receiving components of the International Space Station from Europe and North America and part of it was repaved by the autumn.

The vibration test facility, Baikonour cosmodrome.

The final area of development is the launch complex used for Zenith missions. Although Zenith and Energiya have shared components, the Zenith complex was built far away, to the south of the second R-7 launch site, pad B. Completed in the 1980s, there are two pads for the Zenith rocket, 45L and 45P. Adjacent to them is a launch site for the new Rokot small launcher, first flown in 1994.

Baikonour now has nine rocket complexes, 14 launch pads (seven active at present), 35 technical facilities and three propellant fuelling stations. There were 19 launches from Baikonour in 1995. From the early 1990s, Baikonour has been host to a growing number of Western journalists and fare-paying tourists. In March 1994, a senior American military delegation toured the facilities, and was led by the Secretary of State for Defense, William Perry. Despite the evident decay in facilities in some parts of Baikonour and the unhappy abandonment of the Buran–Energiya system, Baikonour remains an impressive spaceport. When the American space shuttle Atlantis, waiting to fly a Russian–American crew to Mir in June 1995, was grounded in Cape Canaveral owing to thunderstorms, visiting Russians managed a wry smile, being used to tunnelling through snow to launch rockets in temperatures of –30°C in wintertime. Turnaround times in Baikonour are the fastest in the world—five hours on the Zenith pad, six on the R-7 (the minimum at Cape Canaveral is a month). The Zenith launching system is the most sophisticated in the world. By autumn 1995, independent experts took the view that Baikonour had turned the corner after the difficult winter of 1993–4 and that facilities at the cosmodrome were improving.[40]

GETTING THERE: THE BOOSTERS

The Soviet space programme used only six basic rockets for its entire range of space initiatives from the 1950s to the 1980s. Today's Russian space programme has modernized a number of the older rockets and is introducing a new, flexible range of rockets.[41]

Russia's rockets

Name	Designer	Service	Length	Payload
R-7 (Vostok)	Korolev	1957–88	38.4 m	4.73 tonnes
R-7 (Soyuz)	Korolev	1966–	49.5 m	7.5 tonnes
R-7 (Molniya)	Korolev	1960–	45.2 m	1.6 tonnes to high LEO
R-12 (Cosmos)	Yangel	1962–77	30 m	500 kg
R-14 (Cosmos)	Yangel	1964–	31.4 m	1.78 tonnes
UR-500 (Proton)	Chelomei	1965–	59.5 m	20.6 tonnes LEO
				2.3 tonnes GEO
R-36M (Tsyklon 2)	Yangel	1966–	35 m	4 tonnes
R-36 (Tsyklon 3)	Yangel	1977–	39.3 m	5.5 tonnes
N-1	Korolev	1969–72	93.7 m	98 tonnes
Zenith	Yangel	1985–	57 m	13.7 tonnes
Energiya	Glushko	1987–8	60 m	140 tonnes
Rokot		1994–	30 m	1.85 tonnes
Topol, Pioner	Nadirazhde	1993–	29 m	700 kg

LEO = Low Earth Orbit; GEO = Geostationary Earth Orbit.

An understanding of Soviet rockets is complicated by the many different classifications and names used. The Russians withheld basic information on most of their rockets until the 1980s, and detailed information was not published until the 1990s. This forced Western analysts to develop their own systems to interpret and classify their launchers. To give two examples, the basic launcher of the series, the R-7, designed in 1953, was not shown to the West until 1965; first film of a Proton rocket was not shown until 1984. The principal Western classifications were done by Charles Sheldon for the Library of Congress (A, B, C, etc.); the Department of Defense (SL 1, 2, 3, etc.); NATO (generally a codename beginning with the letter S). The principal Russian classifications are the factory code (letters and numbers), the sequence in which the rocket was ordered (R-1, R-2, etc.) and populist titles (Tsyklon, Zenith, etc.).

SERGEI KOROLEV'S R-7

Sergei Korolov's R-7 booster played a key role in the Soviet space programme from Sputnik onwards. With its core and four strap-ons and twenty nozzles roaring at liftoff, it is unique in the rocket world. As the years went by, the engineers simply added more and more to the top, till the rocket reached to nearly 50 m with the Soyuz escape tower, compared to the more modest 29 m when it started as Russia's first ICBM. The R-7 became the most used booster in history. From two launches in 1957, it progressed to 34 by 1967, 47 in 1972 and 63 in 1980, or more than one a week. One Western expert calculated that the factory which built its engines must at one stage have turned out a new R-7 nozzle every 12 min of the working day! With the designing of a new version of the R-7 in the mid-1990s, its story is far from over. The R-7 has been called the Model-T Ford of the rocket industry, though the production run on the R-7 is likely to be longer.

Versions of the R-7

Factory designation	Stages	Title	First launch
8K71	2	Sputnik	May 1957
8K72	3	Luna	Sep 1958
8A92	3	Vostok	Spaceship 1, 1960
8K78	4	Molniya	Mars missions, 1960
11A57	3	Voskhod	Cosmos 22, 16 November 1963
8K78M	4	Molniya M	19 February 1964
11A511	3	Soyuz	Cosmos 133 (28 November 1966)
	3	Soyuz M	27 December 1971 (Cosmos 470)
11A511U	3	Soyuz U	18 May 1973 (Cosmos 559)

In the West, this rocket was called the A-booster (Sheldon classification), SS-6 Sapwood (NATO classification) and the SL-1, 2, 4 and 6 (US Department of Defense).

The original Sputnik rocket was 29 m long, weighed 267 tonnes and could put 1.35 tonnes into orbit. It was modified as early as 1959, when a small first stage was added, enough to get Luna 1 to 3 off to the Moon. The Vostok rocket was 38 m long, weighed 287 tonnes and could put 4730 kg into orbit. After Vostok it was used for the early military reconnaissance and meteorological satellites and was gradually taken out of service in the late 1980s.

The Soyuz rocket, the most recent version, is 39 m long (without payload), weighs 310 tonnes and can put 7.5 tonnes into orbit. The principal modification was the fitting of a large second stage, 9.4 m long and 2.6 m in diameter. This first appeared in 1963 as Cosmos 22, though it was later redeveloped in a number of subversions. This model turned out to be highly reliable and was used for the Soyuz and Progress missions, photoreconnaissance programmes, materials processing and biosatellite missions.

The Molniya rocket, with four stages, first appeared in 1960, with the attempted Mars launches that autumn. It was used for all the early deep space missions, though enormous difficulties were experienced in making the fourth stage reliable. On a typical mission—let us take Venera 8—the Molniya would rise on its twenty nozzles. The strap-ons would burn out and blast free after 2 min. The rocket would now be 50 km high and well above the thick layers of the atmosphere. The core would fire after a further 3 min. The payload would then orbit our planet for one revolution—possibly two—and it would be aimed at the right keyhole in the sky. The escape stage would light up and fire for a full 243 s—just over four minutes. The long struggle against gravity would be over, Earth vanquished. This version has been used for Molniya communications satellites, the OKO military early warning satellites and other small, high-inclination payloads of less than two tonnes.

An uprated version of the R-7 booster was designed in the mid-1990s, called Rus. Although the same height as the Soyuz booster, it has a broader diameter (2.95 m compared to 2.66 m) and will carry an extra 1000 kg of payload, making a total of over 8 tonnes. First launch was scheduled for 1997. The first engine test took place in December 1994 and production was planned for 1996. Construction was the responsibility of the Progress factory at Samara on the Volga. The Molniya upper stage will be replaced by a new, improved Phobos upper stage.

MIKHAIL YANGEL'S R-12

Responsibility for the development of military rockets was given at an early stage to Mikhail Yangel's design bureau in Dnepropetrovsk, Ukraine. His military rockets were adapted for a range of military and civilian missions. Mikhail Yangel's R-12 was used for small Cosmos scientific missions from 1962. The R-12 is also classified as the B-1 (Sheldon), SL-7 (US Department of Defense), 'Sandal' (NATO) and the small Cosmos rocket or the Cosmos 2 (by the Russians themselves). The R-12 was ordered in August 1960, was in service from 1962 to 1977, and was long, thin, and pencil shaped. It was the smallest of all the Soviet boosters, 30 m high, weighing 43 tonnes. It had enough thrust to put a mass of 500 kg into an orbit of 300 km. The R-12 used the RD-214 engine, developed by Glushko in the GDL design office over 1952–7. The fuel was nitric acid hydrocarbon, thrust 74 tonnes and specific impulse 264 s. It placed in orbit over 60 payloads, civilian and military, mainly from Kapustin Yar, and became the basis of the first Intercosmos series of scientific satellites.

MIKHAIL YANGEL'S R-14, THE COSMOS

In the early 1960s, the Soviet Union lacked a rocket capable of placing in orbit satellites larger than 500 kg, the capability of the R-12, but smaller than 7.5 tonnes, the capability of the R-7. This was a big gap—and there were a variety of satellite needs in between. To meet this need, the R-14 was developed, also called 'Skean' (NATO), SL-8 (Department of Defense), C (Sheldon) and Cosmos 3 (and a derivative, the 3M) by the Russians. Construction was ordered in October 1961. Like the R-12, the designer was Mikhail Yangel.

The R-14 looked like the R-12, but fatter. Both were about the same height. It was 30 m high, had two stages, and could orbit payloads of about 1000 kg. The R-14 first appeared in 1964, with the treble launching of Cosmos 38-40. At the time the USSR admitted that a 'carrier rocket of a new type' had been launched. After nine test flights from

Baikonour, virtually all subsequent missions were shifted to Plesetsk, with just a few from Kapustin Yar. With the retirement of the R-12 in 1977, the R-14 took over its old functions. It was used to fly the BOR-4 tests of the spaceplane over 1982–4. A modernized version of the Cosmos, called Vzliot, will be available from 1998. The R-14 is produced in Krasnoyarsk (the Cosmos 3) and Omsk (the Cosmos 3M, by Polyot enterprises).

VLADIMIR CHELOMEI'S UR-500, THE PROTON

Vladimir Chelomei's UR-500K Proton, with its origins deep in the Soviet man-around-the-Moon effort, became in the course of time the workhorse of the deep space programme, geostationary satellites and the orbiter of heavy payloads into Earth orbit. Despite its unreliability in its early years—and problems which helped to cost the Russians the Moon race—it became very solid and reliable, rarely malfunctioning after 1970. Proton was called the D booster (Sheldon).

Proton's famous high-performance engine, the RD-253, designed by Valentin Glushko.

The UR-500 Proton has several versions. In its original form in 1965, called UR-500, SL-9 (Department of Defense), it put the 12-tonne Proton scientific satellites into low orbit. The heavier versions from 1968 on were able to put large payloads of around 20 tonnes into low Earth orbit (SL-13 version, Department of Defense). The most commonly used version was used for geosynchronous and deep space missions (SL-12, Department of Defense). Its capability is 6000 kg to the Moon, 5 000 kg to the near planets, or 2500 kg to geosynchronous orbit.

Increasingly, Proton became used for satellites heading for stationary orbit at 36 000 km. So reliable did Proton become that in 1983 the USSR offered it to Western commercial companies on an economic basis. The Proton rocket is 44 m high. By 1995, it had flown 210 times. From 1990 the Salyut OKB began to design an uprated Proton rocket, the 'M' version, capable of launching payloads of 23.7 tonnes to low Earth orbit and 4.5 tonnes to geostationary orbit. This will be ready during 1998–2000. The Proton rocket is manufactured in the Khrunichev plant in Moscow, now part of Lockheed Khrunichev Energiya.[42]

MIKHAIL YANGEL'S R-36, TSYKLON

The R-36, Tsyklon rocket was introduced as a military booster in the mid-1960s and was initially used for the Fractional Orbital Bombardment System (FOBS) and hunter-killer satellites. From 1967 it was used to put up a series of nuclear-powered ocean surveillance satellites and other military electronic intelligence-gathering missions. Tsyklon was ordered in August 1965 and first flew on 17 September 1966, and was subsequently called the R-36M or Tsyklon-2 (Tsyklon-1 was retrospectively applied to the R-16 of Nedelin notoriety). A second version was ordered in January 1970, entering service in June 1977, being called the R-36 or Tsyklon-3.[43] In the West, the designations used are F1 and F2 booster (Sheldon) and the SL-11 and 14 (Department of Defense).

Tsyklon has two stages, both burning UDMH fuel with either nitric acid or nitrogen tetroxide as oxidizer. Tsyklon-3 is 39 m high and can put payloads into 150 km to 10 000 km orbits from Plesetsk. There are two automated pads at Plesetsk which can launch Tsyklons rapidly in all weathers, from +50°C to −45°C.

ZENITH, OF YUZHNOYE NPO

Zenith also comes from Mikhail Yangel's bureau in Ukraine, though after his death in 1971 it became NPO Yuzhnoye. The Zenith rocket, also known as the SL-16 (Department of Defense) or the J rocket (Sheldon), was ordered in December 1974, first flying in April 1985 in a suborbital test. Its first successful mission was Cosmos 1697 in October 1985, and it became operational with Cosmos 1833 in March 1987.[44]

Zenith serves as the strap-on booster for the Energiya rocket, but is a powerful rocket in its own right, standing almost as high as Chalomei's famous Proton. Zenith has a capacity of 13.7 tonnes to low Earth orbit and 1.7 tonnes to geosynchronous orbit. Its height is 57 m, weight 445 tonnes, diameter 3.7 m and its main RD-170 engine burns for 133 s, the second stage for 303 s. The RD-170 engines and the second stage RD-120 were developed by the Energomash NPO in Khimki, formerly the Leningrad Gas Dynamics Laboratory (GDL).

Zenith rocket, seen here as a strap-on rocket for the Energiya system.

The Zenith complex was completed at Baikonour in 1985: it comprises supply and service sheds and six-floor multistorey buildings capable of processing several Zenith rockets at the same time. Zenith has a unique, automated system whereby the payload is mated, the Zenith transported on a railcar to its pad and put into position for firing. Once the railcar arrives, automatic systems connect the Zenith to 25 fuel lines and 3500 electrical circuits. Zenith is clamped to the pad by vices sufficient to hold the rocket down at full thrust and then raised into firing position. Once secured, it can be fuelled within minutes by pumps drawing off silos which are located underground close to the pad. The entire fuelling and launch sequence is conducted automatically. The hoses and pumps are withdrawn 12 min before launch. At 4 min before launch, the railcar makes its way back to the integration building. A system of sprinklers is available to extinguish fires. 15 s before launch, the cooling system is activated, drowning the base of the pad in water to cool it and dampen vibration. The pad can be ready for another launch in five hours.

On 28 December 1985, Zenith suffered a failure when its second-stage engine failed to ignite. Zenith's early payloads were heavy electronic intelligence (elint) satellites sent into 850 km orbits at 71 deg from Baikonour. There was a long gap in Zenith launches between November 1988 (Cosmos 1980), by which time it had carried out 13 launches, and May 1990 (Cosmos 2089), due to financial difficulties. Zenith entered a second difficult phase in the early 1990s. After fourteen successful launches, on 4 October 1990, a Zenith exploded 70 m high, right over its launch pad at Baikonour, destroying the Cosmos elint payload and damaging the launch tower. There was another launch failure in August 1991, when the second stage exploded during the third minute of flight. Zenith suffered a pad explosion on 5 February 1992, completely destroying the military communications satellite (comsat) on board and the launch pad itself. Zenith has an important role in the building of the international space station. Zenith is designed to fly the main Russian supply craft for the station, the Progress M freighter, which weighs 13.3 tonnes. Western analysts consider Zenith to be a powerful, efficient launcher.

Zenith launches

Date	Designation	Purpose
13 Apr 1985	Suborbit	
21 June 1985	Suborbit	
22 Oct 1985	Cosmos 1697	Elint
28 Dec 1985	Cosmos 1714	Elint
30 July 1986	Cosmos 1767	Recon.
22 Oct 1986	Cosmos 1786	Failure
14 Feb 1987	Cosmos 1820	Recon.
18 Mar 1987	Cosmos 1833	Elint
13 May 1987	Cosmos 1844	Elint
1 Aug 1987	Cosmos 1871	Recon.
28 Aug 1987	Cosmos 1873	Elint
15 May 1988	Cosmos 1943	Elint
23 Nov 1988	Cosmos 1980	Elint
22 May 1990	Cosmos 2082	Elint
4 Oct 1990		Failure
30 Aug 1991		Failure
5 Feb 1992		Failure
17 Nov 1992	Cosmos 2219	Elint
25 Dec 1992	Cosmos 2227	Elint
26 Mar 1993	Cosmos 2237	Elint
16 Sep 1993	Cosmos 2263	Elint
23 Apr 1994	Cosmos 2278	Elint
26 Aug 1994	Cosmos 2290	6th generation photoreconnaissance.

KHRUNICHEV'S ROKOT

A new entry in 1994 was Rokot, a small, 30 m high launcher adapted from the SS-19 ballistic missile (NATO designation). Fired from Baikonour on 26 December 1994, Rokot comprised two solid stages and a third, liquid-fuelled stage. Rokot placed a Rosto radio test satellite into orbit, but the test was somewhat marred by the explosion of the third stage 3.5 h after liftoff, scattering debris in a 2000 km orbit at 64.6 deg. Rokot can fire up to 1.85 tonnes to low Earth orbit. In 1995, Khrunichev formed a company with German Daimler-Benz Aerospace (DASA), to market Rokot, offering it at $7m a launch.

KOMPLEKS' TOPOL AND PIONER

Another converted military launcher is available in two versions: Pioner or the SS-20 or START-1 (NATO designation) and the Topol or SS-25, also called the START-2 (NATO designation), conceived in the 1960s by Alexander Nadirazhde (1914–1987). The Moscow Kompleks Technical Centre converted them into modern, solid-fuelled rockets which could place 700 kg class satellites into orbit. Pioner is four-stage and Topol five-stage.[45] The first Topol launch took place on 25 March 1993 from Plesetsk, placing a small test satellite in orbit. This was the first solid rocket launch by Russia. All appeared to go perfectly on the first operational attempt, which took place in Plesetsk on 28 March 1995. The modified rocket carried a Russian satellite called EKA2, a Mexican meteorite detection system and a private Israeli satellite called Gurvin. However, the fourth stage shut down 12 s prematurely and the fifth stage did not ignite, the payload impacting into the Lama river near the Laptev Sea.

NEW RUSSIAN ROCKETS

Several new launchers have been built in recent years, or are in construction or design. They will join Russia's rocket fleet by the turn of the century.

BLACKJACK BURLAK

New rocket designs have been offered in recent years. At the 1995 Paris Air Show, the Tupolev 160 Blackjack strategic bomber was the show-stopper. Underneath, the Tupolev carried a new air-launched rocket, the Burlak, designed to be flown to altitude by the Blackjack, where it would be released to carry on to orbit by itself. The Blackjack/Burlak combination could put either 800 kg into Polar orbit or 1100 kg into conventional orbit. Burlak is a two-stage, 32 tonne, 25 m long rocket. The concept is similar to Pegasus, a private American air-launched rocket, which since 1990 had been launching small satellite payloads into orbit from an airfield in California, brought to altitude by a Lockheed Tristar civil airliner. It will be ready from 1998.

MOLNIYA'S MAKS

Designs have been put forward by the Molniya design bureau for seven-tonne rockets to be carried aloft by the enormous Antonov 225 large cargo plane, originally designed as a transporter for the space shuttle Buran. Called MAKS (Mnogotselevaya Aviationno Kosmicheskaya Sistema, or Multi-purpose aerospace system), the system envisages a large teardrop-shaped external tank being lifted to altitude by the Antonov 225. Designed by Boris Katorgin at NPO Energomash, MAKS uses an RD-701 engine which is a closed-cycle, twin-chambered tripropellant with a thrust of 4000 kN and a chamber pressure of 300 ats. Assembled on top of the Antonov 225, the MAKS stack of orbiter and tank is 36.3 m long and weighs 275 tonnes, of which 237 tonnes is propellant. The orbiter, based on the Spiral spaceplane design, is 19.3 m long, has a wing span of 12.5 m and weighs 27 tonnes. The system runs on liquid oxygen, kerosene and liquid hydrogen, which are held in the aluminium–lithium alloy tank. The two-person shuttle could carry a payload of 8.5 tonnes into 200 km, 51.6 deg orbit. The MAKS orbiter was similar in size and shape to the European Space Agency's small shuttle, the cancelled Hermes. The mission profile for MAKS is for the orbiter and tank to be ferried to an altitude of 9000 m, possibly some distance from the airfield (the Antonov's range is no less than 10 000 km). During the later stages of the ascent, the MAKS switches from tripropellant to liquid hydrogen and oxidizer only so as to get the greatest efficiency out of the two different fuels.[46]

TsIAM'S SCRAMJET

Development of scramjets in Russia goes back to 1972, when the first work began in the Russian Central Institute of Aviation Motors, TsIAM. It continued at a low level until 1986, when the Americans announced plans (since scrapped) to build a national aerospaceplane, the X-30. TsIAM's work came to fruition on 28 November 1991 at Baikonour when the first scramjet was tested, using an old military missile. The rocket reached an altitude of 30 km, a speed of mach 8, and impacted 180 km downrange. The 11 m long scramjet performed two burns, one of 20 s, the other 10 s.[47] In cooperation with, and funding from, a French organization, ONERA, a second scramjet test took place at Baikonour on 17 November 1992. NASA made arrangements with TsIAM for the tests to resume in 1996.

KHRUNICHEV'S ANGARA

Development of a new rocket began in 1995, the Angara. Approved by the Russian government in 1994, first funding began to flow the following year. The manufacturer is the Khrunichev factory in Moscow. Angara has a performance significantly better than the Proton. Working from the new Zenith pad at Plesetsk, the two-stage version can place 28 tonnes into 63 deg orbits; the three-stage version 4.5 tonnes into geostationary orbit. Angara uses a liquid oxygen and kerosene first stage, and a liquid oxygen and hydrogen upper stage. In an unusual arrangement, the oxygen tanks are strapped on the outside of the rocket half way up. The first stage will use RD-174 engines burning kerosene, the second RD-0120 engines using hydrogen. It will be operational in 2000–2002.

Russia's new rockets

Name	Payload	Scheduled availability
Rus	8 tonnes to LEO	1996
Vzliot	Over 1000 kg to LEO	1998
Proton M	23.7 tonnes to LEO	1998–2000
	4.5 tonnes to GEO	
Burlak	1100 kg to LEO	1998
MAKS	8.5 tonnes to LEO	1998
Angara	28 tonnes to LEO	2000–2002
	4.5 tonnes to GEO	

Soviet rockets experienced many difficulties during their early years, and there was a high failure rate on the lunar and interplanetary missions in the 1960s. This was not a uniquely Soviet phenomenon, for similar problems afflicted American and European efforts—the Americans, for example, took several years to tame their powerful Centaur rocket. Russian rockets have now achieved very high standards of reliability—the commercial claims are 98% for the Soyuz, 96% for the Molniya, 96% for the Tsyklon 2, 100% for the Tsyklon 3, 97% for the Cosmos, 86% for Proton and 71% for the Zenith.

Success rates of Russian launchers to June 1994[48]

Launcher	Introduction	Successes	Failures
Proton SL-12	1967	165	18
Proton SL-13	1968	22	5
Soyuz	1963	1013	6
Cosmos	1964	395	17
Tsyklon 2	1966	118	3
Tsyklon 3	1977	105	5
Zenith	1985	17	4
Energiya	1987	2	0

RUSSIA'S ROCKET ENGINES

Engines are the single most important element in a rocket's design, and are crucial for high performance and reliability. Russia's rocket engines have been designed in four bureaux.[49] The most important one is the Gas Dynamics Laboratory (GDL), now NPO Energomash; the others are the Kosberg bureau, the Isayev bureau, and the Kuznetsov bureau.

GDL

The most famous engine design bureau is GDL, whose history has been intimately associated with the greatest of Russia's rocket engine designers, Valentin Glushko. His engines may be divided into three groups: the RD-100 series, which use liquid oxygen and non-storable propellants; the RD-200 series, which use nitrogen and storable propellants; and the RD-300 series, which use fluorine oxidizer. RD stands for rocket motor (*raketny dvigatel*).

The first engines from GDL were those which drove the Soviet version of the German A-4 rocket. The Soviet version of the A-4, the R-1, used the R-100 engine, which ran on liquid oxygen and alcohol. Improved versions, the RD-101 and RD-103, fired the R-2 and R-5 rocket respectively for the V-2 and V-5 geophysical series of sounding rockets.

Perhaps the most famous engines from the bureau were the RD-107 and RD-108, used for the R-7 rocket, used initially to launch Sputnik and since then developed in the Vostok, Molniya and Soyuz versions. The RD-107 marked the transition from alcohol as a fuel to kerosene. The RD-108 was used as the core stage on the R-7 (block A), the RD-107 on the

Valentin Glushko, Russia's greatest rocket engine designer.

four strap-on stages (blocks B, V, G, D). Each RD-107 weighed 1155 kg dry and had a thrust of 1000 kN.

The most recent operational engine using kerosene is the RD-170, used on the Zenith and as strap-on to the Energiya. The RD-170 weighs 8755 kg and has a thrust of 7905 kN. The RD-170 has a chamber pressure of 3560 psi and can be throttled from 40% to 105%. It is 4.3 m high and is 4.1 m in diameter. An indication of the progress of rocketry may be gauged from the fact that chamber pressure rose from 16 atmospheres on the RD-100 to 250 atmospheres in the RD-170, the highest thrust of any Soviet engine.

GDL developed a second range of engines which uses storable propellants: the RD-214 and RD-216, used on the R-12 and R-14 Cosmos rockets, the RD-219 used on the R-36 Tsyklon, and the RD-253 used on the UR-500 Proton. The RD-301 was an experimental engine developed in 1969–76 using flourine and ammonia generating a thrust of 98 kN for 750 s. It has not been used operationally.

KOSBERG BUREAU

The engines designed by Semyon Kosberg (1903–65) are used for the upper stages of rockets. The Kosberg bureau was set up in 1954, working initially on aircraft engines and then, from around 1956, rocket engines. The Kosberg KB developed engines for the upper stages of the R-7, namely the block E (Luna, Vostok), block I (Soyuz) and block L (Molniya), all of which used liquid oxygen and kerosene; and the upper stages of the Proton, namely the block B and block V, using nitrogen tetroxide and UDMH, which gave so much trouble in the late 1960s. Kosberg built the RD-465 and RD-473 Proton upper stages.

RD-170 engine, used on the Energiya rocket.

ISAYEV BUREAU

The Isayev bureau was set up in 1944. His engines were used in the rocket programme as small propulsion systems, manoeuvring and orientation engines. Examples are the KDU-414 (used on the early planetary probes), the KTDU-1 (employed on Vostok), the KTDU-5A (used for the Luna soft-landings), the KTDU-53 (for Zond), the KRD-61 (for the Luna 16 ascent stage) and the KTDU-35 (used for Soyuz). The Isayev bureau made the systems of the Soyuz T and the thrusters used on Salyut and Mir.

KUZNETSOV

Kuznetsov is an aviation design bureau headed by Nikolai Kuznetsov (1911–95), which became involved with the space programme when Valentin Glushko refused to cooperate with Korolev in building the engines of the Soviet Moon rocket, the N-1. Accordingly, they were built by the Kuznetsov bureau, which developed the engines of the lower and upper stages of the N-1.

The experimental RD-301 engine made by the Gas Dynamics Laboratory, now NPO Energomash.

ROCKET FACTORIES

Russia's biggest rocket factory is the Progress plant in Kyubyshev, now Samara, on the Volga.[50] Originally it was the Duks bicycle factory, set up by a German businessman, Jules Muller, in the Baltics in 1884, which by World War I had expanded into the production of motorcycles, cars and trolleys. Duks was nationalized in 1918 as State Aviation Plant no.1, evacuated to Kyubyshev in 1941 (Goebbels once trumpeted its demise) and during the war turned out Il-2 dive bombers. In 1958 it was named Progress and became the constructor of the R-7, during 1963–74, the N-1 and subsequently Buran. By 1994, it had turned out 1500 rockets and 800 satellites in the Nauka, Bion and Resurs series.

In Ukraine, the largest military combined design bureau and rocket plant was OKB-586, of Mikhail Yangel, established at Dnepropetrovsk. OKB-586 built the R-12, R-14, R-16 and R-36 rockets, though some construction has since been contracted out to other plants in Russia. After Yangel's death, it was renamed NPO Yuzhnoye (the Russian word for 'southern'). The Yuzhnoye design bureau became the biggest missile production plant in the world, at its peak having 185 500 m^2 floor space devoted to rocket production and employing 50 000 people.

Russia's rocket engines

Rocket	1st stage	2nd stage	3rd stage	4th stage
R-7 (Vostok)	RD-107	RD-108	RO-7	
R-7 (Soyuz)	RD-107	RD-108	RD-461	
R-7 (Molniya)	RD-107	RD-108	RD-461	RO-7
R-12 (Cosmos)	RD-214	RD-119		
R-14 (Cosmos)	RD-216	RD-211		
UR-500 Proton	RD-253	RD-465		
UR-500K Proton SL-12	RD-253	RD-465	RD-473	Block D
UR-500K Proton SL-13	RD-253	RD-465	RD-473	
R-36M (Tsyklon-2)	RD-219	RD-219		
R-36 (Tsyklon-3)	RD-219	RD-219	?	
N-1	NK-33	NK-43	NK-39	NK-31
Zenith	RD-170	RD-120	Block D	
Energiya	RD-170	RD-0120		

INFRASTRUCTURE[51]

The organization of the Soviet space programme required a massive managerial effort—in the case of the Moon race, not a very successful one. A study of how the Soviet space programme is run suggests that it is organizationally more complex than its American equivalent. Under the American system, NASA is responsible for space policy and programmes. The Administrator of NASA is appointed by, and reports to, the President. NASA presents its budget to both the President and the Congress, and both argue over the details, adding some programmes and striking others out. Once programmes are agreed, it is the task of NASA to coordinate them and deliver the results.

The Soviet programme, by contrast, was guided by the Party and the Government acting in parallel, and ran through a number of institutions. The chain of command of the Soviet space programme originally ran through the Ministry of Aircraft Production. From 1965, it was channelled through the Ministry of General Machine Building (MOM, or Ministerstvo Obshchego Machinostroyeniye) and the Commission on Military Industrial Issues, which was responsible to the Council of Ministers through the First Deputy to the Prime Minister and was responsible to the Communist Party through the Politburo. This system was created by Dmitri Ustinov, an engineer in the tank industry, who attracted rapid promotion for a legendary ability to get things done in the elaborate web of Party and State that comprised Soviet society in the 1950s and 1960s. The Commission brought together the nine main agencies and ministries concerned with defence, industry and space research, of which the Ministry of General Machine Building was one.

The Ministry of General Machine Building was created for the express purpose of being the umbrella for the space industry in 1965 (the Ministry of Medium Machine Building was the cover for the nuclear industry; only the Ministry of Heavy Machine Building had an appropriate title, being responsible for cranes and excavators).

During the key period of the Moon race and subsequently, all the key decisions of the Soviet space programme were taken by the Commission on Military Industrial Issues and within it, the Ministry of General Machine Building. The Minister of General Machine Building during the critical years from 1965 to 1983 was Sergei Afanasayev, replaced that year by Oleg Baklanov. In 1988, Mikhail Gorbachev promoted Baklanov to a uniquely powerful position which combined Ministry of General Machine Building and the Commission on Military Industrial Issues—a reward he reciprocated by joining the *putsch* against Gorbachev in 1991. Baklanov ended up in prison.

In 1985, Gorbachev tried to bring better cohesion and coordination to the Soviet space programme by the creation of Glavcosmos, directed by Alexander Dunayev. In practice, Glavcosmos was more of a marketing than coordinating body. In 1986, the USSR formally announced that it was placing the Proton rocket and other launchers on the world market; and Glavcosmos sent marketing teams abroad the following year to promote the offer. After the fall of the Soviet Union, both Glavcosmos and the Ministry of General Machine Building disappeared, Boris Yeltsin creating the Russian Space Agency (RKA) in their place.

The nature and purpose of both the Commission on Military Industrial Issues and the Ministry of Medium Machine Building were secret. The visible, public face of the Soviet space programme during this period was the Moscow Institute for Space Research, established in 1965. Its first director was Georgi Petrov. Born 1912 in Archangel, he came from a background in applied gas dynamics and space aerodynamics, and had been with the Academy of Sciences since 1958. After his untimely death in 1973, the second director was Roald Sagdeev, who held the post until 1988, when it had a prominent public role in articulating the Soviet space programme and as a contact point for international activities. After Sagdeev, it was directed by Albert Galeev.

The Academy of Sciences of the USSR played an important role in the Soviet space programme. It was not under direct governmental control, for the Academy is a self-perpetuating body of learned men and women of science—about 300 full members and 300 corresponding members—that long predated the Revolution of 1917. It had only a limited formal role in the organization of the Soviet space programme, but was influential, especially during the presidency of Mstislav Keldysh, when it was called several times to adjudge programmes and projects for manned and unmanned spaceflights. After 1991, the Academy was renamed RAN (the Russian Academy of Sciences).

TRACKING AND CONTROL

The scale and scope of the Soviet space programme required a national and international network for the tracking, control and recovery of spacecraft. Tracking of objects in space is provided by the Russian space surveillance system, set up in 1962. It comprises radio, radar and optical devices. The radar systems are based on the Ballistic Early Warning Missile System, which has sensors in Irkutsk, Murmansk and Pechora; and the Anti-Ballistic Missile Defence in Moscow. Russian radio-tracking stations are located in Bear's Lake, Moscow; Kolpashevo and Ulan Ude in Siberia; and in the Far East, Petropavlovsk Kamchatsky and Ussuriyisk. Optical trackers are based in Irkutsk, Kourova, Ushno-Sakhalinsky and Zvenigorod (Moscow). The largest optical tracker, in Zvenigorod, weighs 25 tonnes, has a focal length of 75 cm and can track satellites in geostationary orbit. Some laser-tracking systems were introduced in 1977. The number of objects tracked has risen from 250 a year in 1969 to 1000 a year in 1975 and 7500 in 1994.[52]

There are two flight control centres—in Kaliningrad, just northeast of Moscow outside the garden ring in the direction of Pushkino; and Yevpatoria, on the west coast of Crimea, Ukraine, the first to be constructed. During the period of the USSR, most interplanetary missions were controlled from Yevpatoria. After Ukrainian independence, the Yevpatoria system briefly withdrew from the network, but has since returned.

Mission control in Kaliningrad includes the flight control centre, which controls manned space flights. This is called TsUP (Tsentr Upravleniye Polyotami), the present building dating to 1974. It is not unlike Western mission control centres, with banks of

A view of the flight control centre, taken during the Soyuz T15 mission in 1986. The cosmonauts may be seen speaking to ground control (top right). The screen (top) marks the path of the station over the Earth's surface. The position of comships is also marked. Mission controllers monitor the mission behind banks of consoles.

consoles, central wall display, a television link to the Mir crew and maps of operational tracking stations. In addition to TsUP, there are other important centres for the control of space flights. The Priroda Scientific Centre takes responsibility for controlling Earth observation satellites and their downlink data; biology missions are delegated to the Institute for Medico-Biological Problems; Intercosmos missions are monitored from the Tarusa centre south of Moscow; and all operational satellites are monitored in the Computing and Coordinating Centre of the Academy of Sciences.

COMSHIPS

A world-wide tracking network is essential for the long-range tracking of interplanetary and lunar spacecraft. During the early 1960s, the United States was able to set up tracking dishes in allied countries such as Australia. Lacking similar or strategically located allies abroad, the USSR was compelled to put its global tracking network aboard ship. As part of the Moon effort, large tracking ships were constructed. The first, the *Cosmonaut Vladimir Komarov* (17 500 tonnes) appeared in the English Channel late in 1967. Two more followed—the *Cosmonaut Yuri Gagarin* (45 000 tonnes), which became the flagship, and the *Academician Sergei Korolev* (21 250 tonnes).

After the Moon race, the comships were used to improve communications between manned orbiting space stations and the ground. Until then, communications between manned spacecraft and the ground were limited to the periods when cosmonauts overflew Soviet territory, which they did for about a third of the day. Whenever these big ships sailed from their home ports in the Black Sea or the Baltic, it was a sure sign of a major manned mission coming up. Once the fleet was under way, the ships could then be found taking up position in three or four standard locations, such as the Newfoundland banks, the Caribbean, the Gulf of Guinea, the South Atlantic and the Sea of Japan. The last comship, the *Academician Nikolai Pilyugin*, was laid down in Leningrad in April 1988. They were large streamlined white ships, and with their giant aerials and with huge telescope-like domes they looked futuristic. They were accompanied by a fleet of smaller, converted comships—*Borovichi, Kegostrov, Morzhovets* and *Nevel*.

A series of smaller tracking comships was commissioned in 1974—the *Pavel Belyayev* (1978), the *Georgi Dobrovolski* (1978), the *Viktor Patsayev* and the *Vladislav Volkov* (1977). These ships had a displacement of 8950 tonnes, length 121 m and could cruise at 14.7 knots. They were based in Leningrad. The crews varied between 130 and 150, divided between sailors and tracking staff. Each ship could spend six months at sea at a time. The *Georgi Dobrovolski* was launched by Dobrovolski's widow, and included a small memorial museum on board.[53] The Soviet navy also commissioned its own comships, presumably for use in association with its naval reconnaissance satellites. These were the *Marshal Nedelin*, assigned to the Pacific fleet, the *Marshal Krylov*, and a third, huge, nuclear-powered comship, as yet unnamed, which joined the fleet in 1991.

In February 1992, as the economic crisis began to bite in Russia, all the tracking ships were recalled, even though this meant that the then-orbiting Mir cosmonauts were out of touch with ground control for up to nine hours at a time. The *Borovichi, Kegostrov, Morzhovets* and *Nevel* were sold and the *Vladimir Komarov* became an ecological monitoring ship in the Gulf of Finland. In 1994, the *Yuri Gagarin* and *Sergei Korolev*, after

Simplified table of some of the principal design bureaux

Name	Directors	Location	Present name	Speciality
OKB-1	Lavrentin Beria 1945 Sergei Korolev 1950–66 Vasili Mishin 1966–74 Valentin Glushko 1974–89 Yuri Semeonov 1989–	Podlipki, Moscow	RKK Energiya	Manned spacecraft
OKB-2 Then OKB-52	Vladimir Chelomei 1955–84 Yuri Semeonov 1984–8 G Efremov 1988–	Reutovo, Moscow	NPO Mashinostroyeniye	Manned spacecraft
Salyut Formerly no. 1 branch, OKB-52		Khrunichev	KB Salyut	Space stations
GDL OKB-486	Mikhail Tikhomirov, 1921 Valentin Glushko (post-war)	Moscow Leningrad Kazan Khimki	NPO Energomash	Rocket engines
Krasnoyarsk 26 Babakin	Mikhail Rechetnev 1959– Georgi Babakin 1965–71 Sergei Kryukov 1971–8 Vyacheslav Kovturenko 1978–	Krasnoyarsk Moscow	NPO Prikladnoi Mekhaniki NPO Lavochkin	Applications Lunar, interplanetary
OKB-23 OKB-56	Vladimir Myasishchev 1951–60 Pavel Tsybin	Transferred to Salyut KB		Spaceplanes Spaceplanes
OKB-586	Mikhail Yangel 1954–71	Dnepropetrovsk	NPO Yuzhnoye	Military rockets
Molniya	Gleb Lozino-Lozhinsky	Moscow	NPO Molniya	Spaceplanes
OKB Kosberg	Semyon Kosberg 1941–65 Alexander Konopatov 1965–	Voronezh	NPO Khim Automatiki	Upper stages
OKB Isayev	Alexei Isayev 1944	Kaliningrad	KimMash	Small engines

Note: some data are incomplete, owing to lack of full availability of information, archives and frequent changes of designation.

lying idle in Odessa for some time, came under the control of the Ukrainian Space Forces, who at once tried to sell them—but no buyers appeared.

DESIGN BUREAUX

A central organizational element of the Soviet space programme was the design bureau. The failure of the political leadership to control and regulate these bureaux was a significant element in the failure of the Soviet Union to reach the Moon.

The premier design bureau during the Moon race was OKB-1, directed by Sergei Korolev, which designed the R-7, Vostok, Voskhod, Soyuz, the N-1, the Zenith spy satellites, and the first generation of lunar and interplanetary probes. When Korolev died, OKB-1 became NPO Energiya under his successor Vasili Mishin (1966–74), Valetin Glushko (1974–89) and then Yuri Semeonov. When it was privatized in 1994, it was renamed RKK Energiya and now employs 30 000 people.

The main rival to Korolev was OKB-52, directed by Vladimir Chelomei, who masterminded the building of the Almaz space station, the TKS modules, the Proton rocket, and a range of space planes and military projects. After his death in 1984, it was renamed NPO Mashinostroyeniye and was directed by Yuri Semeonov (1984–8) and then G Efremov.

As OKB-1 became overloaded with work in the mid-1960s and the urgency to beat America became overwhelming, many elements were hived off to new or existing design bureaux. The unmanned lunar programme was first to be hived off, in 1965. Georgi Babakin was chief designer there from 1965 to 1971, succeeded by Sergei Kryukov (1971–8) and then Vyacheslav Kovturenko. Meteorological and communications satellites were devolved to the Electromechanics Scientific Research Institute (NPO-PM) in Krasnoyarsk. Upper stages became the preserve of the Kosberg bureau in Voronezh; and the Kozlov bureau in Kyubyshev took responsibility for military and Earth resources missions.

REORGANIZING THE SPACE PROGRAMME

The collapse of the Soviet Union brought a series of consequences for the space programme. These were political, organizational, financial and territorial. Initially, the programme contracted sharply as Russia slipped into financial crisis and government investment fell.

Government funds allocated to the space programme bore little relationship to the payments which actually arrived, even taking inflation into account. Many enterprises reported that they received only 30% of their actual allocation, some even less. One Western analysis reckoned that the real level of investment fell 80% from 1989 to 1995 and trailed not just the United States but France, Japan, China and Germany.[54] Whatever the reality of funding, the actual effects of the collapse of the command economy were not in doubt. By 1994, staff in many enterprises had not been paid for months. 205 000 technicians and other employees had left. It is estimated that total employment in the Russian space industry fell from one million at its peak in the mid-1980s to 295 000 in 1993, levelling out at around 200 000.[55] Several space enterprises were, on paper, bankrupt. Rocket launchings were held up because subcontractors, still unpaid, would not deliver components and fuel until accounts had been settled. Even in the Mir programme, launchings were delayed because nozzles and nosecones were unavailable, R-7 launchers being borrowed from the military stock. There were warnings that many comsats had exceeded their lifetimes and that, without new launches, many communications services, especially across Siberia, would simply break down. Flights to Mars were delayed; scientific missions were put on hold.

Originally, it had been thought that the space programme would continue as a unified effort by the former republics of the Soviet Union. These were, effectively, the fifteen republics bar the Baltics. The agreement setting up the successor body to the Soviet Union, namely the Commonwealth of Independent States, specified space research as a defined area of cooperation between the member States. In practice, the space programme became essentially a Russian space programme, and within a short period departing cosmonauts sported Russian flags and little pretence was made that the programme was a united effort of the CIS.

Russification presented its own problems. Many design bureaux, space factories and production plants were located outside the territory of Russia: several key production plants were in Ukraine. In practice, relationships with these plants were relatively unaffected by Ukrainian independence. More critically, the space programme's most important launch base was in the Republic of Kazakhstan. Virtually all recoveries of manned and unmanned spacecraft took place in its territory. In 1993, Kazakhstan made it plain that it intended to charge Russia for the use of the cosmodrome and for recovering crews from

A Soyuz manned cabin returning to Earth. When the Kazakh government began to charge Russia for spacecraft recoveries, Russia began to retrieve as many spacecraft as possible on Russian territory just south of the Ural mountains.

orbit. Things came to a head in January 1994 when Kazakhstan began to charge Russia prohibitive rates for basing its recovery helicopters in Kazakhstan during the return of the Soyuz TM17 crew of Vasili Tsibliyev and Alexander Serebrov. Russia based its helicopters in Chelyabinsk on Russian territory, flying them into Kazakhstan only for the immediate period of the recovery itself. Even then, they had to file flight plans in advance and carry parachute bags full of cash for fuelling stops.

The Russians responded to the Kazakh threat in several ways. First, they began to transfer as many launches as they could to the Plesetsk cosmodrome in northern Russia. They also began to recover capsules in Russia, in preference to Kazakhstan, when they could. The first such spacecraft to be landed in Russia was the Raduga capsule of Progress M18, which came down in the Russian steppe on 4 July 1993. Second, they began to cast around for an alternative launch site to Baikonour, but within Russian territory. Third, they began to work out a more permanent arrangement for the use of the Baikonour cosmodrome.

It was not feasible to move all space operations to Plesetsk. The manned space station and flights to geosynchronous orbit required the more southerly latitude offered by Baikonour. The cosmodrome in Baikonour was the only one with Proton rocket pads. Negotiations between Kazakhstan and Russia rumbled on in the course of 1993–4. At one stage, funding problems for Baikonour became acute. During the winter of 1993–4, the city of Leninsk suffered acute shortages of heat, light, gas and water. Many of its workers left. Several blocks of apartments were deserted, boarded up and abandoned.

Eventually, in March 1994, agreement was reached whereby Russia would take a 20-year lease on the cosmodrome, with a ten-year option of extension. The area of the cosmodrome would be sovereign Russian territory, under the command of Russian troops. Russia had hoped to strike a bargain for the use of the cosmodrome, offering Kazakhstan access to its space programme, sweetened by seats on missions to Mir. In the end, the Kazakh fee was $115m a year, backdated to 1991, paid in cash, and they took up an outstanding offer of a flight to Mir in any case. In no time, Russian parliamentarians were complaining that the rental was using up half the manned space programme budget even before the cost of using Baikonour was totted up.

A NEW COSMODROME?

This strengthened the hand of those who favoured Russia developing an entirely new cosmodrome, and surveys of an alternative were made in 1993–4. Three locations, all in the far east, were examined: Svobodny - Blagoveschensk, Vladivostok, and Khabarovsk. Svobodny, the favourite, was an old missile base: the 27th division there had once controlled 60 SS-11 missile silos, though all but five of these had been destroyed under the Russian–American treaty for the reduction of missile forces. It already had facilities worth 180bn roubles comprising technical, residential and production complexes.

In the course of 1993–5, debate broke out on the wisdom and desirability of converting Svobodny to a new, full-scale cosmodrome. In July 1994, President Boris Yeltsin visited the Amur region and Blagoveshensk. He said that a decision on the new cosmodrome was 'a complex matter' and that there was a need for a proper feasibility study. When pressed about the desirability of a new cosmodrome, he is reported as saying that 'you can't go on leasing Baikonour for ever' and that Russia 'did need' a new cosmodrome. But in October 1994, the Defence Committee of the Russian parliament, the Duma, rejected the plan for Svobodny cosmodrome. It declared that the Baikonour leasing agreement was satisfactory. The best way to deal with Russia's launching problems was to upgrade Plesetsk. In June 1995, the decision was taken to postpone the conversion of Svobodny for five years, but it was to remain an option.

NEW SPACE AGENCY, PROGRAMME

The controversy about Svobodny coincided with organizational changes. Within Russia, a new Russian Space Agency, RKA, had been formed by the decree of President Yeltsin on 25 February 1992. Yuri Koptev, formerly involved in managing the space programme through the now-abolished Ministry of General Machine Building, became its first director. A week later, on 2 March 1992, Ukrainian President Leonid Kravchuk decreed the formation of the National Space Agency of Ukraine (NSAU), with centres in Kharkov and Dnepropetrovsk.

In April 1994, the Russian government approved a *Space programme for the period 1994–2000*, drawn up in consultation with the Russian Academy of Sciences (RAN) and the Russian Space Agency, RKA. Its principal elements were: open, legal, competitive and planned development; the application of space technology to the economy; the conversion of defence production for economic benefit (in Russian, *konversiya*); and commercialization of the space industry.[56] The plan committed the government to spending R16 trillion over the period. Russian economists calculated that this was the equivalent of 0.23% of the national budget (compared to 0.97% spent on space research in the United States).[57]

COMMERCIALIZATION

Commercialization must not have come easy to the Russians. In 1975, during the Apollo–Soyuz Test Project, an American journalist once asked Intercosmos council chairman Boris Petrov how much the USSR was putting into the project. He rambled on for half an hour. In the end he gave up, saying he didn't know. 'What's the use?', he said: 'I don't count the money and here we have everything we need'.[58]

The initial commercialization of the programme took some bizarre and well-publicized forms. The cosmonaut training centre, TsPk, offered cosmonaut training to tourists, several days costing up to $10 000, including several minutes weightless in an Il-76 trainer. In December 1993, Sotheby's auctioneers sold off 200 rare items of Russian space history, including spacesuits (Leonov's, Gagarin's and the Moon suit); space cabins (e.g. Cosmos 1443); the dummy which flew on Spaceship 4; Vasili Mishin's diaries; and Sergei Korolev's slide rule. To the surprise of the auctioneer trade, the hardware fetched the least money, and the personal mementoes of cosmonauts and designers the most.

Ultimately, the future of the programme would depend on maintaining a reasonable level of government funding and making the programme a commercial part of the world space industry. The Russians, for their part, were aware that their rocket programme contained some real industrial, commercial and intellectual assets, and sought to market them so that their respective design bureaux and companies could continue in existence.

Commercialization proceeded swiftly, accompanied by the establishment of trading alliances with American companies. The largest design bureau in the Russian space industry, Energiya, was ordered to be part-privatized by Presidential decree. The order specified that 49% of its R1bn equity (then $650 000) be offered to management, its employees, citizens, institutional investors and foreign interests. The privatization of other leading aerospace companies was expected to follow.

The first Russian–American commercial enterprise was initiated by the American aerospace giant Lockheed, which, following a surprise visit by Lockheed officials to the Khrunichev factory in December 1992, quickly formed a joint company with the Khrunichev plant, manufacturers of the Proton rocket, called Lockheed–Khrunichev Enterprises (LKE). The Khrunichev factory, which had produced bicycles before the Russian Revolution, was a subsidiary of the Korolev OKB, though in the 1960s it had been subcontracted to build Chelomei's Proton rocket. LKE expanded on both sides when in the United States Lockheed merged with Martin Marietta, and Energiya was formally tied into the company, which became Lockheed Khrunichev Energiya International (LKEI). Proton became part of a giant Russian–American company able to offer Atlas and Titan as well. LKEI offered Proton on the world market at $70m (Europe's Ariane rates were around $70–$120m). LKEI won its first foreign contract in 1992, when the international maritime satellite organization, INMARSAT, paid $75m for it to launch an INMARSAT navigation satellite on the Proton. The company quickly attracted contracts for the European Astra-1, Loral's Tempo and PanAmsat 6. In late 1993, the Loral company signed a $250m deal with Lockheed Khrunichev to launch its small new communications satellites. By 1995, it had 20 confirmed orders, representing 15% of the world market. In 1995, LKEI announced plans to invest $23m in Baikonour. These involved upgrading the airport, dressing the roads between the airport and the Proton pads and improvements in the clean rooms. LKEI was renamed again in 1995 as International Launch Services (ILS).

Fear of Khrunichev undercutting the world market led the United States to restrict Russia to not more than eight commercial satellite launchings by 2000 and prohibited Russia from offering launches at less than 7.5% below the nearest Western offer. Quite how these restrictions squared with free enterprise and America's professed interest in helping the Russian economy was never explained by Washington. The quota applied to all the Western world, not just the United States, even though other countries were not consulted. American satellite manufacturing companies have tried to work their way round these restrictions and quotas, seeing no reason why they should fly on expensive American or European rockets when cheaper Russian launchers are available. In a relaxation of export licences, the US Commerce Department permitted the Greenbelt, Maryland company Final Analysis to fly a small 114 kg satellite called Faisat-1 with a Tsikada satellite. Launched on 23 January 1995 on a Cosmos rocket out of Plesetsk, Final Analysis hopes that it is the first in a 26-satellite system. In 1995, Vice-President Al Gore visited the Khrunichev plant, and there was growing confidence that the quotas would either be dropped or lapse.

NPO-PM in Krasnoyarsk took advantage of commercialization to earn income from its business as the world's largest manufacturer of comsats. NPO-PM was approached by Rimsat, a small company based in Fort Wayne Indiana, which had the licence to provide telecommunications services for the Kingdom of Tonga, and in turn for India, Malaysia, Philippines and the southwestern Pacific. First, Rimsat hired an existing Gorizont comsat already in orbit and which had exceeded its planned lifetime. Second, it leased Gorizont 41 and Gorizont 42 from NPO-PM, paying $130m. Two further comsats were ordered. The contracts were organized through a subsidiary of NPO-PM, in which all employees are shareholders. NPO-PM has also entered a joint venture with Sovcanstar of Canada for a five-satellite world-wide comsat system; and in 1995 sold China three Gals satellites.

ROCKET ENGINES

American aerospace companies were quick to realize the potential of Soviet-designed rocket engines and establish commercial ventures. In 1992, NPO Energomash signed an agreement with America's prime engine manufacturer, Pratt & Whitney, to market its engines, including the RD-170 and RD-701 tripropellant, in the USA. In summer 1994, year-long tests were begun in both Moscow and Marshall Space Flight Center, Alabama, of the RD-701 and RD-704 tripropellant engines with a view to the engines competing for the US Air Force's new Expendable Launch Vehicle contract and for American single stage to orbit (SSTO) technology contracts. In March 1994, NASA's *Access to space* study cited the RD-714 as the reference point for all future single-stage-to-orbit propulsion systems.

The American Aerojet company signed a contract with the Samara Progress NPO to market the NK-33 engines used on the N-1 Moon rocket. Samara made a total of 450 NK-33s in the 1960s. Although instructions had been issued for all N-1 equipment to be destroyed, Samara kept 90 complete units which Aerojet bought for $4m each in 1995 to enter as its candidate for the engine in the competition for the US Air Force's new Evolved Expendable Launch Vehicle. Aerojet's evaluation of the engine found that it could deliver 10% more performance than any other American engine, and enthused over its simplicity, lightness and low production costs. In August 1995, the NK-33 arrived in Sacramento, California, for testing by Aerojet. In the same competition were their ancient rivals Energomash, who had entered a smaller and modified version of the RD-170 called the RD-180. Also in autumn 1995, Pratt & Whitney received the engine of the second stage of the Zenith, the RD-120, for testing at its West Palm beach site.

Aerojet also teamed up with Lyulka, jet engine manufacturers and makers of the jet engines for Buran, to test out the liquid oxygen–hydrogen D-57, originally made in the 1960s as a 4th stage of the N-1, similar to the NK-31 actually adopted. Four models survived the 1974 cancellation (105 had been built) and by then the D-57 had accumulated 53 000 s of tests. Aerojet regarded the D-57 as the ideal candidate for the single-stage-to-orbit rocket, viewing with particular favour the ability of the D-57 to throttle back to 10%, which was perfect for the final landing manoeuvre.[59]

Ukraine has followed a similar path to Russia. The Ukrainian National Space Agency has attempted to develop a separate identity and role for the space facilities based in the State. Relationships between Ukraine and the Russian space industry remained relatively smooth, compared to the long tussle between Russia and Kazakhstan over Baikonour. By autumn 1995, Russia and Ukraine were on the verge of signing a bilateral agreement to regulate their relationship. A series of agreements between Ukraine, on the one hand, and Russia and the United States, on the other, tied in those elements of the International Space Station which are built in Ukraine. In November 1994, Presidents Leonid Kuchma and Bill Clinton signed a space, trade and *konvērsiya* agreement permitting direct cooperation between NASA and the Ukrainian National Space Agency, though it did not yet permit Ukraine to market its Zenith, Tsyklon and Cosmos rockets competitively on the world market. An early item on the working agenda between the two was the flight of a Ukrainian cosmonaut on the space shuttle, set for 1997, with welding equipment devised in the Boris Paton Institute.[60]

These partnerships have not necessarily met with total approval in Russia. They have drawn criticism that they will lead to a brain and patent drain to the United States, and that the once-great Russian rocket industry will lose its ingenuity and ability to innovate. Some Russian engineers are taking this in their stride, one in Samara being recently overheard saying that they had coped with two revolutions already this century (1917 and 1991) and 'we're still here'.

Some Russian–western collaborative partnerships

Western company	Russian company	Area of collaboration
Boeing (US)	Niichmash	Environmental support systems
CNES (France)	Russian Space Agency (RKA)	Manned spaceflight, materials processing
Dassault (France)	NPO Yuzhnoye	Rocket engines
Kayser-Threde (Ger)	TsSKB, Samara	Materials processing
Lockheed (US)	Khrunichev/Energiya	Proton rocket
		International Space Station
Loral (US)	Khrunichev/Energiya	Comsats
Matra (France)	Ukrainian Space Agency	Comsats
McDonnell Douglas (US)	Moscow Institute for Space Research (IKI)	
	NPO Lavochkin	Mars 96, Mars 98, robotics
	NPO Energomash	Rocket engines
Rockwell (US)	Energiya	Space shuttle docking system
	NPO Energomash	Rocket engines
Space Commerce (US)	Machinostroyeniye	Almaz Earth resources station
	Zvezda	Spacesuits
Space Systems (US)	Fakel OKB	Plasma thrusters
Spar, Ontario (Can)	NPO-PM	Comsats
Pratt & Whitney (US)	NPO Energomash	Engines
OHB Bremen (Germany)	{OKB Tupolev	Burlak air-launched rocket
STS System Technik (Ger)	{OKB Raduga	
DASA (Germany)	Khrunichev	Rokot small launcher

ASSESSMENT

By the mid-1990s, the Russian space programme had changed markedly compared to a decade earlier. Although it had contracted compared to Soviet years, privatization, commercialization and alliances with Western companies inspired hopes for a brighter future. Russia's advanced rocket engine technology, its ultramodern rockets like Zenith, and the reliable performance of older boosters like Proton should enable the Russian space programme to thrive and expand. As confidence began to return to the programme, Russia made plans for a range of new launchers, missions, launch complexes and modernized versions of old rockets. Cosmodromes were re-equipped and updated, and new launching centres were in the pipeline. Vladimir Barmin, the great builder of cosmodromes and the last of Korolev's colleagues from the 1940s, died in July 1993, but he would surely have approved.

5

The space fleet

From the rocket we can see the huge sphere of our planet. We can see how the sphere rotates and how within a few hours it shows all its sides successively. This picture is majestic, attractive and infinitely varied.

Konstantin Tsiolkovsky, 1911.

Most public interest in the Russian space programme has focused, unsurprisingly, on the prestigious manned missions, space stations, spaceplanes and robotic flights to the Moon and planets. However, Russia also sustains a comprehensive unmanned space programme for both civilian and military purposes. This chapter describes the nature of the unmanned space effort, most of which takes places within the Cosmos programme. It dissects the many categories and sub-sets of military Cosmos missions, from photoreconnaissance to single-orbit bombs. It examines declassified parts of the Cosmos programme, now flying as civilian missions. It describes the range of space applications, such as communications and weather satellites. The principal scientific programmes are outlined. The chapter concludes with examination of multilateral cooperation programmes.

UNMANNED SPACE PROGRAMME

From 1962, the Soviet Union operated a large programme of unmanned Earth orbiting spacecraft. With a few exceptions, these spacecraft were given the 'Cosmos' designation. When Cosmos 1 went up on 16 March 1962, it was announced as a new series of satellites for the scientific exploration of outer space. 100 had flown by December 1965. The 1000 mark was passed in 1978, by which time a Cosmos launch was a weekly event. The 1500 mark came in 1983 and the 2000 mark in February 1989. Taken at face value, the programme would have represented a fanatical concern for science. Of course it did not and the Cosmos programme was essentially military, though the title 'Cosmos' was used for scientific satellites, stranded Moonshots, abandoned space stations, experimental modules, manned spaceflight tests, and as a flag of convenience for missions that failed. Although Cosmos 1 and many of its successors were genuinely scientific missions, they were a minority. 'Cosmos' designation was to become the most overused classification in the history of classifications.[61] Not until *glasnost* and the need to market non-military un-manned spacecraft commercially did much information become available about the extensive range of applications of the Cosmos programme. The Soviet space programme, like the American, had always had a substantial military element. Of Russia's 51 launches in 1994, 27 (60%) were military.

UNMANNED SOVIET SPACE PROGRAMMES

Military

Purpose, acronym	Name and subtitles used	Dates
Photoreconnaissance	Cosmos (Zenith, Yantar, Cometa)	1962–
Hunter-killers	Cosmos	1968–82
Single orbit bomb	Cosmos	1967–71
Radar ocean reconnaissance	Cosmos	1967–88
Ocean reconnaissance	Cosmos	1974–
Electronic intelligence	Cosmos	1967–
Communications	Cosmos (Potok)	1964–
Navigation	Cosmos (Parus, Tsikada, GLONASS)	1967–
Military early warning	Cosmos (OKO, Prognoz)	1972–

Civilian

Purpose, acronym	Name and subtitles used	Dates
Navigation	Nadezhda	1989–
Biosatellites	Cosmos (Bion)	1965–92
Meteorology	Cosmos, Meteor, Elektro	1964–
Earth observation	Cosmos, Meteor-Priroda, Resurs F, Resurs O, Okean O, Resurs T, Almaz	1977–
Materials-processing	Cosmos, Foton	1985–
Communications	Cosmos, Molniya, Raduga, Gorizont, Ekran, Ekran, Gals, Express, Informator	1965–
Geodesy	Cosmos, Geo-1K, Etalan	1968–
Space science	Elektron, Proton, Prognoz, Interball	1964–95
Astronomy, astrophysics	Astron, Granat, Gamma, Koronas	1983–94
Microsatellites	Iskra, Radio, Pion	1981–
International (multilateral)	Intercosmos	1969–91

SPIES IN THE SKY

Mission control at Cape Canaveral simply could not believe it. Trains? Aircraft? But that's what the man said. Was he still sane?

But he insisted. Mission control was listening as astronaut Gordon Cooper reported back on the phenomenal sights from orbit. As he flew his 22 orbits around the Earth, he claimed to see the tracks of boats in the Gulf of Mexico, a plane flying toward land on the east coast and a steam train in northern India. Then to cap it all, he saw cars on a highway in Texas. No one really believed him. Astronaut doctors did recall that Cooper's eyesight was unusually good. But it was not until Cooper flew aloft with Charles Conrad in 1965 who confirmed his findings that the truth sunk in: the atmosphere was no obstacle, and in fact was a help, to observations from space. It seemed to have some kind of magnifying effect that was not visible to high-flying aircraft. The military had known this all along, but a civilian appreciation of the benefits of spotting objects from space was not well appreciated till the flight of Gordon Cooper.

Spy satellites have been the largest single element of the Soviet space programme, accounting for about a third of all launches.[62] The Soviet use of spy satellites dates to 1957, when Korolev was ordered to develop a space reconnaissance programme. The 2.3 m diameter spherical satellite that he designed, called Zenith, two years later became the basis of the Vostok manned spaceship. In 1962, the USSR introduced its first military photoreconnaissance satellite, the Zenith programme. The first attempt to orbit Zenith was 11 November 1961, and the first partly successful one was Cosmos 4 on April 1962. There were serious difficulties with its camera system and Cosmos 7 was the first fully successful mission. Three days later it was recovered. Zenith was transferred from OKB-1 to the Kozlov OKB in 1964. Of the first 20 Cosmos missions, ten were Zenith missions. Zenith carried four cameras. The swath was 180 km. The cameras could be turned for either downward looking or oblique views of the Earth's surface. The aim of each mission was to cover an area equivalent to the United States, 10 million square metres. Each camera could take up to 1500 frames. This, the first series of photoreconnaissance satellites, operated from 1962 to 1967. Cosmos 153 in 1967 was the last. On average the payload flew for eight days, and all but one flight was in summertime. In mid-1964 the 65 deg orbit was replaced by one of 51.2 deg; in 1966 the missions also flew out of Plesetsk at 64.6 deg.

The second generation of photoreconnaissance satellites, a further development of Zenith, was introduced in 1963 (Cosmos 22) and ran to 1978 (Cosmos 1004). It was heavier, taking advantage of the uprated R-7 booster used in the Voskhod and later Soyuz series. The second generation flew out of Baikonour at 51.8 deg and Plesetsk at 65.4 deg and 72.9 deg. The second-generation type came in three versions: a low-resolution mode; a high-resolution one (also recoverable after eight days); and an extended-duration model which stayed aloft 12 days. The last-mentioned could carry a stubby cylinder attached to the front. It was a standard small scientific payload which was normally left behind in orbit when the military film canisters returned.

The third generation, also based on Zenith, was introduced in October 1968. This model was still operating in the nineties (Cosmos 2281, 7 June 1994). The first one, Cosmos 251, was called a Morse code satellite—for some reason it transmitted its data in morse code. Not that it did not require decoding—it did—but the use of Morse was unexpected. The Morse code series ended in 1974. Of the rest of the third generation, there were five categories: low, medium, and high resolution, one-month missions and extended-duration flights. The low-resolution satellites operated at 212-245 km, skipping the outer edges of the Earth's atmosphere. They flew at 82.3 deg, and about two went up each year. Filming was in black-and-white, like the rest of the series. The first was Cosmos 470 and the last Cosmos 1597 in 1985. Medium-resolution satellites went into low orbit around

200–370 km and then manoeuvred up to 355–400 km. Orbits were 62.8 deg, 70.4 deg, 72.9 deg and occasionally 82 deg. The first was Cosmos 867 and the last was Cosmos 2006 in 1989. High resolution ones, starting with Cosmos 364, used low orbits at 62.8 deg, 82-83 deg and 72.9 deg (Plesetsk) and 70 deg and 70.4 deg (Baikonour). All came back after about two to three weeks and most used Plesetsk. In the 1990s, third-generation Zenith photoreconnaissance satellites principally flew at 62.8 deg and 82 deg from Plesetsk. They became the basis for the civilian Resurs F satellite.

The principal shortcoming of the third-generation reconnaissance satellite was that military ground controllers had to wait until the return to Earth in order to analyse film. This problem was partly solved by the fourth-generation series. They were sophisticated, skimming just over the atmosphere; each week they used their motors to keep them just high enough to prevent their burning up. Small capsules are ejected for re-entry, up to two on each mission. Pictures may then be analysed when the satellite is still up there and the satellite ordered to concentrate on new areas. The main cabins are often reused, up to three times. The fourth generation of spy satellites appeared in September 1975, with Cosmos 758, and went operational in 1980. The fourth generation was based on the Soyuz cabin with solar panels. The length of missions gradually increased, from the 20 days of Cosmos 805 in 1976 to 59 days of Cosmos 1585 in 1984. Most missions last between 44 and 60 days, and have a low point of 170 km. Fourth-generation satellites are subdivided into global surveying missions (the Cometa series) and close-look analysis of specific targets (the Yantar series), or a mixture of the two. Global survey missions generally last 40 to 45 days at 64.9 deg or 70 deg, both from Baikonour, with a typical orbit of 200–280 km. Close-look satellites orbit between 170 and 350 km, manoeuvring up and down as targets require, using orbits of 62.8 deg and 67 deg from Plesetsk, and 65 deg and 70.4 deg from Baikonour. Close-look missions are especially in evidence at the time of tense military situations. In the autumn of 1990, several fourth-generation Cosmos performed close-look manoeuvres over the Persian Gulf to observe the buildup of military forces in the region. Fourth-generation photoreconnaissance satellites are still in operation. The most recent of the Yantar series are Cosmos 2274 (March 1994) and Cosmos 2311 (March 1995).

The fifth generation of photoreconnaissance satellites was introduced in December 1982 (Cosmos 1426). This generation returns all its information electronically, onboard devices scanning pictures and transmitting them back to Earth almost immediately. The first operational mission was Cosmos 1552 in 1984. The fifth generation is launched from Baikonour into circular orbits of 225 km at inclinations of 65 deg, with regular engine boosts to maintain this altitude. The series is thought to use the Soyuz service module, with a length of 7 m, a diameter of 2.3 m, but with a Vostok-style spherical cabin. They have long lifetimes, in the order of seven to nine months. Russia likes to have at least one in orbit at any given time, preferring to have two operating in conjunction. The most recent are Cosmos 2305, launched 29 December 1994 from Baikonour on a Soyuz into 70 deg, 89.89 min, 240 by 298 km. It replaced Cosmos 2267, recovered 28 December 1994, after operating at 70.4 deg. Cosmos 2267 in turn had operated in conjunction with Cosmos 2280, launched 28 April 1994 on a Soyuz V rocket.

A series of explosions in Earth orbit has led observers to conclude that fifth-generation satellites are deliberately destroyed at the end of their mission. Thus Cosmos 2031 (1989), Cosmos 2101 (1990), 2163 (1991), and 2225, 2262 and 2243 (1993) have all exploded at

200 km at the end of their missions. Russia may lack a means to recover them or for some other reason prefers to self-destruct them. Such deliberate destruction runs counter to growing international concerns about the problem of space debris. All previous Cosmos reconnaissance satellites have carried explosive devices, and these have been used when previous missions have run into difficulty, but this is the first example of explosive destruction being used as a norm.

In May 1994, Russian television reported that the Progress works in Samara had created a new large spaceship 'capable of spotting matchsticks from orbit', but that it was so secret that, even in conditions of *glasnost*, no further information could be revealed. What is considered to be the sixth-generation photoreconnaissance satellite appeared not long afterwards on 26 August 1994 with the launch of Cosmos 2290. It was orbited by Zenith from Baikonour, carrying a payload of up to 13 tonnes into an orbit of 212–293 km, 89.5 min, 64.8 deg, the first photoreconnaissance satellite to be orbited by Zenith. It used a series of engine firings to maintain its perigee at 200 km but several times raised its apogee, first to 350 km, then 450 km and finally 550 km. It de-orbited in April 1995 after 221 days.

HUNTER KILLERS

Of all the Soviet boosters, the R-36 Tsyklon had the most sinister purpose: over the years 1967–8 it introduced weapons of destruction to near-Earth space. These were SIS (Satellite Interception System), popularly called hunter-killers and FOBS (Fractional Orbital Bombardment System), or the single-orbit bomb.

At the height of the cold war, Khrushchev ordered the development of a system that could track, intercept and destroy American spy satellites or, worse, satellites carrying weapons or bombs. Tests of orbital manoeuvring systems took place in November 1963 and April 1964, and were given the title Polyot, the Russian word for flight. At the time, the Polyots were thought to be connected to the manned space programme, but it later transpired that they were connected to anti-satellite weapon tests by Vladimir Chelomei's OKB-52. In 1965, these tests were made the responsibility of the Yangel bureau, then developing the R-36 rocket. It was soon put to the test.

On 19 October 1968, Cosmos 248 rose from Baikonour and entered orbit of 475 by 543 km, 62.2 deg. Nothing unusual, until a second flight left Baikonour the next day, Cosmos 249. It manoeuvred rapidly and then shot past 248 on a rapid intercept trajectory. It manoeuvred further, headed up into a high orbit of 493 by 2157 km, and then blew apart into hundreds of fragments. Cosmos 252 then did exactly the same thing on 1 November.

To observers, two things were clear. First, that a new and versatile rocket was in operation; and second, that the USSR had developed a means of knocking unfriendly satellites out of orbit. With a fleet of these rockets, all America's satellites—be they spying or on more innocent errands—could be knocked out within two or three hours. In the event of a nuclear confrontation, America's eyes and ears would be put out of action.

It was a system the USSR perfected quickly and in 1970 it was put through its second full test. Cosmos 373 was the target of a fast interception by Cosmos 374, and a week later, 375. Clearly, the system worked. Once the basic interceptor system had been tested, the USSR moved on to fly it in more demanding combinations. Three tests were carried out in 1971. Cosmos 397, launched from Baikonour, intercepted 394, which had been launched from Plesetsk. Cosmos 397's interception path was a slow one—suggesting the possibility of 'sleeper' interceptors whose hostile intentions might not be immediately apparent. By contrast, Cosmos 404 was a fast intercept, but instead of exploding and showering its target with debris, it re-entered the atmosphere, demonstrating the possibility of photographic inspection followed by recovery.

In 1976 the interceptor tests were suddenly resumed with manoeuvres of new complexity. The target was Cosmos 803 (Plesetsk, 12 February). On the 16th, 804 made a slow intercept and then returned to Earth after close scrutiny and inspection of the target. On 13 April, 814 intercepted 803, closed in for investigation, and returned to Earth—all within one orbit. In December, 886 closed in on 880, and exploded. 21 tests had been made by 1983. Typical was Cosmos 1375 (6 June 1982) which flew into the standard target orbit (65.8 deg, 979–1012 km, 105 min). Twelve days later, 1379 went up from Baikonour at 11.08 a.m. Its first orbit was 65.1 deg, 91.4 min, 140 by 542 km. Using its powerful third stage, it manoeuvred rapidly to an orbit of 537 by 1019 km. By repeatedly burning its boosters, guided by ultrarapid computers, separate manoeuvres were made as little as four minutes apart. At 2.30 p.m., 1379 made a fast intercept of its target at 400 m/s. At 2.50 p.m. it re-entered over the Pacific Ocean. Flight time was 3 h 42 min. No further tests were made after 1982.

SINGLE-ORBIT BOMB

The FOBS system was in the long run less important than the interception system. 15 tests were carried out over 1967–71 and it may have become obsolete not long afterwards. But they highlighted the militarization of space generated by the Cold War. Again, the R-36 Tsyklon was used.

Suspicion that something new was afoot began in 1966 with the launch of two unannounced Cosmos flights—now called the U1 and U2. Then came the orbiting of Cosmos 139 in 1967, orbiting at 135–215km, 49.6 deg. The odd thing about 139 was that it made just less than one orbit—although there was no sign that anything had gone wrong.

American defence experts soon grasped what was going on. Their defence strategy was based on a Soviet missile attack over the North Pole, with the missiles coming from Siberia. Hence the radar warning lines stretching across Alaska and Canada. FOBS undid all that. Cosmos 139 orbited directly south, over the southern hemisphere, came round from behind, approaching America from the Gulf of Mexico. It was also a 'fractional' bombardment system—meaning that the warhead split into several parts. It had the Pentagon worried: even one Cosmos, coming in from the 'wrong' direction, could do untold damage.

The last test was on 9 August 1971. For several years, FOBS gave the USSR the edge in the nuclear weapons stakes. With the Strategic Arms Limitation Talks the following year, the Baikonour FOBS pads were abandoned. At best the system had been barely legal, for the 1963 Test Ban Treaty had forbidden the flying of weapons into space. The Russians argued that FOBS was not 'in space' or 'orbiting' since it did not quite complete a full orbit.

NUCLEAR SPIES

Northern Canada. January 1978. Ice and snow covered the endless wilderness. One silent starry evening the few Eskimos and Canadians who lived there looked up and saw a fireball plunging to the northeast. It burned in an arc and disappeared, breaking up in red-hot fragments high in the upper atmosphere. Twenty minutes later, the metallic remains of the fireball crashed into the ice and snow near the small settlement of Yellowknife.

The Canadians who saw the fireball probably knew by this stage that they were being visited by something different from the normal run of astronomical objects like aurora borealis or a meteor. It was a satellite: and not just any satellite, but one that had gone out of control; and not just any satellite out of control, but a nuclear satellite out of control. The Canadian government, with United States help, lost no time in trying to locate the wayward satellite, now identified as Cosmos 954, origin USSR. 'Operation Morninglight' was mounted. It was an eerie title. They cynic would say that they were more interested in finding and analysing Soviet space debris than making the area safe for the few people who lived there. The Americans may well have called the shots anyway because Canadian search gear could be charitably described as primitive: they had nothing better than hand-held geiger counters.

Hercules aircraft fanned out in grid patterns across the desolate landscape. Occasionally they passed settlements with names like Snowdrift, Great Salt Lake or Fort Reliance. It could not have been colder as the temperature was −40°C. And as their luck would have it, the area was full of underground minerals and ores, including uranium, which gave false readings which confused the instruments. It was four days before anything was found. Some resident meteorologists—not the search teams at all—came across a patch of melting snow. Parts of Cosmos 954 had crashed there, melted through the ice and sunk below it.

The search was abandoned in March 1978. Only 10% of the reactor was found, and a total of 50 kg of debris. Even fewer bits were exhibited to the public and no one, not least the Canadians, knows what happened to the rest, though it is suspected that it was analysed and buried later in the United States. Eskimos living in the area were told not to eat hunted animals for fear of nuclear poisoning. So ended 'Morninglight'. There were two sequels. One was a prolonged legal wrangle between Canada and the USSR, the former billing the latter $12m to clear up the mess. The second was a less dangerous repeat of the incident by another Cosmos five years later. But what was Cosmos 954 up to in the first place? And why the nuclear intrigue?

The story goes back to the mid-1960s, when Khrushchev demanded a means of following American nuclear submarines, aircraft carriers and other naval vessels at sea. The ever-alert Vladimir Chelomei offered a means of dealing with this threat by spy satellites equipped with powerful radar. Construction was carried out by a section of his bureau, Krasnaya Zvezda ('red star' in Russian; it later became independent). The difficulty was that these radars gulped electrical power.

They required so much energy as to be well beyond the range of existing solar panels and solar cells. The only alternative was to use nuclear power. As of 1964, the most advanced Soviet reactor was 'Ramoshka', exhibited that year at a show in Geneva. The

Soviet nuclear space programme went back to 1962, when it was authorized by Khrushchev. The Kurchatov Institute produced the 'Ramoshka' reactor, a 508 kg reactor using 49 kg of 90% enriched U235 and capable of generating 500 to 800 w with a graphite moderator. It was tested in space on Cosmos 300 and Cosmos 305. 'Ramoshka' had a core temperature of 2173 K, and with no coolant system it acted as a long-life and highly efficient battery. It was small but had two disadvantages: it did not produce enough power and at 500 kg it was very heavy.

So when Chelomei's programme of ocean surveillance was approved in the years 1964–5, orders went out to produce a new reactor. It emerged in due course as 'Topaz' and worked on the same principle of converting heat to electricity, except that in this case the conversion was carried out by conductors and diodes. 'Topaz' was infinitely more sophisticated than 'Ramoshka'. Weighing only 105 kg, it had 50 kg fuel (93% enriched uranium 235) and a boron moderator; it produced 5 to 10 kW; and had a design lifetime of 300 days. It had no moving parts. But 'Topaz' had its drawbacks. It was liable to meltdown; and the only way radiation protection could be provided was to surround the reactor with heavy metallic shielding, thus increasing the payload weight. Finally, the reactor had to be brought to power before launch, which meant that for safety's sake, the launching always took place from a silo. Evidence of pre-launch power-up came when a launching failed some minutes into flight on 25 April 1973: zeon traces were found in the crash path.

The R-36 booster, true to its general military usage, was employed for this series of satellites which in time became known as RORSAT, from Radar Ocean Reconnaissance SATellite. The RORSAT itself was a large satellite, weighing four tonnes, 10 m long, 1.3 m in diameter, its main element being a giant side-looking radar, the others being the instrument module, the 390 kg reactor and the small kick motor to boost it to high orbit. The first flight was Cosmos 198, late in 1967, after the R-36 had been tested out in FOBS tests. Cosmos 954, ten years later, was the 16th such mission.

RORSATs had remarkably consistent characteristics. All used Baikonour, all entered orbits of 250 by 265 km (±2 km) at 65 deg. The mission profile was a trade-off between the need to be close to Earth to identify targets, but high enough to ensure that atmospheric drag would not end the mission in too short a period. At the end of the operational phase, the reactor was separated from the instrument compartment and its huge radar, to be boosted out of harm's way into an orbit of 900 km which should last nearly 600 years. One flight was made each year until 1974, when RORSAT went operational. With the launch of Cosmos 651 and then 654 two days later, the USSR began to operate a system of two-satellite reconnaissance. They were spaced in the same plane of orbit, normally 25 min apart.

Cosmos 954 was the first to suffer a public failure. What happened was simple, but lethal enough: the rocket failed to fire the reactor into high orbit. Surrounded by its heavy metallic casing, it simply decayed after a normal lifetime, crashed and spread debris over a wide area. Flights were then suspended for two years. After Cosmos 954, new safety procedures were developed; with Cosmos 1249 and 1266 in 1981 the system returned to operational status. A fresh controversy blew up over Cosmos 1402. When its turn came to rise to higher orbit on 28 December, 1982, once again the motor failed to fire. It was at this stage that safety procedures developed since the 954 incident came into play. The reactor separated from its casing, and without the heavy metallic casing the reactor did not make it to the ground but instead scattered its radioactivity around the upper atmosphere—not ideal, but preferable. Cosmos 1900, launched in October 1987, which later operated in conjunction with Cosmos 1932, got into difficulty when on 10 April 1988 it failed to eject into higher orbit. Finally, as it got closer and closer to Earth, on 30 September a trigger touched off a rocket motor which fired the nuclear core to a new, high orbit of 695 by 763 km. The main craft burned up over west Africa on the night of 3 October, when it dipped to 115 km altitude.

RORSAT programme

Number	Launch	Lifetime (days)
Cosmos 198	27 Dec 1967	1
Cosmos 209	22 Mar 1968	1
Cosmos 367	3 Oct 1970	0
Cosmos 402	1 Apr 1971	0
Cosmos 469	25 Dec 1971	9
Cosmos 516	21 Aug 1972	32
Cosmos 626	27 Dec 1973	45
Cosmos 651	15 May 1974	71
Cosmos 654	30 Jul 1974	74
Cosmos 723	2 Apr 1975	43
Cosmos 724	7 Apr 1975	65
Cosmos 785	12 Dec 1975	0
Cosmos 860	17 Oct 1976	24
Cosmos 861	21 Oct 1976	60
Cosmos 952	16 Sep 1977	21
Cosmos 954	18 Sep 1977	43
Cosmos 1176	29 Apr 1980	134
Cosmos 1249	5 Mar 1981	105
Cosmos 1266	21 Apr 1981	8
Cosmos 1299	24 Aug 1981	12
Cosmos 1365	14 May 1982	135
Cosmos 1372	1 Jun 1982	70
Cosmos 1402	30 Aug 1982	120
Cosmos 1412	2 Oct 1982	9
Cosmos 1579	29 Jun 1984	90
Cosmos 1607	31 Oct 1984	93
Cosmos 1670	1 Aug 1985	83
Cosmos 1677	23 Aug 1985	60
Cosmos 1736	21 Mar 1986	92
Cosmos 1771	20 Aug 1986	56
Cosmos 1818	1 Feb 1987	183
Cosmos 1860	18 Jun 1987	40
Cosmos 1867	10 Jul 1987	365
Cosmos 1900	12 Dec 1987	124
Cosmos 1932	14 Mar 1988	66

The RORSAT programme was terminated with Cosmos 1900, although Cosmos 1932, already in orbit when 1900's accident took place, was permitted to conclude its mission. Cosmos 1932 was the 35th launch in the series. The RORSATs cannot be said to have been a very successful programme. Despite a design life of 75 days before 1980 and 135 days after 1980, few RORSATS ever achieved that: Cosmos 1176 was the first to reach a full operational lifetime in 1980. Many failed after a few days, owing to poor electronics. The RORSATs never achieved year-round coverage of American naval movements.

NUCLEAR PROGRAMME

RORSATs were the only visible side of a considerable Soviet programme for the use of nuclear power in space.[63] An improved Topaz, 1000 kg in weight, also built by Krasnaya Zvezda, with 5–6k W (some quote 10 kW) of power, was launched on two experimental missions—Cosmos 1818 (February 1987) and Cosmos 1867 (July 1987) into 800 km orbit, providing electrical power for over a year. The new Topaz had multicell units, much like the way batteries are stored in torches. It seems the new Topaz was intended to provide the same power as the RORSATs, but for a year in high orbit, rather than 2–3 months in low orbit. It is doubtful if Russia has the resources to operate this programme now, or, since the end of the Cold War, has the same need.

Two other design bureaux have developed nuclear power reactors for use in space. The original nuclear laboratory, the Kurchatov Institute, developed a single-cell reactor with 6 kW output, called Enisy. Enisy uses single uranium crystal fuel elements which may be tested on the ground without the use of radioactive fuel. 28 Enisy units were built between 1970 and 1988, one reactor being successfully tested for 14 000 h in 1979. In 1992, the United States Ballistic Missile Defense Organization bought two Enisy reactors for $13m and shipped them to Albuquerque in the University of New Mexico for testing, and a further four Enisy reactors the following year. In effect, the Kurchatov Institute traded the secrets of the Enisy programme for cash to keep the institute open. The Americans, for their part, were anxious to examine this advanced technology. Their payments also had the intended effect of keeping Russian nuclear experts working in Moscow, rather than seeking employment abroad with hostile powers like Iran or Iraq.

A third nuclear space programme was also under development at NPO Energiya in the 1980s. This bureau developed a lithium-cooled 150 kW reactor, and although some ground tests were conducted, no full-up test was ever run. Officially, it was developed for a manned flight to Mars, but American intelligence linked it instead to a Soviet Star Wars programme for particle-beam weapons.

ELINTS AND FERRETS

RORSATs were only part of a rapidly developing programme of military surveillance by the superpowers. One key area was ferreting—locating the other side's military radio and radar stations. Ferrets listen in to enemy radio traffic and pick up conversations; from their information it is possible to guess enemy intentions and their equipment, or, as it is put in military parlance, the Electronic Order of Battle (EOB).

Most Soviet electronic intelligence satellites, called elints or ferrets, orbited at 400 to 850 km. Typical inclinations used were 74 deg, 65 deg and 81.2 deg. The USSR flew a combination of larger and smaller ferrets. The first generation of ferrets flew in 1967 (Cosmos 148), the first of 48 in the series. Later that year, with Cosmos 189, a second type was launched, the first of forty. The third generation began with Cosmos 895 in 1977, weighing four tonnes and operating in constellations of six. From the mid-1980s, elints have flown on the Zenith rocket, starting with Cosmos 1697 in 1985, which was the start of a new four-satellite constellation. The use of the Zenith rocket has enabled very large ferrets to be flown. Subsequent launches were Cosmos 1980 (1988), 2082 (1990), 2227 (1992), 2237 (1993) and 2278 (1994). The most recent is Cosmos 2297, which flew on a Zenith from Baikonour on 24 November 1994, into an orbit of 849-854 km, 101 min, 71 deg. Its weight is 9000 kg.

An important type of ferret is the EORSAT, the Elint Ocean Reconnaissance SATellite, which orbits from Baikonour at 65 deg, 400 to 445 km. These are ferrets devoted to ocean surveillance and were originally designed to complement the RORSATs. Their particular task was to track American aircraft carriers at sea. The standard EORSAT constellation comprises four to six spacecraft. They must operate in precise, unchanging orbits, so as to precisely triangulate the objects they are tracking: to do so, they use ion microthrusters which continually readjust their flight paths. The first was Cosmos 699 (December 1974). The programme developed in three phases: a testing phase, during 1974–9; an operational phase (1980–6); and a second operational phase from 1987 (Cosmos 1834). In the first two, the satellites were observed to self-destruct at the end of their missions. During the third phase, the end of orbit manoeuvre would de-orbit the spacecraft to natural destruction, but not explosively.

Normally two EORSATs operate together, one in conjunction with the other. In 1995, two EORSATs were operating, Cosmos 2264, launched in 1993 and Cosmos 2293, launched in 1994. Cosmos 2293 orbited at 404–417 km, 92.7 min, 65 deg out of Baikonour. At certain times, as many as five EORSATs have operated together, for example during the Gulf War in 1990–1. With the end of the RORSAT programme, the EORSAT became a priority military programme and Russia's prime source of naval electronic intelligence.

MILITARY COMMUNICATIONS

From the early 1960s, the Soviet Union defined a need to provide state-of-the art communications between its military commanders, its navy on the high seas and other far-flung outposts. Development of a military communications system began in the summer of 1964 (18 August) when the USSR announced that it had put three satellites into orbit on one rocket—Cosmos 38, 39 and 40. This mission was also the first flight of the R-14 Cosmos rocket. Why three?

As the R-14 entered orbit, a spring was fired, pushing each of the three satellites into the required orbit in turn. As a result, they became spaced out. A ground radio could use one, then another, then another satellite to communicate as each came over the horizon. Cosmos 38–40 were followed by two more 3-in-1s and three 5-in-1s. By the end of this series, the Russians had not only tested the viability of the spring-launching device but also the military communications system itself. Since then, the system evolved to constellations of 8-in-1 satellites (octets), 6-in-1 satellites (sextets) and single satellites operating as a group of three. The system was finally operational in 1970 as part of an 8-in-1 mission and the complete system involved three 8-in-1s, or 24 satellites all told. Cosmos 336–343 orbited at 74 deg, 1450 km altitude, from Plesetsk, an orbital slot followed faithfully since. The 8-in-1 satellites have a mass of about 60 kg each and fly at 800 km at 74 deg. The sextets weigh about 250 kg and orbit at 82.6 deg. The most recent military field communications set was the sextet launch of Cosmos 2299–2304 on 28 December 1994 on a Tsyklon from Plesetsk. Each satellite weighed 225 kg and went into an orbit of 1402–1416 km, 114 min, 82.5 deg.

Between them, they can provide constant global communications. The purpose of the system is to provide both real-time radio communications and a facility whereby messages can be relayed from abroad to one satellite for retransmission when passing over a control centre in Russia itself (this is called the store-dump technique). Store-dump was thought to be linked to the work of KGB agents in the field. Using tiny wrist transmitters an agent was supposed to be able to send a message up to a Cosmos travelling overhead. Once over a ground station some time later in the orbit, the vital intelligence was beamed down. Cosmos 2298, 20 December 1994, is the most recent example. The single satellites weigh about a tonne and fly at an altitude of around 800 km.

Cosmos satellites have also been located in geosynchronous orbit for military communications purposes. This is the Potok system of data relays. The Potok system started with Cosmos 637 (1974) and Cosmos 775 (1975), becoming operational with Cosmos 1366 in 1982. Several of these 2.5 tonne Cosmos have been launched, starting with Cosmos 1366, followed by Cosmos 1540 (1984) 1738 (1986), 1888 (1987), 1961 (1988), 2085 (1990), 2172 (1991) and 2155 (1991). The most recent example is Cosmos 2291, put into 24 h orbit on 21 September 1994 at 1.5 deg E.

NAVIGATION SATELLITES

The USSR began its first launches of navigation satellites in 1967. Working on a similar principle to the military communications satellites, constellations of communications satellites can provide extremely accurate coordination and reference points for ships at sea and aircraft in the air. Russia operates a low-altitude system (Nadezhda, Tsikada and Parus) and a high-altitude system (GLONASS). All launches within the low-altitude system used to take place within the Cosmos label. Subsequently, these were divided into three systems: civilian (*Nadezhda*, the Russian word for 'hope'); a semi-military system, *Tsikada* (Russian for 'chirping cricket'); and *Parus*, which still operates within the Cosmos label.

The Nadezhda system consists of a constellation of four satellites orbiting at 83 deg, 1000 km altitude. Nadezhda is a 810 kg civilian navigation satellite which carries a search-and-rescue satellite beacon system. Nadezhda 1 was launched on 4 July 1989 out of Plesetsk into a 979–1026 km orbit at 83 deg. The beacon is a transponder system which ships in distress may use to summon help: since 1982 it has saved 1700 lives and is widely used in the West as well.[64]

Civilian navigation satellites

Nadezhda 1	4 Jul 1989
Nadezhda 2	27 Feb 1990
Nadezhda 3	12 Mar 1991
Nadezhda 4	14 Jul 1994

The semi-military system was declassified on 24 January 1995 with the launch of 825 kg Tsikada 1 from Plesetsk on an R-14 Cosmos rocket. It went into a 965–1021 km, 104.97 min, 82.97 deg orbit and was co-planar with Cosmos 2123. The military system is used by the Soviet navy and merchant marine to provide coordinates as accurate as 80 m and consists of a constellation of six satellites operating at 83 deg at 1000 km. The wholly military Parus system is part of the Cosmos programme, the most recent example being Cosmos 2315, launched 5 July 1995 into a 988–1027 km, 83 deg orbit.

GLONASS

The Soviet Union introduced a single high-altitude navigation system, GLONASS, which parallels the American Global Positioning System (GPS). GLONASS operates in a constellation of 24 satellites (21 plus three spares) in 64.8 deg orbits with a period of 675 min. The present GLONASS military and civilian aircraft navigation system was inaugurated with Cosmos 1413–5 on 12 October 1982. By 1990, over 1200 ships had been equipped with GLONASS receivers so that they could accurately fix their position. A ship, or aircraft, must be able to receive such signals from three satellites, either simultaneously or in succession. The GLONASS system is launched in trios on Proton rockets. After several years of testing, the first fully operational GLONASS system was commenced in 1989 and completed on 7 March 1995 when a Proton put Cosmos 2307, 2308 and 2309 into space, entering orbits of 64.8 deg, 11h 15min, 19 132 km. A second-generation GLONASS system, called GLONASS-M, is planned for the second half of the 1990s.[65]

MILITARY EARLY WARNING SYSTEM

When Iraq launched its Scud missiles during the Gulf War of 1991, the only possible advance notice of an impending attack was a satellite picking out the hot gas plumes of the Scud as it left its mobile launch pad. Although the Gulf War was the first of its kind involving one of the superpowers, the use of infrared detectors to give early warning of impending missile attack was the focus of efforts by both the United States and the Soviet Union during the Cold War. The United States operated two systems—Midas, from 1960 to 1966; and the Defense Support Program (DSP) satellite series, from 1970.

The Soviet early warning system was introduced in 1972 (Cosmos 520) and became operational in 1976 (Cosmos 862), expanding into a nine-satellite constellation in 1980. Called OKO, it used a constellation of nine satellites in 12 h orbits, designed in such a way that at least two satellites were high over the continental United States land mass at any given time. The 1900 kg OKO satellites, built by the Lavochkin bureau, have a 350 kg, 0.5 m diameter, Earth-pointing infrared telescope, quick-deploy 4 m conical sunshield, topped by an instrument bus and solar panels which deliver 2.8 kW of power. The most recent OKO to join the constellation is Cosmos 2312 (May 1995). From 1976 to 1983, it was standard Soviet practice to destroy an OKO satellite at the end of its mission, though on some occasions the explosive charge went off prematurely.

One problem about the OKO system was that it did not cover the Pacific Ocean. To guard against American missile attacks from Pacific bases, geosynchronous satellites were placed in orbit high over the Pacific at 335°E, starting with Cosmos 775 (October 1975), followed by Cosmos 1546, 1629 and 1894, all of OKO design. In 1988, these were re-placed by a new design called Prognoz (not to be confused with the solar observatories of the same name), the first of which was Cosmos 1940, launched on 26 April 1988, and which functioned until 14 September that year. This ill-defined programme was initially linked to Earth resources surveys from geosynchronous orbit but it appears that this expla-nation was devised as a cover for the extension of the OKO programme. The subsequent Prognoz were Cosmos 2133, 2209, 2224 and Cosmos 2282 (7 July 1994) stationed at 335°E. The Russians propose to build up a system of seven active Prognoz. Prognoz is made by the Lavochkin NPO, weighs 3 tonnes and has a 600 kg Cassegrain optical assem-bly with aluminium-coated beryllium mirrors which scan the Earth's surface every 7 s and are so sensitive that they can pick out the afterburner of a jet fighter.[66]

MILITARY COSMOS: OTHER USES

Despite the best attempts of American and Western experts to categorize the Cosmos se-ries, there are always small numbers of Cosmos missions which defy analysis. In any case, the dividing line between 'military' and 'civilian' missions is never clinically clear (this is true of some aspects of American programmes as well). For example, Earth resources flights and navigation systems may collect information or provide facilities that may be of value to both parties. Likewise the GLONASS system is of equal value to military or civilian aircraft.

As if to emphasize the flexible boundary between the two, a distinct group of military Cosmos missions carried scientific payloads. From Cosmos 208 in 1968 onward, the Russians began to add small, drum-shaped scientific modules to the front of the Vos-tok/Zenith cabins of the third-generation photoreconnaissance spacecraft. These were called Nauka modules ('nauk' is the Russian word for science) and they carried both civil-ian and military scientific experiments. 64 Nauka modules were carried from 1968 to 1982, of which 24 were civilian. Such modules were later fitted to the Vostok cabins used in the biology programme. Nauka experiments focused on the detection of gamma rays, cosmic rays, X-rays, micrometeorites, and some tested electron beam generators and mag-netoplasmadynamic thrusters.[67]

Starting in 1986–9, many of the civilian parts of the Cosmos programme were declassi-fied and received separate designations: it also became standard practice that a new civil-ian series should receive its own name, rather than be designated within the Cosmos pro-gramme.[68]

CIVILIAN COSMOS PROGRAMME

Because of the heavy military emphasis of the Cosmos programme, it would be natural to conclude that applications and space science were given a very low priority in the overall Soviet space programme. This was not the case, for since 1962 there was a continuing scientific programme of observations, and since 1965 a programme to apply the benefits of space research to communications, meteorology and Earth observation. Most took place under the Cosmos programme, but long before the late 1980s declassification there were specific scientific programmes, such as Elektron, Proton, Prognoz, Intercosmos and Astron. Most concentrated on the environment of space and the never-ending particles and radiation that stream through it; others probed deeper still.

Scientific Cosmos satellite.

WATCHING THE EARTH

During the early days of the space race, the United States emphasized the success with which they applied space technology for the benefit of the consumer and the ordinary citizen. With good reason: America's first meteorological satellite, TIROS (short for Television and Infra Red Observation Satellite), flew in April 1960 and at once transmitted useable weather pictures. Within several years the United States had developed a system of Automatic Picture Transmission, APT, using store-and-dump techniques. From 1966 the Americans started to use weather satellites from 24 h orbit, from which position the entire Earth could be scanned at a glance and continuous observation provided. This became operational in 1974 with the Synchronous Meteorological Satellite, SMS 1.

Whether because of the Moon effort or for other reasons, a Soviet meteorological system was slow to develop. A number of experiments were made first—with Cosmos 44, 58, 100, 118, 122 and 144 over 1964–6. Cosmos 122 was the key model and featured a cylindrical body with TV cameras and two solar panels. The first operational launch was on 26 March 1969 and it was called Meteor 1. The first Meteor 1s had orbital periods of 97–98 min, the later ones 102.4 min.

The Meteor 1 series of meteorological satellite, introduced in 1969. The advanced Meteor 3 series was introduced 20 years later. Meteor is the basis of the Resurs O series of scanning Earth observation satellites.

A second-generation series began in 1975, called Meteor 2, the two generations overlapping each other. Meteor 2s orbited in 102.4 min orbits. By 1993 there had been 21 Meteor 2s, and the series appeared to be winding down.

Meteor 3 satellites were introduced and became operational in 1989. They also followed Polar orbits but had a higher altitude. Meteor 3 metsats are larger (2.15 tonnes, with 700 kg of instruments) and have small electric ion jets for attitude control, based on Glushko designs dating back to the 1920s. The 5 m high spacecraft comprises a hermetically sealed instrument container and two solar panels orientated to the Sun by an electromagnetic solar tracking drive providing 500 W power. Meteor 3s carry scanning telephotometers, infrared radiometers and spectrometers, a multichannel ultraviolet spectrometer and a radiation measurement device. Its scanning equipment is designed to observe the Earth by night as well as day. The most recent was Meteor 3—6 (January 1994) which also carried French and German experiments. Meteor 3–5 (August 1991) carried TOMS, an American device to study ozone depletion. Meteor 3s operate from Plesetsk at 82.6 deg at 1200 km.

Meteor transmits to over 50 ground stations in Russia, using Automatic Picture Transmission—which means that foreign stations can and do use its data. Information on water moisture in the atmosphere and temperature is transmitted daily down to Moscow and St Petersburg. The hydrological service, with its centres in Moscow, Novosibirsk and Kharbarovsk, needs its pictures so as to predict rainfall and snow runoff. Further information is passed on to planes, ships and agricultural institutes. Meteor spacecraft are built at the Research Institute for Electro-Mechanics, VNIIEM, directed by NK Sheremeyevsky. Generally, a constellation of three operates at any given time.

Starting in 1974, Meteor satellites began to take on an Earth resources monitoring role. Cameras were fitted with multispectral cameras, enabling photographs of the ground to be taken in infrared and other colours. Such missions received the subdesignation of Meteor-Priroda (*priroda* is the Russian word for 'nature'). A more advanced Meteor-Priroda appeared in 1980 with a 10-band scanner with a resolution of 30 m. Using the many colours, different categories of objects appeared in the different scans. Thus it was possible to detect healthy crops from diseased crops, identify oil and gas deposits, follow the progress of sowing and harvesting, identify soils, and so on.

Despite the fact that America experimented with a 24 h weather satellite as far back as 1966, a Soviet version was remarkably slow to appear. In 1975 the USSR announced that it would participate in the 1978-9 Global Weather Watch programme. Its contribution would be a 24 h weather satellite called GOMS. The project was repeatedly postponed owing to financial difficulties and software problems, even the final countdown being held up when the fuel suppliers demanded payment in cash. Eventually, Elektro 1 was launched on 31 October 1994, 16 years behind schedule, on a Proton from Baikonour. It reached its geosynchronous destination at 76°E several days later. Elektro was a large, 2.5 tonne, observation satellite, 6 m high with a diameter of 1.4 m and a solar wing span of 12 m, equipped with radiometric instruments operating in the visible and infrared bands. Elektro 1 was designed to work for three years, when it would be replaced by Elektro 2. Electro was designed to transmit images of Earth 48 times a day to Moscow, Tashkent, Kharbarovsk and local stations.

EARTH RESOURCES

The Russian Earth resources programme is called Resurs (resources), which now has a number of subprogrammes.[69] The terminology used requires some attention. The subprogrammes comprise recoverable cabins (the F1 and F2 series); non-recoverable cabins (the O and O-1 series); Resurs Okean (which observes the oceans) and its successor Okean O-1 and Okean B; and other subprogrammes such as Resurs T and Resurs R (the Almaz series).

Like many other series, its roots were buried in the Cosmos programme. 45 Resurs missions were flown under the Cosmos label, starting with the Cosmos–Priroda missions in 1977, dedicated Resurs missions running from 1979 (Cosmos 1127) to 1989 (Cosmos 1990). In addition, between 1975 (Cosmos 771) and 1989 (Cosmos 2029), 39 Cosmos satellites carried out remote sensing work in a related programme.

The recoverable Earth resources cabin is called Resurs F, which in turn is subdivided into F1 (short duration) and F2 (long duration). Even after declassification, Russian announcements rarely distinguish between F1 and F2 missions, thereby complicating identification of the category.

Resurs F1 is a recoverable Vostok-style cabin equipped with cameras for the study of the Earth's resources. Resurs F1-1 was launched on 25 May 1989 on the R-7 from Plesetsk. It manoeuvred to 254–273 km, 89.9 min a day later and was recovered in Kazakhstan on 17 June. The next Resurs satellites were flown later that year, on 27 June, 18 July, 15 August and 6 September, and others have followed this midsummer pattern. Although the last series of summer Resurs missions was flown in 1993, the programme is still operational.

Resurs F1 orbits at 250–400 km at either 62.8 deg or 82.6 deg. Each mission lasts 25 days and involves close-look photography. Resurs F1 carries two SA-34 topographic cameras which provide stereo pictures in three spectral bands; and two SA-20M long-focus wide-frame cameras which take up to 1800 frames. Pointing is done by use of a star sensor.

Resurs F2 missions last between three weeks and 45 days and use cabins weighing up to 6.3 tonnes. The F2 series concentrates on mapping from higher altitudes. The F1 and F2 spacecraft are similar in appearance, F2 carrying solar panels. Resurs is to be replaced by Kuban in 1996, which will have a 45-day service life. It carries an SA-M multizonal camera with a resolution of 5 m, aimed by a star sensor. Resurs F2 operates at 210–450 km at either 62.8 deg or 82.6 deg.

A special Resurs mission was flown in October 1992 to mark the 500th anniversary of Christopher Columbus' landfall on the islands off the North American coast. Called Resurs-500, it was launched from Plesetsk, Russia, on 15 November and splashed down off the coast of Seattle on 22 November, to be picked up by the US coastguard, conveying anniversary greetings from President Yeltsin to President Bush and a cutglass replica of the Statue of Liberty.

Whereas Resurs F capsules are returned to Earth, Resurs O scans photographs on board and transmits them to the ground in real time. The comparison echoes the way in which recoverable spy spacecraft gave way to more sophisticated onboard scanning reconnaissance missions. While Resurs F is based on the Vostok cabin, Resurs O is in effect a

Meteor satellite with an MSU-E high-resolution charge-coupled device (CCD) scanner, an MEU-SK multiband conical scanner, an RSL-BO side-looking radar and a UHF radiometer. Resurs O flies at 650 km. The Resurs O series, which is made by VNIIEM, divides into two parts: the 600 kg Resurs O, which operated within the Cosmos programme and was based on the Meteor metsat (first flown as Meteor 1-30 in 1980, operational as Cosmos 1484, 1689 and 1939); and the newer, declassified Resurs O-1.

Resurs F series

Resurs F1	25 May 1989	F1-1
Resurs F2	27 Jun 1989	F1-2
Resurs F3	18 Jul 1989	F1-3
Resurs F4	15 Aug 1989	F2-1
Resurs F5	6 Sep 1989	F1-4
Resurs F6	29 May 1990	F1-5
Resurs F7	17 Jul 1990	F2-2
Resurs F8	16 Aug 1990	F1-6
Resurs F9	7 Sep 1990	F1-7
Resurs F10	21 May 1991	F1-8
Resurs F11	28 Jun 1991	F2-3
Resurs F12	23 Jul 1991	F1-9
Resurs F13	21 Aug 1991	F2-4
Resurs F14	29 Apr 1992	F2-5
Resurs F15	19 Aug 1992	F1-10
Resurs F16	23 Jun 1992	F1-11
Resurs F17	21 May 1993	F2-6
Resurs F18	25 Jun 1993	F1-12
Resurs F19	24 Aug 1993	F1-13
Resurs F20	26 Sep 1995	F2-7

The first Resurs O-1, called Resurs O-1/1, was flown on 4 November 1994 on the Zenith from Baikonour. The 1900 kg satellite entered an orbit of 661–663 km, 97.9 min, 98 deg. Resurs O1 carries high-resolution optical sensors with a resolution of 15 m. Each mission is expected to last three years.

OKEAN—EYE ON THE WORLD'S OCEANS

The main sea observation programme is called Okean (ocean). The series was first tested by Cosmos 1500, 1602, 1766 and 1869. The system became operational with the launch of 550 kg Okean 1 on 5 July 1988, which was lofted by a Tsyklon rocket into an 82.5 deg orbit from Plesetsk. Okean carries a multizonal scanner, microwave scanner, radiometer, visual and infrared sensors, 1.5 km resolution side-looking radar and a device to receive and transmit information from buoys. The radar is able to measure the height of waves. Designed by the Ukrainian Institute for Radiophysics and Electrics, it has a swath of

450 km by 500 km. Images may be transmitted to up to 570 ground stations. Information on the state and nature of polar ice was transmitted to the State Centre for Remote Sensing and the headquarters of the fishing industry. Okean flies at 670 km. Okean and its predecessors have had an important role in tracking hurricanes, warning of floods in the Gulf of Finland and helping ice-breakers through Antarctica.

Okean sea observation satellite, introduced operationally in 1988.

The second Okean was launched in February 1990, the third in June 1991. A more advanced Okean 4, also called Okean O-1, was launched on 11 October 1994 from Baikonour on Tsyklon into a 632–666 km, 97.7 min, 82.5deg orbit. A Ukrainian version of Okean, called Sitch, was launched in August 1996. Other upgrades of the Okean, called called Okean B, are planned by the Yuzhnoye design bureau.

Other variants have been reclassified under the Resurs programme, such as the Resurs R, which is also the Almaz radar observatory, and Resurs T, which was introduced within the Cosmos programme in 1993 when Cosmos 2260 carried a new KFA-3000 camera with a resolution of 75 cm.

Okean series	
Okean 1	5 Jul 1988
Okean 2	28 Feb 1990
Okean 3	4 June 1991
Okean 4	11 Oct 1994

MATERIALS PROCESSING—FOTON

Soviet experiments with materials processing date to the Almaz and Salyut space stations in the 1970s. In the 1980s, the Vostok cabin was adapted as an unmanned, recoverable, materials processing laboratory called Foton (also written as Photon), which was able to fly 14–16 days at a time.

Foton precursors in the Cosmos programme were 1645, 1744 and 1841. Foton was formally introduced on 14 April 1988 as a programme for the manufacture of semiconductors and extrapure materials. Foton was built by the Kozlov design bureau in Samara. Foton weighs 6.2 tonnes and orbits at 62.8 deg at 220 km to 400 km from Plesetsk. Chemical batteries provide 400 W of power. The 2.3 m diameter cabin has a payload of 700 kg and a volume of 4.5 m^3. Standard equipment includes the Splav-02 furnace, the Zona furnace and the Kashtan electrophoresis unit. The purpose of the Foton mission is to enable experiments to be conducted in processed alloys and optical materials, and the testing of semiconductors. A feature of the series is that it uses already-flown capsules. Foton has been a modest earner for the Russian space programme, enabling Western companies and agencies to have access to zero gravity in a way not otherwise possible. There is no equivalent of the Foton programme in the United States or Europe (though there is in China).

The main Foton customers have been the French space agency, CNES, and the German company of Kayser-Threde, which has flown experimental packages from Foton 7 onward. Foton 2 (28 April 1989) carried a French crystal growth device and other experiments, and was recovered on 11 May. Foton 3 flew from Plesetsk on 11 April 1990 for a 16-day CNES mission. Foton 9, on 14 June 1994, carryed a French experiment, Gezon, to study the melting of materials and space, and a European biopan experiment to study the behaviour of amino acids in space.

	Foton series
Foton 1	14 Apr 1988
Foton 2	28 Apr 1989
Foton 3	11 Apr 1990
Foton 4	4 Oct 1991
Foton 8	8 Oct 1992
Foton 9	14 Jun 1994
Foton 10	15 Feb 1995

Note: Foton designations exhibit the most confusing aspects of the Cosmos declassification process. The earlier Foton missions within the Cosmos programme were announced in 1991 and backdated to Foton 5, 6 and 7, even though they had flown long before Foton 1.

Foton 10 was a joint ESA/CNES mission, which ended in disaster. Launched on a 15-day mission out of Plesetsk on 16 February 1995, the Foton carried semiconductors and a biobox with shrimps and urchin. The cabin returned to Earth perfectly on 3 March near Orenberg in the Urals, but when it was lifted out of the recovery area the next day, the helicopter flew into thick fog and dropped the payload from an altitude of several hundred metres. Most of the experiments were smashed. Two more Foton missions were listed for 1996—Foton 11 and 12. A successor for Foton, Nika, has been planned and should be able to carry a 1200 kg payload and fly for 120 days at a time.Three large solar panels will generate 6 kW of power. Nika is to fly out of Plesetsk on the Zenith rocket.

COMSATS

Molniya (*Molniya* the Russian word for 'lightning') was the USSR's first communication satellite, or comsat. Russia was a poor second into the comsat race after the United States and its comsat technology always tended to lag about five years or more behind the United States. American comsat development was determined by urgent commercial imperatives absent in the USSR.

Molniya is cone shaped. Its eyes, antennæ and shiny metallic shapes glisten. At the base are six vane-like panels spread out like a sunflower or a windmill about to turn. Each weighs about 816 kg. 4 m high, 1.4 m in diameter, Molniya provides telephone and TV links. Like other Russian comsats, Molniya is built by the Applied Mechanics NPO in Krasnoyarsk, now NPO-PM, directed by Mikhail Reshetnev.

The Molniya communications satellite, introduced in 1965 and still Russia's basic comsat in the 1990s.

Ironically it was General Eisenhower—the man who was not interested in space—who was the first to use a comsat. It was Christmas 1958 and the President had a tape-recorded message broadcast to the world from an orbiting Atlas Score booster. Come 1960 and NASA was experimenting with beaming signals off a huge orbiting balloon called Echo. The real breakthrough came in July 1962 when American Telephone and Telegraph paid for NASA to put up a commercial communications satellite called Telstar. It was the first fare-paying satellite. Within two weeks, AT&T had linked Telstar up with a set of ground-receiving stations in Maine, Britain and France, and set up the first live broadcast. In one blow, the cables that had linked the world for a century over land and under sea bed were redundant. People waited up all night for Telstar. Telstar came into position. The lines on the TV sets flickered, straightened out and the image of a man could be made out sitting at a desk. Soon a live conversation developed between the American and another man in Britain. The old world and the new were linked forever in a new way.

It was not long before the enormity of Telstar sank in—helped along a little by a pop record called 'Telstar', which stayed at the top of the pop charts for months. Telstar paved the way for an even more momentous development. In 1945, writing in *Wireless World*, science fiction writer Arthur C. Clarke put forward the concept that a satellite, in an orbit of 36 000 km, circling the Earth once every day (and thereby appearing to be stationary), could act as a transmitter in the sky for world radio broadcasting. In July 1964 NASA put up Syncom 3 into just such a 24 h orbit to act as a global television relay, first sending back TV of that summer's Olympic Games. Later that year, Intelsat was formed, a multi-national user corporation. Intelsat quickly showed its worth. Its first satellite, Early Bird, began operations in May 1965. It demonstrated its potential through an 80-minute world-wide *tour de force* in a opening global hook-up, with scenes from Hong Kong, India, America and everywhere else.

A Soviet comsat duly appeared on 23 April 1965 as Molniya 1. Molniya became the base of the Soviet comsat system. It used a system of orbits not hitherto used by any other type of satellite system—one explicable in terms of the geography of Siberia. In designing a comsat system, the 24 h orbit presents difficulties. A stable 24 h orbit can only be located on the equator, and a transmitter from equatorial orbit would simply not be strong enough to reach the far northern Arctic latitudes of Siberia for which comsat technology would be most useful. At the other extreme, a conventional orbiting satellite in a low orbit covering Siberia would present major tracking problems because it would be overhead only for periods of ten or fifteen minutes at a time.

Hence the compromise 12 h orbit stretching up to the 24 h altitude of 40 000 km, but with a perigee of 600 km. Apogee was nearly always over Siberia, so that it climbed slowly across that part of the sky over a period of eight hours, before whizzing around its perigee at a much faster velocity. Three satellites were needed for an operational system. A series of 12 m receiver dishes called Orbita were built throughout the USSR to pick up Molniya signals. Molniya 1s operate in a constellation of eight at a time, thus ensuring continuous coverage.

An improved version, Molniya 2, appeared in 1971. Heavier, at 1250 kg, it had greater capacity than Molniya 1 and was used internationally with Orbita ground stations in the East European socialist countries and with Ulan Bator in Mongolia and with Havana, Cuba. This development coincided with the establishment of a Soviet version of Intelsat, called Intersputnik. As well as the socialist countries, it included the then Soviet-leaning states of Vietnam, Laos, Afghanistan, Algeria, Syria and Yemen.

The Molniya 2 series was phased out in 1981, replaced by Molniya 3, which first appeared in 1974. Molniya 3 was able to use much smaller ground stations, and by the early 1970s terminals were as small as 7 m. Like Molniya 1, the 3 series operates in constellations of eight. At a general level, Molniya 1 concentrates on domestic, governmental and military communications links, and Molniya 3 the international and civilian. On 14 December 1995, the Molniya 1 series reached 88. 47 satellites in the Molniya 3 series had been flown.

DIRECT TO THE HOME

Despite the success of Syncom in 1964, and Early Bird the following year and a series of Intelsat communications satellites after that, the USSR was very slow to develop 24 h satellites. The first operational one did not appear until 1975, and three types emerged: standard TV and communications satellites, Gorizont (*gorizont*, the Russian word for 'horizon'), which were civil; Raduga (*Raduga*, the Russian word for 'Rainbow'), which were government and military; and direct broadcast, called Ekran (*ekran*, the Russian for 'screen') which was civilian.

The first 24 h satellite flew in 1974, and it was an experimental prototype (Cosmos 637). It was a once-off mission called Molniya 1-S and it went up on 30 July. The tests were evidently successful, for Raduga, Gorizont, and Ekran followed over the next two years.

Raduga 1's channels were used from the beginning to transmit facsimiles of newspapers from Moscow to Irkutsk in the central USSR, to Kharbarovsk in the Pacific. Thus *Pravda* was available in the far east within minutes of leaving the printer's works in Moscow. No picture of Raduga has been released, though it is thought to have a mass of around 1960 kg. In June 1989, a new version of Raduga was introduced, called Raduga 1, and the series has since been labelled 1-1, 1-2, and so on. Raduga 1-2 flew in December 1990, Raduga 1-3 flew in February 1994. The first generation of Raduga reached 32 in December 1994.

Gorizont looked like an automaton out of science fiction. Arrays of shutters, engines, tanks and instruments sat atop a cylinder base. On top of the structure was a huge dish, pointing earthwards. A typical Gorizont weighed 2.5 tonnes and carries 11 antennæ and eight transponders. The last Gorizont was Gorizont 26 in July 1992. Gorizont is to be phased out and replaced by Express, which made its first appearance on 13 October 1994 with the launch of Express 1 by Proton from Baikonour, heading for 24 h orbit. Weighing 2.5 tonnes, it was stationed on the Greenwich line at 0 deg E at an altitude of 35 800 km.

Ekran, introduced in October 1976, carried television only, and was one of the first national television systems designed to broadcast direct to the homes of isolated communities. The target area was a footprint covering Novosibirsk, Irkutsk and northwest Mongolia. All the people needed on the ground was a small dish rooftop aerial.

Ekran continued the tradition of putting more and more power on the satellite and less and less receiving power on the ground. Ekran had a broadcasting power of 200 W, compared to a mere 8 to 10 W on the Raduga. The service as a whole covered 40% of the USSR, or 9 million square kilometres, with Ekran hovering over Sumatra, Indonesia at 99 deg E longitude. Ekran weighed two tonnes and had a lifetime of over two years. This precision delivery to scattered communities was made possible by the unusual design of the Ekran: a cylinder pointing earthwards. On top were two solar panels stretching from a long beam. Underneath was a flat electrical board, and spread out on it, 200 pencil-shaped antennæ, pinging downwards.

An improved version, Ekran M, was introduced with Ekran 16, which was also termed Ekran M1. The last Ekran was Ekran 20 on 30 October 1992. Over 5000 Ekran-receiving stations are now in operation, and its transmissions are also picked up by Russian ships at sea. Ekran is due to be phased out by a new series called Gals. The first Gals direct broadcast satellite was lofted on 20 January 1994 by Proton from Baikonour. Weighing 2.5 tonnes, the satellite will transmit to 90 cm dishes. Gals is designed to have a much longer operating life—five to seven years. Gals 2 flew in November 1995.

By the mid-1990s the USSR had done much to restore the gap created by Telstar and Early Bird and Intelsat. An outstanding problem for the Russians has been that the operational life of their satellites has been much shorter than that of comparable American or European comsats. Short operational lifetimes have attracted considerable negative comment in the Russian press. The average life of Raduga was 50 months, Ekran 26 months and Gorizont 69 months. One Gorizont even operated for ten years (Gorizont 3). The purpose of Gals and Express is to radically upgrade the standard of service, capacity and lifetimes of the Ekran and Gorizont systems.[70]

Finally, Informator-1 was an experimental new communications satellite which appeared on 29 January 1991. Launched from Plesetsk, the 800 kg satellite entered 83.5 deg orbit and was designed to assist communications among rescue teams in the event of a natural disaster. Tests were conducted with the help of geologists working in remote locations in Siberia. It was designed by Alexander Klnyshkev of the Polyot OKB in Omsk. It also carried two amateur radio transponders.

GEODETIC PROGRAMME

The Soviet Union began to launch geodetic satellites in 1968, starting with Cosmos 203. Geodetic satellites are important primarily for the accurate mapping of the Earth's magnetic and gravity fields, but also for the targeting of weapons and earthquake prediction. The geodetic programme took place within the Cosmos series. There were six geodetic launches from 1968 to 1972, all into 74 deg orbits on the Cosmos rocket from Plesetsk. Typically, the satellites orbited at 1180–1,200 km, period 109 min, perfect for geodetic measurement. A new series of eleven geodetic satellites opened in 1972—similar missions but at 83 deg with the 74 deg flights taking a higher, 1350–1400 km altitude. The satellites are thought to be cylindrical with a long boom at one end.[71]

In 1981, the Tsyklon launcher was used to launch the second generation of geodetic satellites, the Geo-1K series, which orbited in higher, circular orbits of 1500 km at 73.6 deg or 82.6 deg. Satellites in this series were Cosmos 1510, 1660, 1732, 1823, 1950, 2037 and 2088 at 73.6 deg, and Cosmos 1312, 1410, 1589 and 1803 at 82.6 deg. An example of the former series was Cosmos 1950, orbited in 1988, which carried doppler transmitters, a flashlight system and laser reflectors. The lifetime of each satellite was designed to be over a year. Signals were transmitted 12 h a day and could be heard on 150 MHz and 400 MHz.

The first declassified satellite of this series was identified as Geo-1K, launched 29 November 1994 on Tsyklon from Plesetsk into an orbit of 1480–1527 km, 73.6 deg, 116 min. Geo-1K is a 900 kg cylinder 2 m in diameter, 2.1 m long, with a gravity-stabilizing boom and ten vanes of solar panels.

A third class, orbiting at 19 000 km, was introduced in 1989. Called Etalan, these were launched with GLONASS satellites en route to high orbits. The first examples were Cosmos 1989 and 2024, also named Etalan. The first was launched on 10 January 1989, riding piggyback on a Proton GLONASS launch. It was a passive 306 mm cube optical laser reflector, 1.3 m in diameter, weighing 1415 kg, which entered a 65 deg orbit at 19400 km. The purpose of Etalan was to enable scientists to draw accurate maps of the Earth's shape and gravitation fields, and to enable better prediction of satellite orbits. Its visibility is stellar magnitude +11.5. Etalan 2 followed, piggyback with another GLONASS, on 31 May 1989. The American satellite most similar to Etalan is LAGEOS.

Geodetic programme

First series

Cosmos 203	20 Feb 68
Cosmos 256	30 Nov 68
Cosmos 272	17 Mar 69
Cosmos 312	24 Nov 69
Cosmos 409	28 Apr 71
Cosmos 457	20 Nov 71
Cosmos 480	25 Mar 72
Cosmos 539	21 Dec 72
Cosmos 585	8 Sep 73
Cosmos 650	28 Apr 74
Cosmos 675	29 Aug 74
Cosmos 798	12 Feb 75
Cosmos 770	24 Sep 75
Cosmos 842	21 Jul 76
Cosmos 911	24 May 77
Cosmos 963	24 Nov 77
Cosmos 1067	26 Dec 78

Second series

Cosmos 1312	30 Sep 81
Cosmos 1410	24 Sep 82
Cosmos 1510	24 Nov 83
Cosmos 1589	8 Aug 84
Cosmos 1660	14 Jun 85
Cosmos 1732	11 Feb 86
Cosmos 1803	2 Dec 86
Cosmos 1823	20 Feb 87
Cosmos 1950	30 May 88
Cosmos 2037	28 Aug 89
Cosmos 2088	30 Jul 90
Geo-1K	29 Nov 94

Third series

Cosmos 1989/Etalan 1	10 Jan 89
Cosmos 2024/Etalan 2	31 May 89

BIOLOGY PROGRAMME BION

The Cosmos programme included an international biosatellite programme which dates to June 1962, with the bilateral agreement between NASA and the USSR Academy of Sciences for the compilation of a treatise called *Foundations of space biology and medicine.* Although this was never stated publicly at the time, it is likely that cooperation of space medicine was considered to be the area of space cooperation least likely to cause political problems or difficulties. Further arrangements were made for cooperation on joint missions under the Nixon–Kosygin agreement on space cooperation signed in Moscow in May 1972. National precursor biology missions were flown on Cosmos 92 and 94, which carried plants, seeds and aquatic plants in 1965. The first jointly planned mission was Cosmos 936 in 1975. Interestingly the series survived the freezing of cooperation in other fields which took place under the Carter administration in 1978–9. The programme provided the only opportunity for space scientists and biologists to have regular access to dedicated medium-duration orbital space biology missions during the Cold War period.

The series was called Bion, though this designation was only used formally at a later stage in the series. The objectives of the programme were to study the effects of weightlessness on living organisms on short flights, the effects of radiation on animals, to better understand the adaptation of living bodies to weightlessness and to study means of protecting animals from the effects of weightlessness. The prevention of space sickness, suffered by up to 50% of astronauts and cosmonauts during their first five days in orbit, was an important aim.

Ten Bion missions have flown. Although two more missions have been pencilled in, it is uncertain that they will be flown. The missions used a 2.3 m diameter Vostok-derived cabin with a hatbox battery pack located on the front. All Bion launches were into 62 deg or 83 deg orbits from Plesetsk on R-7 boosters. Some results of the later missions were published. Information and publicity concerning the earlier missions were limited. At a 1988 conference in the United States, it was learned that the animals lost muscle strength and suffered from a suppressed immune system, confirming evidence from manned flights that exercise was an essential element in combating zero gravity. The outcome of the rat experiments on the Cosmos 2044 (Bion 9) mission was that injuries to skin and muscles heal very slowly in zero gravity; heart degeneration decreased the natural release of hormones; cholesterol rose; there was decreased immune response; larvae hatched in space had a short lifespan; and flies were conceived in space but many did not hatch and others had short lifespans. These findings pointed to the evolution of life having a gravity-dependent stage, and that being sick in space or sustaining physical injuries were undesirable.

Cosmos 1887 went wrong from the start. Despite being selected from fifty candidate monkeys, Yerosha proved ill-suited to spaceflight. First, Yerosha's pulse reached a record 200 a minute during launch. Second, eight days into the mission, Yerosha broke free of his restraint, removed electrodes from his head and began tampering with the controls. Finally, though this could not be laid at Yerosha's door, the cabin was misaligned at re-entry and came down 3000 km northeast of the planned landing site. The temperature at the landing site was −15°C: local people kept the monkeys warm until rescue crews arrived.

Bion series

---

31 Oct 1973	Cosmos 605/Bion 1	221/424 km, 62.8 deg, 90.7 min. Landed 22 Nov. Tortoises, rats, insects, fruit flies. Beetles bred in 0 g. Fungus.
23 Oct 1974	Cosmos 690/Bion 2	223/389 km, 62.8 deg, 90.4 min.
21 Nov 1975	Cosmos 782/Bion 3	227/405 km, 62.8 deg, 90.5 min. Experiments from USSR, Czechoslovakia, USA. Commenced US participation. Centrifuge on board. Cancer cells. Fish eggs.
3 Aug 1977	Cosmos 936/Bion 4	219/396 km, 62.8 deg, 90.6 min. Experiments from USA, France, Czechoslovakia, Poland, Rumania, Bulgaria, GDR. Landed in Siberia after 19 days. Fruit flies, seeds. Main experiments with white rats, half in 0 G, half in centrifuge made in Bratislava. Calcium loss recorded.
25 Sep 1979	Cosmos 1129/Bion 5	218/377km, 62.8deg, 90.45mins. Soviet–American biology satellite with 38 white rats and 60 quail eggs. Carrot seeds and tumour studies. Rats and insects. Embryos of birds and mammals. First attempt to breed rats in space. Carrots with bacteria, tumours in plants. Landed in Kazakhstan after 14 days. Experiments from Bulgaria, Hungary, GDR, Poland, Rumania, France, Czechoslovakia.
14 Dec 1983	Cosmos 1514/Bion 6	214/259 km, 82.31 deg, 89.3 min. Two monkeys, Abrek and Bion. Fish and 18 rats. First time USSR flew monkeys (from Institute of Biomedical Problems of Ministry of Health). First mission at 82.3 deg orbit. Recovered after six days.
11 Jul 1985	Cosmos 1667/Bion 7	211/270 km, 82.36 deg, 89.3 min. Week-long mission by monkeys Verny and Gordy; white mice, tritons, fish, insects. Partners: France & United States.
29 Sep 1987	Cosmos 1887/Bion 8	216/383 km, 62.82 deg, 90 min. Two monkeys, Yerosha and Dryoma; insects; 10 rats, fish; recovery in Siberia after 13 days. Joint project with NASA and ESA. Plants, spleen and bone marrow cell tests.
15 Sep 1989	Cosmos 2044/Bion 9	206/264 km, 82.33 deg, 89.2 min. Two macaque monkeys, Zhakonya and Zabiyaka (backup monkey Zemlyanin); rats, tritons, fish, flies, beetles, ants, worms, stick insects. Twenty nations participating, including USA, France, UK, Canada, Denmark, Germany, Norway, Spain, ESA, Intercosmos. School experiments. Landed Kustanai, 29 September. 3 000 samples.
29 Dec 1992	Cosmos 2229/Bion 10	218/376 km, 62.81 deg, 90.45 min. Monkeys Krosh and Ivasha. Russia, United States, Canada, Czech Republic, Lithuania, Poland. Recovered 10 January.

FROM ELEKTRON TO ASTRON

Until the declassification of parts of the Cosmos programme from 1989, few missions flew under independent designations. Those which did concerned themselves with radiation and astronomical studies—Elektron, Proton, Prognoz and the observatories Astron, Granat and Gamma.

Elektron was a short series—there were only two launches. The idea was a double study: two satellites were launched simultaneously into widely differing orbits. Overlapping in their orbits, they relayed back real-time information as they passed through the radiation belts. Elektron 1—2 went up on 30 January 1964, and Elektron 3—4 on 11 July 1964. Between them they investigated and mapped the doughnut-shaped radiation belts surrounding Earth. They used irregular orbits: Elektron 1 406 by 71 026 km and Elektron 2 460 by 68 200 km. Between them—the first in the series being a cylinder with paddle wings and the second a cylinder glistening with solar cells—they returned a deluge of data on the radiation belts, and made it safer for cosmonauts to follow in their tracks. As a bonus, they found the presence of hydrogen and helium high in the atmosphere.

PROTON

The huge, gangly Proton series terminated after four launches over 1965–8. Proton was kettle-shaped with four paddle wings. The first weighed 12.2 tonnes and the last 17 tonnes. The prime purpose of the mission was to test Chelomei's new UR-500 Proton rocket, but these large scientific satellites were important in their own right. Proton 1 (July 1965) and 2 (November 1965) studied cosmic ray and gamma radiation. Proton 3 (July 1966) attempted to locate the smallest cosmic particles known to exist—quarks; and Proton 4 (November 1968) researched high-energy cosmic rays.

Proton series	
Proton 1	16 Jul 1965
Proton 2	2 Nov 1965
Proton 3	6 Jul 1966
Proton 4	16 Nov 1968

PROGNOZ

The Soviet Union was late to develop a specialized programme of solar observation satellites. The United States launched its Orbiting Solar Observatory Series from 1962 to 1971. Several early Cosmos satellites carried equipment to study the Sun: Cosmos 230 (1968) and Cosmos 481 and 484 (1972). There were several reasons for a series of solar observatories: the Sun, as a typical star, could be studied accurately from space, free of the interferences of Earth's atmosphere; second, the Sun's emissions and electrical disturbances interfered with Earth's physical environment, producing such effects as auroræ, which were poorly understood; and third, solar radiation was a potential threat to cosmonauts in low Earth orbit, and early warning of danger was desirable.

Prognoz weighed 850 kg, had a square base, a dome-shaped top from which an array of instruments emerged, and four stretched-out solar sails. The first flew in 1972, taking a highly eccentric orbit of 965 by 200 000 km, 65 deg, 97 h. A second launch took place in the same year, and there was one each in most of the following years. Its four-day slow curving orbit, taking it out in an ellipse nearly to the distance of the Moon, gave it a good vantage point for studying conditions on the Sun. The orbit, half way out to the Moon, was so chosen because at apogee it could intercept and analyse solar radiation before the processes of near-Earth space had interfered with it. Prognoz' main task was to monitor solar radiation, solar flares, and dangerous emissions that might disrupt Earth's weather and cause radio interference. Spacecraft designer was Ivan Savenko.

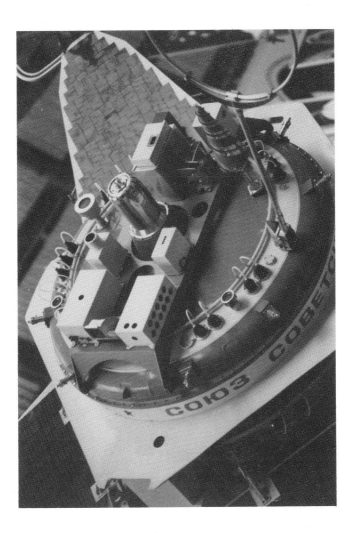

The instrument compartment of Prognoz.

In addition to its main target, the Sun, Prognoz carried instruments for observing gamma and X-ray radiation. Prognoz 2 carried French instruments to study neutrons. Instruments were later flown from the east European countries and Sweden. For example, Prognoz 7 carried a Swedish mass spectrometer, a French instrument to record gamma bursts, a Swedish electromagnetic analyser, and a Soviet magnetometer. Prognoz 1 and 2 operated in tandem, one being at apogee while the other was at perigee, and vice versa.

A second-generation Prognoz, Prognoz 9, weighing 1000 kg, was launched in July 1983, followed by Prognoz 10 in 1985. Prognoz 9 went into an extreme orbit of 380 by 720 000 km, 26.7 days, so extreme that it could almost be perturbed into solar orbit. The second generation carried a new suite of instruments. Prognoz 9 carried instruments to study gamma flashes, solar corpuscular and electromagnetic radiation and ions: one of its tasks, called Project Relikt, was to try to detect residual radiation from the formation of the universe, the big bang, for which it carried two antennæ and an amplifier to transmit the results. Prognoz 10 carried instruments to study the magnetosphere, cosmic rays and electric fields: a joint experiment with Czechoslovakia, called Intershock, was designed to study what happened when solar winds reached the electric environmental of the Earth. Following the second generation, a third model was planned, Prognoz M, later called Interball, to study the tail end of Earth's magnetosphere. After very long delays, the mission was finally launched from Plesetsk on 2 August 1995 into an orbit of 91 h 40 min, 193 000 by 797 km, 62.8 deg. 9.5 h after launch, the 50 kg Magion 4 Czech subsatellite separated to begin its independent programme of activities. Interball was made by the Lavochkin design bureau.[72]

Prognoz series

Prognoz 1	14 Apr 1972
Prognoz 2	29 Jun 1972
Prognoz 3	15 Feb 1973
Prognoz 4	22 Dec 1975
Prognoz 5	25 Nov 1976
Prognoz 6	22 Sep 1977
Prognoz 7	30 Oct 1978
Prognoz 8	25 Dec 1980
Prognoz 9	1 Jul 1983
Prognoz 10	26 Apr 1985
Interball 1	3 Aug 1995

ASTRONOMICAL AND ASTROPHYSICAL OBSERVATORIES: ASTRON, GRANAT, GAMMA AND KORONAS

Soviet astronomical missions took place several years after comparable launchings of American, British and European astronomical and astrophysical observatories. Referred to ambitiously as 'the world's first orbiting astronomical space station', Astron went up on 23 March 1983, on a Proton, into a highly eccentric orbit of 2000 by 200 000 km,

51.5 deg, 98 h. It was modelled on the Venera 9 and 10 Venus probes. Astron carried ultraviolet and X-ray telescopes—the ultraviolet one was built by the Crimean observatory and the Byurakan observatory in Armenia, with a French-built spectrometer. The Astron weighed 3.5 tonnes. Astron was an attempt to look deep into the universe: pulsars, quasars and the Crab nebula were listed as specific objectives. By midsummer 1983, Tass could report that it had obtained the spectra of distant galaxies. The Astron mission ended in late 1989, when its fuel supplies ran out. When it concluded, Astron had been given 10 000 commands and held 628 communication sessions.

The telescope of Astron, launched 1983.

Granat, also a Venera derivative, was a 4.4 tonne, 6.5 m tall, R46m astrophysical observatory launched by the Soviet Union on 30 November 1989 on a Proton booster from Baikonour. The aim of the mission was to study the sources of X-rays and gamma rays, neutron stars, black holes, traces of supernovæ, the centre of the universe and the interstellar medium. Equipment for the Granat mission was made in the USSR, Bulgaria, France and Denmark. Granat's four-day orbit took it as far out as 200 000 km where its X-ray telescopes would be undisturbed by Earth's magnetic field. The largest instrument on Granat was a one-tonne, 3.5 m long Sigma telescope built by the French space agency CNES. Four Soviet-made telescopes were aligned alongside, with an X-ray detector, gamma burst detector and gamma ray detector. The operational lifetime of the observatory was one-and-half years. The observatory was soon making measurements of radiation, supernovæ, neutron stars, the temperature of intergalactic gas and making X-ray images of galaxies in Perseus constellation. In 1991, ground controllers reported that they had found, in the centre of the galaxy, a zone of electron–positron annihilation, or, in ordinary language, a black hole.

Gamma was a high-energy astrophysics observatory launched on 11 July 1990 into a 400 km, 51 deg orbit from Baikonour. Gamma was 7.3 tonnes in weight, was based on the Progress cargo spacecraft design, and carried a gamma ray telescope, a low-energy telescope (Disk-M) and an X-ray telescope called Pulsar X-2. The craft was powered by two solar arrays 11.75 m wide. The programme had been long delayed—it had been conceived in 1972, originally set for launch in 1982, redefined as a small module for Mir and eventually launched independently and was a Soviet, French and Polish project. The observatory studied gamma-pulsars, high-energy sources, solar flares and was also turned earthward to examine this planet's radiation belts.

A new solar observatory was launched on 2 March 1994. Koronas 1 was sent up by Tsyklon from Plesetsk into an orbit of 501–541 km, 94.7 min, 82.5 deg and was given an operational lifetime of five to seven years. Although other countries participated, it was primarily a Russian–Ukrainian project. The aims of Koronas 1 were to study the Sun's internal structure (helioseismology), to investigate solar activity and to discover the reasons for periodic discharges and eruptions from the Sun. Equipment included a heliometer and X-ray telescope.

Astronomical and astrophysical missions

Astron	23 Mar 1983
Granat	30 Nov 1989
Gamma	11 Jul 1990
Koronas 1	2 Mar 1994

MICROSATELLITES: ISKRA, RADIO, PION

Like the United States and Europe, the Soviet Union and Russia have both made use of very small satellites, jettisoned from larger payloads or launched from orbiting stations. Iskra 2, a modest 28 kg, achieved space history when on 25 May 1982 it became the first spacecraft to be launched from a space station, Salyut 7. The two cosmonauts on board at the time simply pushed it through the airlock hatch. It was built by the students of the Moscow Aviation Institute and was a radio amateurs' target for use by radio societies in the USSR, Cuba and Laos. Iskra 3 was also pushed out of Salyut 7, in November 1982. It had been brought up there by the space freighter, Progress 16. Iskra 1 had been lofted on Meteor 1-31 in 1981 but had failed to deploy.

Iskra 2 followed a tradition of amateur radio satellites. Radio 3–8 were part of a 6-in-1 shot in December 1981 and followed from Radio 1 and 2, which hitched a lift with Cosmos 1045 on 27 October 1978. To judge how well equipment would work in the vacuum, one was hermetically sealed, the other not. They provided a relay station for the USSR's 26 000 amateur radio users.

Pion subsatellites are generally released at the end of Resurs F2 missions. Pion satellites have a diameter of only 70 cm: their only equipment is a transmitter, and they are designed to test ground tracking systems. Two Pion satellites were released from the

Resurs F1-1 spacecraft on 8 June 1989, both having been constructed by students of the Korolev Aviation Institute in Kyubyshev. Pions 3 and 4 were released from Resurs F1-3 on 7 August 1989; Pions 5 and 6 from Resurs F1-13 in August 1993. Generally, Pions orbit for about two months before decay.

INTERNATIONAL COOPERATION

Despite the closed nature of the Soviet space programme in its early years, a certain level of international cooperation developed. This developed in two forms: bilaterally, principally with France and the United States; and multilaterally, with the other socialist countries.

Bilateral cooperation with the United States found its most lasting expression in the Bion programme. France was the most regular partner in the bilateral programme. In January 1973 the USSR put up a French satellite, Aureole, which was purpose-built to study the strange phenomenon of the Polar lights and the way in which electrical fields could light up the northern summer skies. Aureole 2 followed in December 1974, and Aureole 3, a 1000 kg powerful atmospheric probe, in 1981. Two other French satellites were flown around the same time: Signe 3, a 102 kg satellite for X-rays and gamma rays, left Kapustin Yar in June 1977. Arcad-3 (September 1981) was much heavier at 1100 kg and spent six months studying the magnetosphere at high latitudes.

There has been bilateral cooperation with other countries, though it has been less extensive. India is one example. The USSR put an Indian satellite, Bhaskara, into orbit from Kapustin Yar in 1979. On 15 March 1988, the Soviet Union launched an Indian Earth Resources satellite, the 940 kg IRS-1A, for which India paid a nominal price of $2million. Fifty Indian scientists were invited to Baikonour to supervise the launch. IRS-1B was launched by the USSR on 29 August 1991, IRS-1C on 28 December 1995.

Multilateral cooperation was organized through the Intercosmos Council, brainchild of Boris Petrov, who in the mid-1960s put together a council comprising representatives of the USSR, the east European socialist countries and later, Cuba and Vietnam. Its purpose was twofold: to give Soviet allies a chance to participate in the Soviet space programme and to enable the USSR to benefit from the special scientific expertise developed in other countries. It was formally set up in the Academy of Sciences on 31 May 1966.

The first of the Intercosmos satellites sponsored by the council took off from Kapustin Yar on 14 October 1969 on an R-12, and it was the first of nine such missions. All were in the 300–400 kg class. Each of the small satellites had a specialized task. Intercosmos 1, 4, 7, 9, 11 and 16 were solar probes; Intercosmos 2, 8, 12, 22, and Bulgaria 1300 were ionospheric missions; Intercosmos 3, 5, 6, 10, 13, 14, 17 and 18 were magnetospheric; and 20 and 21 were Earth resources. One, Intercosmos 6, was supposed to return to Earth. Intercosmos 1 was built by scientists from Czechoslovakia and the German Democratic Republic, and different combinations of countries and scientists built different probes. Intercosmos 8—the last of this series out of Kapustin Yar on the R-12—was called Copernicus 500 in honour of the great Polish scientist's 500th anniversary in 1973, and was built in Poland.

From Intercosmos 9 on, the R-14 was used. From Intercosmos 15 on, a standard base spacecraft for station-keeping in orbit, orientation, power and transmission, called a 'bus' was introduced. It could thus be mass produced, and different instruments added on top as specialized equipment. Intercosmos 18 broke new ground by releasing a subsatellite, Magion 1. Built in Czechoslovakia, it was a mere 15 kg. It drifted away from its parent, to see how much atmospheric drag affected a satellite orbit. Intercosmos 20 (1 November 1979) used the R-36 Tsyklon for the first time. The satellite itself belonged to a new, long-life design, and it was the first Earth applications satellite in the series. Similar to Cosmos 1076 and 1151, it carried equipment designed to measure the exact temperature of the sea to within 1°C, which is important for fishing, forecasting, and ice warnings. Intercosmos 21, two years later, was similar. There was also a once-off Soviet–Bulgarian flight in August 1981. Called 'Intercosmos–Bulgaria 1300' (also Intercosmos 22) it used a Meteor design and carried 12 experiments built by the Bulgarian School of Space Research to investigate the Earth's magnetic field.

Intercosmos series

Intercosmos 1	14 Oct 1969
Intercosmos 2	25 Dec 1969
Intercosmos 3	7Aug 1970
Intercosmos 4	14 Oct 1970
Intercosmos 5	2 Dec 1971
Intercosmos 6	7 Apr 1972
Intercosmos 7	30 Jun 1972
Intercosmos 8	1 Dec 1972
Intercosmos 9	19 Apr 1973
Intercosmos 10	30 Oct 1973
Intercosmos 11	17 May 1974
Intercosmos 12	31 Oct 1974
Intercosmos 13	27 Mar 1975
Intercosmos 14	11 Dec 1975
Intercosmos 15	19 Jun 1976
Intercosmos 16	27 Jul 1976
Intercosmos 17	24 Sep 1977
Intercosmos 18	24 Oct 1978
Intercosmos 19	27 Feb 1979
Intercosmos 20	1 Nov 1979
Intercosmos 21	6 Feb 1981
Intercosmos 22	7 Aug 1981
Intercosmos 24	28 Sep 1989
Intercosmos 25	18 Dec 1991

Intercosmos 24 was also known as Aktivny, which was a small scientific satellite launched from Plesetsk by Tsyklon on 28 September 1989. Designer was Valentin Shevchenko. The purpose of the R4.8m Aktivny project was to study low-frequency radio waves in the Earth's magnetosphere and the Van Allen radiation belts. Its orbit measured 511–2479 km,

82.6 deg, 116 min. The equipment for Aktivny, which included a neutral gas injector and a plasma generator, was made in Hungary, Poland, Bulgaria, Romania, Czechoslovakia and the German Democratic Republic. Aktivny weighed 1000 kg and carried a 20 m unfurlable magnetic aerial and a 5 kW low-frequency 10 kHZ transmitter. A 50 kg Czechoslovak subsatellite, Magion 2, was released from Aktivny on 3 October, with the purpose of measuring plasma. Magion 2 carried an ion electric propulsion system for station-keeping with Aktivny at a distance of between 100 m and 100 km; however, this part of the mission is not thought to have been a success, and the two satellites drifted far apart. The mission cost R3million.

The last Intercosmos was Intercosmos 25 on 18 December 1991, which went into a 437 by 3073 km, 82.5 deg, 121 min orbit from Plesetsk and released a 52 kg, 52 cm Magion 3 subsatellite. Intercosmos 25 was also known as Active Plasma Experiment (APEX). The purpose of the mission was to study the effect of active electron and plasma beams on the Earth's ionosphere and atmosphere so as to better understand auroral phenomena and the Polar lights. Once released, Magion 3 deployed a 1.7 m aerial and kept station from distances of 10 m to 2000 km using a small pulsar engine.

After the fall of communism, Russia began to integrate itself more fully into the world's international organizations. In July 1994, Russia became the 41st member of the European telecommunications satellite organization, Eutelsat.

ASSESSMENT

In assessing the unmanned Soviet, now Russian space programme, one is first struck by its sheer size. The number of Cosmos missions alone passed the 2326 mark in the spring of 1996, and that before the range of hundreds of other unmanned missions is taken into account.

Second, the priorities of the Russian programme are broadly similar to the unmanned programme of the United States. Resources are allocated to military, applications and scientific programmes in that descending order. Soviet military programmes have, broadly speaking, matched those of the United States, in the fields of photoreconnaissance, electronic intelligence, navigation, military communications and early warning. The OKO and Prognoz programmes carry out missions comparable to American programmes, even if their methods differ slightly. This is not to suggest that the Soviet Union copied the United States: far from it, for superpowers have similar military needs which they meet in similar ways. In four programmes, the USSR developed capabilities which the Americans did not match—the hunter-killer programme, the FOBS system, the RORSATs and the orbiting nuclear reactors Ramoshka, Topaz and Enisy.

Despite the contraction of the space programme since the end of the Soviet Union, Russia has continued to maintain the pace of its military space programme. Military tasks have steadily transferred to the new Zenith launcher, evidence of purposeful moderniza-tion. The 'matchstick-finding' new series of Zenith-based, sixth-generation, large pho-toreconnaissance satellites was introduced in 1994. Electronic ocean reconnaissance satellites continue to be a priority.

Some Western analysts have criticized the large unmanned programme as uneconomic, wasteful, exhibiting poor performance, and producing low-quality results. For the most part, this is not justified, though some parts of it, like the RORSATs, must have disappointed. Economy is achieved by the adaptation of basic equipment to a wide range of diverse missions and tasks. The Zenith cabin was used not just as the basis for the Vostok and Voskhod manned spacecraft, but for the second and third generation of spy satellites, which were still flying in the 1990s. In the civilian sphere, the Zenith cabin was also adapted for the Resurs and Foton applications programmes. The Meteor cabin is the basis for Resurs O1 and so on. Considerable economies are achieved by such a mass production approach—moreover one where the development costs were essentially paid off in the 1950s.

Excellence is evident is several aspects of the programme. Although Soviet photoreconnaissance standards were long considered inferior, the release of Soviet photographs from orbit for commercial purposes under the Resurs programme forced Western military agencies to declassify their own photographs if they were to have any chance to compete. The hunter-killer programme exhibited very considerable military prowess. The Foton series provides access to zero gravity in a programme unmatched elsewhere at a reasonable price.

On the downside, the availability of mass production of application satellites and the lack of Western cost-accounting meant that the Soviet Union had no incentive to invest in extending the life of their applications satellites. Commercialization and cost-accounting have already begun to change that, for the new Gals and Express comsats, introduced in 1994, are specifically designed for much longer on-orbit lifetimes. This will undoubtedly set the trend for the rest of the applications programmes for the remainder of the decade.

6

Moon, Mars and Venus

One day we shall fly to Mars!

Friedrich Tsander (1887–1933)

While the centrepiece of the Soviet space programme during the 1970s was the establishment of Earth-orbiting space stations, the Soviet Union also conducted programmes for the exploration of the Moon, Mars and Venus. The Moon exploration programme was abandoned in 1976, and the programme for the exploration of Venus concluded in 1985. Soviet efforts to explore Mars were dogged by failure throughout. In the 1990s the Mars programme remained the only element of a once extensive programme of unmanned deep space exploration.

The difficulties experienced by the USSR in its deep space programme were so acute that it made no attempt to match America's missions to the distant parts of the solar system and beyond. From the early 1970s, a succession of American probes—Pioneer 10 and 11, Voyager 1 and 2—swept past Jupiter, Saturn, Uranus and even Neptune. The world held its breath as one astonishing series of colour images unfolded after another, revealing strange worlds never before imagined. Nor did the Russians match the American mission to nearby Mercury, Mariner 10, in 1973.

There were political and technical reasons. Politically, the need for an 'inexpensive, risk-free alternative' to Apollo receded once the Apollo programme itself was over. Poor outcomes from successive Mars missions convinced the political leadership that the level of results did not match the level of investment. With the Moon race over, impressive exploits in deep space were less necessary, symbolic or important.

These factors were not unique to the Soviet Union. In the United States, funding for deep space missions fell off sharply after the mid-1970s. Congress funded only three probes to Venus (two Pioneer Venus probes and Magellan), one Mars probe (Mars Observer), and one Jupiter probe (Galileo). NASA was not able to resume a systematic programme for the exploration of the planets until the mid-1990s. Even then, costs were cut rigorously under the rubric of 'smaller, faster, cheaper', and only a small suite of scientific instruments could be carried.

In the Russian case, technical factors were also important. Deep space missions required advanced electronic equipment able to navigate spacecraft long distances over extensive periods of time, ensuring that equipment worked precisely and faultlessly at its destination months or even years after leaving Earth. Of the small number of Soviet deep space probes which did successfully get away from Earth in the 1960s, communications broke down long before they reached their destination. It was no coincidence that the more successful probes were those which flew to Venus, where journey times are comparatively short. By contrast, the Americans were quicker to develop microcircuits, or chips as they came to be called, and these had the advantage of lightness, flexibility and sophistication. American computer technology and electronic performance became more and more advanced, driven by the rapid commercialization of computers and processors in the American economy, a factor absent in the Soviet Union.

IN THE SHADOW OF BLACK SEPTEMBER

When Luna 15 was smashed to pieces in the Sea of Crises in July 1969, Russia's plan to upstage Apollo by the first automatic recovery of lunar soil came unstuck. But the Soviet Union permitted the programme to continue, for two reasons: first, because the series could produce a credible automatic programme for the exploration of the Moon; and second, because the series was important if the Soviet man-on-the-Moon programme were completed after all. Such hopes still existed up to the summer of 1974.

Inside the third generation of the Luna programme (Lunas 15 to 24) were three separate models: the Moonscooper, the lunar rover and the orbiter. They all used common components and a similar structure. The base was 4 m wide, consisting of four spherical fuel tanks, four cylindrical fuel tank nozzles, thrusters and landing legs. Atop the structure rested either a sample-return capsule, a lunar rover or an instrument cabin for lunar orbit studies.

Both the lunar rover and the orbiter had their origins in the manned Moon programme. The lunar rover was designed first (it was called the Ye-8) and was intended to test the surface of the intended site for the first manned landing; later versions would carry cosmonauts across the Moon.[73] The lunar orbiter, called the Ye-8LS, was intended to provide detailed maps of intended landing sites. The first attempt to launch the lunar rover came on 19 February 1969, but the Proton launcher crashed 40 s into the mission.

New third-generation probes were ready to fly again just months after the disaster in the Sea of Crises. At this stage, the unreliability of the Proton reasserted itself, block D failures stranding the new Moonscooper Lunas in low Earth orbit on 23 September 1969 and 22 October 1969. A lunar orbiter to scout landing sites for future missions was sent up by Proton on 19 February 1970. It crashed into the Pacific Ocean. Success was to elude the planners and designers until 12 September 1970, when Luna 16 was launched. Like Luna 15 it headed out Moonwards on a slow four-day coast. Right up to the landing, its characteristics were identical to those of Luna 15.

Despite the great media interest which Luna 15 had attracted, Luna 16 went virtually unremarked by the Western media. This was a pity, for Luna 16 was a remarkable technical achievement by any standard. Its flight coincided with what became known to the world as Black September. Four airliners were seized in the space of a few hours by Palestinian fighters; the aircraft were hijacked to a remote airstrip called Dawson's Field in Jordan; King Hussein's army moved in to crush the Palestinians. The world looked on, mesmerized.

Luna 16 entered Moon orbit on 17 September at an altitude of 110 km, 71 deg, 1 h 59 min. Two days later it braked into an elliptical course of 106 by 15 km. Its final path was 15 by 9 km, identical to Luna 15's last erratic orbit and so low as to only barely scrape the peaks of the Moon's highest mountains.

A descent was inevitable. Early on the 20th as Luna 16 skimmed over the eastern highlands of the Moon, the retrorocket of the 1880 kg craft blasted and Luna 16 began to fall. The critical stage had begun. Luna 16 was now over flat lowlands. Sophisticated radar and electronic gear scanned the surface, searching for a suitable landing place. The engine thrust was carefully modulated to prevent the craft from either falling too fast or drifting to the side.

At 20 m the retrorocket cut off and small vernier engines came into play. The craft was aligned and the descent speed cut to zero. At 2 m, sensing the nearness of the surface, these too cut out. Luna 16 dropped silently to the airless surface, bouncing gently on its landing pad. It was down, safe and sound, on the Sea of Fertility, and the local lunar dawn had just broken. The surface was barren, flat and stony, and marked only by a few small craters. Within hours, the USSR had announced its third soft-landing on the Moon—but said no more. Ground observers picked up strong signals, suspecting something was afoot.

They were not wrong. A quarter of a million miles away a long drill arm swung out from Luna 16 like a dentist's drill on a support. It swung well clear of the base of the spacecraft, free from any area that might have been contaminated by gases of landing

The cabin in which Moon dust was brought back to Earth. The drill is on the right.

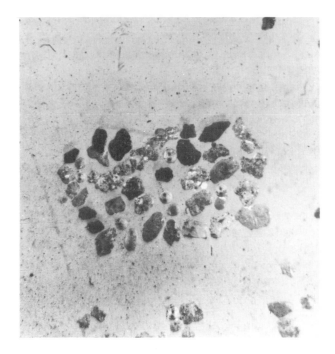

Grains of the 105 g of Moon rock brought back to Earth by Luna 16.

engines. The drill head bored into the lunar surface and then scooped the grains of soil (35 cm long and weighing 105 g) into the container attached to the drill head. Like a robot in a backyard assembly shop, the drill head jerked upwards, brought itself alongside the small 39 kg spherical recovery capsule and pressed the grains into the sealed cabin.

By the 21st, Luna 16 had spent a full day on the Moon. There was still no official indication as to its purpose. Jodrell Bank reported still more strong signals. In fact what Luna 16 was doing was checking out its exact landing coordinates so as to give the best possible return trajectory.

27 h after landing, explosive bolts were fired above the Luna 16 descent stage. On a jet of flame the upper stage shot off and headed towards the white-and-blue Earth hanging in the distance. It curved over, motor still purring, its radio pouring out details from the four aerials poking out the side. The Sea of Fertility returned to the quiet it had known for eons. The descent stage was the only forlorn reminder of the brief visit.

The ascent from the Moon was so accurate that no course change was needed. The returning rocket—capsule, instrument container, fuel tanks and motors—reported back from time to time as it headed for a straight nosedive re-entry. The tiny capsule separated from the instrument and rocket package, plunged into the upper atmosphere, glowed red and then white as temperatures rose to 10 000°C as it hit forces of 350 g. Helicopters were already in the air as a parachute ballooned out. The capsule hit the ground and beacons began sending out a bright beep! beep! signal as rescuers rushed to collect the precious cargo.

It was transferred to a plane and flown at once to Moscow to a laboratory for analysis. How the scientists ever got the soil container open is a mystery, for the entire outer skin of the capsule may well have been welded by the intense heat of the fiery return. Once open, the golden grains of Moon dust poured out—loose lumps of blackish powder like very dark wet beach sand.

It was a tremendous triumph. The Luna 16 mission had gone perfectly from start to finish. The tricky stages of soft-landing, drilling and take-off were just like the book said they should be. 'It's the decade of the space robot!' heralded the Soviet press. The USSR made great play of how such flights were cheaper than manned flights like Apollo; how they did not expose humans to danger; and how versatile space robots could land just about anywhere.

For NASA and Western observers the real significance of Luna 16 lay elsewhere: it confirmed what many, but not all of them, had suspected was Luna 15's real purpose, namely that it was a real challenge to Apollo 11 a year earlier. Russia did have good grounds to celebrate Luna 16. Some of the remarks about its low cost and versatility were exaggerated, and the sample of 100 g was tiny compared to Apollo's sample, each mission of which brought back well over 20 kg.

ROVING IN THE SEA OF RAINS

Any benefit that was gained by the success of Luna 16 was turned to double advantage just two months later by Luna 17. The Moonscooper, pushed to the back page by the eruption of political violence in the Middle East, had made little public impact. The same could not be said of its successor, put up on 10 November 1970.

Luna 17's mission was, at least for its first six days, apparently identical to that of Luna 16 and 15. A four-day coast out to the Moon was followed by lunar orbit insertion at 85 km, 1 h 56 min, 141 deg. On the 16th, the onboard motor lowered the orbit to an altitude of 19 km. Luna 17's target was nearly a hemisphere away from that of Luna 16. The entire western face of the Moon is dominated by a huge, dark 'sea', which is called the Ocean of Storms. In its northwest corner is a semicircular basin, the Sea of Rains.

After only two days in orbit, reflecting the bright sunlight of the setting Sun, Luna 17 skimmed in low over the Jura mountains. The rocket fired. Luna 17 hovered as its radar searched for suitable sites. Down it came, as softly as a parachutist on a wind-free day. The long shadows of the structure stood out starkly toward the darkening east. For two hours, Luna 17 reported back its position. Russia coolly announced its fourth soft-landing. A return capsule would be fired back to Earth the next day—or so everyone thought.

Not so. On the upper stage rested the first vehicle designed to explore another world. It had eight wheels, looking like pram wheels, which supported a shiny metallic car in the shape of a bathtub, covered by a kettle-style lid. Out of the front peered two goggle-like television eyes. Above them peeped a laser reflector and two aerials.

It was an unlikely-looking contraption, on first impression more the outcome of a Jules Verne or HG Wells type of sketch rather than a tool of modern Moon exploration. But the wheels were ideal for gripping the lunar surface and were less prone to failure than caterpillars. The lid could be raised backward to the vertical, and on the other side were solar cells to recharge the batteries in the Sun's rays. There was genius in its simplicity.

The most dangerous part of the vehicle's journey was probably getting off the platform and onto the lunar surface. Two ramps unfolded at each end, so it could travel down either way if one exit were blocked. The vehicle, to be called 'Lunokhod' or 'Moon walker' weighed 756 kg and was 4.42 m long (lid open), 2.15 m in diameter and 1.92 m high. Its wheel base was 2.22 m by 1.6 m. While Lunokhod was still sitting on the landing platform, ground control commanded the dust hoods to fall off the TV eyes. A television picture came back at once, showing the wheel rims, the ramp down to the flat, bright surface and the silhouette of the landing ramps. There was nothing for it but to signal to Lunokhod to go into first gear and roll down the ramp and hope for the best.

The first automatic vehicle to drive on the Moon, Lunokhod 1. Russia had been designing roving Moon explorers since the late 1950s and they would have accompanied the first cosmonauts to explore the Moon.

So it was that at 6.47 a.m. on 17 November 1970, carrying the hammer and sickle, a red flag and a portrait of Lenin, the Moon vehicle edged its way down the ramp and rumbled 20 m across the lunar surface. Its tracks were the first wheel marks made on another world. Its TV cameras showed its every move, and at one stage Lunokhod slewed around to film the descent stage which had brought it there. On day two it parked itself, lying there so that its lid could soak in solar energy for its batteries. On day three it travelled 90 m, 100 m the following day, overcoming a 10 degree hill. On the fifth day, with lunar night not long off, it closed its lid, settled down 197 m from Luna 17, and shut down its systems for the four-day lunar night. A nuclear power source would supply enough heat to keep it going till lunar daybreak.

The Soviet—and Western—press took to Lunokhod with an affection normally reserved only for friendly robot television personalities. There was unrestrained admiration for the technical achievement involved, for it was a sophisticated automated exploring machine. The *Times* called it 'a remarkable achievement'. 'A major triumph' said *The Scotsman*. The *Daily Mail*, in a front page editorial entitled 'Progress on wheels', gave Lunokhod's designers an effusive message of congratulations. It was the main news story for several days.

TO THE PROMONTORY OF HERACLES

The control centre for Lunokhod was, like much else in the venture, a scene straight from science fiction. Five controllers sat in front of television consoles, where lunar landscapes were projected on screens. The crew of five worked together like a crew operating a military tank. There was a commander, driver, engineer, radio operator and navigator.

Night-time on the Moon: temperatures plunged to −150° C and stayed at that level a full two weeks. Lunokhod, lid closed, glowing warmly from the heat of its own nuclear radioisotope, rested silently on the Sea of Rains. It was bathed in the ghostly blue light of Earth as the mother planet waxed and waned overhead. Even as it stood there, laser signals were flashed to Lunokhod from the French observatory in the Pic du Midi and from the Semeis Observatory in the Crimea. They struck the 14 cubes of the vehicle's laser reflector and bounced back. As a result, scientists could measure the exact distance from the Earth to the Moon to within 18 cm.

To the east of Lunokhod rose a ridge, and the sharp rays of dawn crept slowly over its rugged rocks early on 9 December. Had the Moon rover survived its two-week hibernation? Within minutes, ground controllers knew that it had. It raised its leaf-shaped lid and at once began to hum with life. Four panoramic cameras at once sent back striking vistas of the Moonscape, full of long shadows as the Sun gradually rose in the sky.

After a day recharging, Lunokhod set out once more. The drivers on the Earth soon got into their stride and they had the Moon car in second gear, swivelling around, reversing and traversing craters and slopes at will. One day it travelled 300 m, more than it had achieved in its first five days in November. Before Christmas the camera eyes spotted in the distance a range of mountains—the far peaks of the Heracles promontory, part of the vast bay encircling the Sea of Rains.

For ground control it was just like being there. From the cosy warmth of their control post they could direct at will a machine a quarter of a million miles away. This prompted romantic notions in the minds of the Earthbound. Radio Moscow promised 'more Lunokhods, faster, and with a wider range'. Boris Petrov spoke of Mooncars that would collect samples and bring them to craft like Luna 16 for transporting home. Others would instal packages on the Moon and carry telescopes to the far side where there was radio peace free from Earthside interference. Other probes would reach the lunar poles.

Such notions did not seem like daydreaming at the time. As time went on, it became apparent that Lunokhod was not just a playful bathtub on wheels but a sophisticated machine. It carried a soil analyser called 'Rifma', which bombarded the surface with X-rays and enabled ground control to read back the chemical composition of the basalt-type soil. From time to time a mechanical rod jabbed into the soil to test its strength. Lunokhod did not only look Moonwards. There were two telescopes on board—one to pick up X-rays beyond the galaxy and another to receive cosmic radiation. On 19 November, it recorded a strong solar flare that could have injured cosmonauts had they been on the Moon at the time. Lunokhod therefore contained within it several concepts: an exploring roving vehicle; a rock-testing mobile laboratory; and an observatory able to capitalize on the unique air-free low-gravity environment beyond the Earth.

Come the New Year, 1971, Lunokhod was back in action once more, and on 18 January drove back to the Luna 17 that landed it there. A spectacular photograph of the landing vehicle with ramps and wheel tracks all about reminded the world that Lunokhod was still there, prowling about the waterless sea of the Bay of Rains.

By the fourth lunar day, 8 February, scientists were able to compile a map of that part of the Bay of Rains adjacent to Luna 17. On 9 February the Mooncar survived a lunar eclipse when temperatures plunged from +150°C to minus 100°C and back to +136°C, all in the space of three hours. In March the craft drove around a 500 m wide impact crater in ever-narrowing circles. Lunokhod nearly came to grief on 13 April. It got stuck on a crater slope and it needed full power on all the eight wheels to get it out again. It used up so much energy that it had to sit silently on the surface for some time, simply recharging. Later that month it ventured to a crater field full of boulders over 3 m across. Because of a nearby crater impact, all the black lunar dust had piled up against one side of the boulders as if a hurricane had swept through.

Early on 5 August, American astronauts David Scott, James Irwin and Al Worden flew directly over the Mooncar in their Apollo 15 command module and Lunokhod's magnesium alloy frame glinted in the Sun. As it drove slowly, plodding across the Moonscape, the two different Moon explorers stood in stark contrast to one another.

Then suddenly, whilst at work on 4 October 4, Lunokhod's 'heart'—its isotope power source—gave out. Telemetry reported a rapid drop in pressure inside the hermetically sealed cabin. The wheels halted; the TV pictures ceased. It was the end.

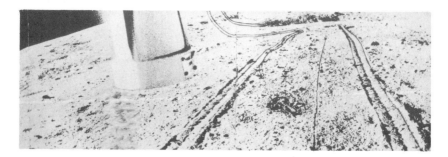

These are the tracks made by Lunokhod 1 as it headed away from its landing stage, skirting a depression (top).

Bearing in mind that Lunokhod had been designed to function for only three months and had worked for nearly a year, its mission was a cause of much congratulation. It was the USSR's most brilliant achievement in the field of automatic space exploration. Crude in design, superbly built, with a reliability that the perfectionist buffs in NASA would have envied, it endeared itself to the public at large, and became the most exciting robot of its day. In statistical terms alone, its achievement was impressive. It had travelled 10.54 km, covered an area of 80 000 m^2, sent back 20 000 pictures and X-rayed the soil at 25 locations. A month later, Radio Moscow announced that a new Moon car was being designed. And why not?

TORRID GULF

Luna 16 and 17 represented two pieces of a three-part programme that involved Moon-scoopers, Moon rovers and lunar orbiters. Warning of a new Moon probe first appeared in January 1971 when predictions of 'low-flying artificial satellites' were made that would fly 'fairly soon'. Sure enough, Luna 19 was launched on 28 September 1971 and entered a circular lunar orbit of 140 km at 40 deg, 2 h 01 min, on 3 October. It settled into a steady orbit of 127 km.

A lunar orbiting mission lacked the appeal or interest of a soil sampler or rover. But it was valuable and important nonetheless. The mission lasted till 3 October 1972, and 1000 communication sessions were held. Luna 19 reported back on magnetic fields, mascons, meteoroids, and sent back televised pictures of an area 30°S to 60°S and 20E° to 30E°, the quality much improved compared to Luna 12 in 1966. In February 1972, it swept over the Torrid Gulf near the crater Eratosthenes, and filmed rock-strewn plains above which reared a volcanic-like summit. In order to take such pictures it had dropped into a new, lower orbit of 77 by 385 km, 131 min.

By this stage, two more attempts had been made to obtain samples from the Moon. Luna 18 appeared on 2 September 1971. After a perfect journey to and around the Moon it fired its braking rockets over an area near the Sea of Fertility on 11 September. The small thruster rockets tried to guide it into a suitable landing site, but the fuel supplies gave out and it crashed. Not even Radio Moscow felt able or thought it worth its while to invent a cover-up story. Something like 'testing new landing techniques' may have been considered, but this time it admitted that the landing had been 'unlucky' in a 'difficult and rugged' upland area.

HIGHLAND SAMPLES

The intentions behind Luna 18 became clear when its backup vehicle was sent aloft on 14 February 1972. Luna 20 fired its engines to come in for a landing late on 21 February. This was the critical stage, and it had gone wrong twice before. Luna 20 was coming down right on the top of mountains. The Sea of Fertility lies on the right of the Moon's visible face, and Luna 16 had landed on one of its flattest parts. About 70 km to the north, hills rise and there are soon mountains 1500 m high. It was in a plateau between these two peaks where Luna 20 was aimed and less than 5000 m from where its predecessor had come to grief on a sharp slope. The area is called Apollonius. It was tougher than anything that the American lunar module would have tried. But Luna 20 made it; whether through luck or skill, we do not know.

And so it came to rest, straddled by towering mountain peaks. Signals at once indicated to relieved controllers that it was safe and secure. Within seven hours, aided by a small television camera, its drill was hard at work scooping up lunar soil. The whole operation took 40 min. The rig encountered stiff resistance at 100 mm, and operations had to stop several times because it overheated. When it reached 150 mm, the samples were scooped into the return capsule to await the long journey home. The onboard computer fired the engines early on 23 February, and the return vehicle climbed away from the lunar peaks. Two days later it headed into re-entry.

An appalling blizzard hit the recovery area during the day. Helicopters spotted the tiny capsule—parachute, antennæ and beacon deployed—heading straight into the Karakingir river. Would the precious samples be lost at this stage? Luckily, the capsule came to rest on an island in the middle of the river and in a snowdrift and trees. But getting it back was easier said than done. The gale was too severe for the helicopters to land. Four cross-country vehicles tried to get across on the ice, but it cracked, so they called it off for fear of falling in.

They retrieved the battered and burnt capsule the next day when the wind abated. Its contents were opened at the Academy of Sciences. They were surprisingly small—only 0.05 g. But it was Moon dust all the same, and the light ash-grey dust was 300 million years old. The records state that it consisted of anorthosite, olivine and pyroxene.

This is what the small Luna 20 capsule looked like when recovered by rescue teams. The parachute lines and homing beacons may be clearly seen.

LEMMONIER

Apollo ended in December 1972. It was Apollo 17's commander, Eugene Cernan, who balefully drew attention to the fact that they would be the last Americans on the Moon till the early 21st century. Apollo's Moon landing programme had lasted a brief three years, during which the Americans had landed twelve men on the Moon in six locations and recovered no less than 380 kg of Moon rock. The last missions had been impressive: the Apollo 17 mission had spent three days on the Moon, two astronauts had spent 11 hours each walking on the Moon, and their lunar rover had taken them far from their lander. Their leaving of the Moon was characterized not so much by a feeling of triumph at what they had achieved but as a feeling of sadness at the promise of the post-Apollo programme that had been cancelled owing to lack of public support.

The original post-Apollo programme planned at least three more landings, including missions to such exciting places as the crater Copernicus. Apollo 20 would fly two astronauts into a lunar polar orbit for a month on a mammoth mapping survey. This too had gone by the board. So were even more ambitious notions like a month-long lunar shelter adapted from the LM ascent stage. So when Apollo 17 splashed down in December 1972, the Russians had the Moon to themselves.

When Luna 21 headed Moonwards on 8 January 1973, the launching was seen as cashing in on NASA's disappointment in Congress's suppression of the post-Apollo programme. In fact, the timing was coincidental. The second Moon car, for that was what Luna 21 carried, had taken a full year to design after Lunokhod 1 had terminated its programme. Luna 21 weighed 1814 kg, and its translunar flight was problematical. False telemetry signals nearly aborted the mission, and then Lunokhod 2's solar lid opened during the translunar coast, without being asked to do so.

On its 41st Moon orbit, Luna 21 began its descent from an altitude of 16 km. The target was Lemmonier crater, only 180 km from the valley just visited by Jack Schmitt and Eugene Cernan. Off the edge of the Sea of Serenity, the Lemmonier crater cut into the edge of the rocky Taurus mountains. Luna 21 came down in a relatively flat area surrounded by the high rims of the old crater.

Lunokhod 2 rolled down the landing ramps not long afterwards. Lunokhod 2 at once made a trial journey over the surface. Lunokhod 2 was a distinct improvement over its predecessor. It was 100 kg heavier. It could travel at twice the speed. It had twice the range. There was an extra TV camera and some new scientific instruments, most notably a photometer to detect ultraviolet light sources in our galaxy.

Lunokhod 2's programme was as follows: it was to sit on the Moon for the first two days, charging up its batteries. Then it was to inspect the descent stage, to which it would not return. Finally it would head south to the mountains 7 km away and explore them as long as its lifetime permitted.

This it did and in one of its early sessions the bug-eyed roving vehicle went 1148 m in six hours—much faster than anything achieved before. On the second lunar day (February 1973) the robot headed south towards the mountains, prowling through craters and ridges. It climbed one hill of 400 m, with its wheels at one stage slipping up to 80%. From the top it sent back an eerie photograph of the Taurus peaks glowing to the north, 60 km away, and the thin sickle of the Earth rising just above. One day it travelled 1.16 km. As it journeyed, it measured and analysed the lunar soil.

It was expected that Lunokhod 2 would continue its work for several months, but on 4 June came the sudden announcement from Radio Moscow that 'the programme had been completed'. No explanation was given, but it seems fair to assume that the rover did not survive the lunar night of May–June. The Russians seem to have been disappointed, but there is little reason why they should have been. Lunokhod 2 had travelled 37 km, sent back 86 panoramic pictures and 80 000 television pictures, and had covered four times the area of its predecessor. It had investigated not only crater floors but much more difficult geological features such as rilles and uplands. One of its most interesting findings actually had nothing to do with the lunar surface, but the suitability of the Moon as a base for observing the sky. While it would be excellent during the lunar night, during the daytime the lunar sky was surrounded by a swarm of dust particles, a kind of atmosphere that would make telescopic observations very difficult.

It was a full year before the next Moon probe, Luna 22, took off on 2 June 1974 and entered Moon orbit at a standard altitude four days later. Late that month it swooped down to 25 by 244 km for special photography, before going back up again to 181 by 299 km. Over the next year, Luna 22 regularly altered its orbit, displaying both versatility and reliability. In April 1975 it was in an eccentric orbit of 200–1409 km out. Then in September 1975 it dipped to a mere 24 km over the surface before returning to a higher orbit of 100 by 1286 km out when its mission ended in November 1975.

BACK TO THE SEA OF CRISIS

The USSR's last Moon missions in this series were in October 1974, October 1975 and August 1976. Luna 23 tried to land in the Sea of Crises but was severely damaged in the course of the landing. The soil-collecting gear was wrecked, although the descent stage was able to continue transmissions for a further three days. A replacement mission was organized. Indeed, Russia's determination to get back samples from the Sea of Crises was nearly becoming obsessive, as it had also been Luna 15's target and the Sea is not thought to be an area of outstanding geological interest. The next Luna failed a year later owing to a rocket booster problem. Finally, Luna 24 came down only a few hundred metres from the wreckage of Luna 23 and at the exact place of Luna 15's targeted spot. Touchdown was on 19 August 1976 and all went well this time. The drill was a radical improvement on its predecessors and was able to penetrate to a depth of about 2 m. It brought up samples, weighing 170 g. The upper stage of Luna 24 blasted off for Earth the next day, and the capsule came down in summertime Siberia near the tundra town of Surgut, a recovery area never used before or since.

This was the last Moon mission by the Soviet Union or Russia. Although there had been many public commitments about teams of robots exploring the Moon's surface and sending back regular supplies of samples, further missions were scrapped in 1976. Plans to recover samples from the lunar far side, using an orbiting satellite as a signal relay, had reached an advanced stage. Lunokhod 3 was built and ready to fly, but ended up in the Lavochkin museum. In its last plan for space development, published in 1989, the Soviet Union proposed a lunar polar geophysical orbiter, but this project was overtaken by the financial crisis.

Final round of Moon missions

Moonscooper missions

15 Apr 1969	Failure
14 Jun 1969	Failure
13 Jul 1969	Luna 15 (failure)
23 Sep 1969	Failure
22 Oct 1969	Failure
12 Sep 1970	Luna 16
2 Sep 1971	Luna 18 (failure)
14 Feb 1972	Luna 20
28 Oct 1974	Luna 23 (failure)
16 Oct 1975	Failure
9 Aug 1976	Luna 24

Lunokhod missions

19 Feb 1969	Failure
10 Nov 1970	Luna 17/Lunokhod 1
8 Jan 1973	Luna 21/Lunokhod 2

Orbiting missions

19 Feb 1970	Failure
28 Sep 1971	Luna 19
2 Jun 1974	Luna 22

DOWN IN ELECTRIS

The USSR's early efforts to explore Mars were unhappy ones. With the Proton rocket available, the designers of the Babakin bureau could think in terms of spacecraft weighing up to five tonnes. Two new-generation spacecraft were prepared for launch on 27 March and 2 April 1969. Each weighed 3495 kg, which was less than the permissible five tonnes, but the launch window was not a very favourable one and extra fuel had to be carried. The Proton was going through its most difficult phase: the first failure was due to a Proton third-stage explosion at 438 s, and the second due to a first-stage engine malfunction.[74]

The Americans returned to Mars in 1969 with two more spacecraft, Mariners 6 and 7. With four solar paddles, they looked like windmills with a box in the middle. America's deep space probes were becoming even more sophisticated: data came back at 16 200 bits a second now compared to 8.3 on the previous Mariner mission to Mars; 200 pictures were sent back rather than 21. The planet, as the probes revealed, was even more bleak than had been thought before. Mars was cold, dry and nearly airless, and the atmosphere was nearly all carbon dioxide. Mariners 6 and 7 passed over crater after crater as desolate

Third-generation interplanetary probe built by the Babakin design bureau.

as an aviator overflying the Western front during the Great War. Ice clung to the crater slopes. These triumphs largely passed the general public by, for they took place barely days after Neil Armstrong and Edwin Aldrin had walked on the Moon, and nothing could ever compare with that ecstatic moment. NASA was less easily overwhelmed and at once ordered up a further two Mars craft whose job would be to map the planet in detail from pole to pole. Mariners 8 and 9 were prepared: they weighed 1032 kg on account of the need for an engine and fuel to put them into Mars orbit.

The original Soviet intention was to send two landers to Mars in 1971, both carrying French equipment to measure solar radiation. However, when the American schedule for the year became available, it was clear that America's Mariner would arrive in Martian orbit just before Mars 2, 3 and 4. Accordingly, the Babakin bureau was ordered to produce an orbiter without a lander, which, although it would leave Earth a day after Mariner 8, would overtake it and reach Mars first. One set of the French equipment was taken off Mars 2 and put on the orbiter instead.

Mariner 8 crashed, however, into the Atlantic Ocean on 9 May. The next day a Proton booster placed the first of three Mars probes in low Earth orbit. One and a half hours after lift-off, the block D should have fired to send the probe Marsward. It did not. The control system designers from the Pilyugin bureau searched through their documentation to try find out what had gone wrong. To their horror, they found that the command for block D ignition had been set, not at 1½ hr after liftoff, but at 1½ years! The spacecraft was called Cosmos 419.

Mars 2 swung out of Earth orbit on 19 May and Mars 3 on 28 May. America's Mariner 9 just beat the end of the launch window by a day on 30 May. The Soviet missions were not long under way before Russia revealed that soft-landings were intended. Each probe carried a mechanical scoop to detect life. And when Mars 2 did get on its way, the French were puzzled as to why their experiments were not transmitting data. The Russians explained that there had been an electronic fault on Mars 2, rather than that they had been put instead on the doomed and now destroyed Cosmos 419.

Both probes were big. Each was a cylindrical doughnut 3 m high. A huge dish antenna was lashed to each side. Two solar wings stuck out the side of the craft like butterfly wings. The main body was full of pipes, lines, aerials, rods and tubes. From the bottom peeped out a retrorocket. On the top sat the precious dome-shaped cone of the landing capsule. Both carried mechanically operated microrovers on skids which were able to venture up to 15 m from the landing capsule.

Throughout the summer and autumn the three probes sped towards Mars. As they did so, the chief designer of the institute responsible for them, Georgi Babakin, died on 26 August, to be succeeded by Sergei Kryukov. At the end of July, Mars 2 was 17 million kilometres from Earth and Mars 3 2 million kilometres behind. Then came trouble. At the end of October the smallest of the three probes, America's Mariner 9, began warming up its cameras as if flexing its muscles for the climax of its journey. And what those cameras saw at the beginning of November meant that the Mars they were journeying towards was very different from the planet they had expected. Far from being the quiet and cold planet with spring gradually warming the southern hemisphere, the whole planet was convulsed in a raging dust- and sandstorm. The likes of it had not been seen since 1937 or 1956. Not a thing was visible—just swirling red and brown clouds.

Mariner 9 fired its 44 cm wide nozzle for 14 min on 14 November and swung into orbit, each revolution lasting 12 h. The bad weather did not bother it terribly—it waited for the duststorm to settle, which it did in January 1972. Mariner 9 went on to map the planet and was an outstanding success. But for the Soviet probes heading in for a landing the effects of the dust storm were nothing short of calamitous. The time at which the landing capsules would be released was already built into the computer programme—and could not be changed.

Mars 2 reached the planet on 27 November. Four hours before arrival the cone-shaped capsule separated from the mother ship. At the fantastic speed of 6 km/s the little cone hurtled into the thin Martian atmosphere. Shock waves formed and gases heated the capsule to thousands of degrees. Mars 2 crashed through the air and was soon over the deserts of Mars. Still supersonic, a giant parachute unfurled.

What happened next no one knows. Mars 2 did not survive the descent with intact instruments although it is known that it did reach the surface. A pennant with the Soviet coat-of-arms was on it and we know that it must have arrived. It was the first direct human contact with the planet Mars. The second craft, Mars 3, headed on. On 2 December the descent capsule blasted free of the mother ship to begin its perilous descent. The entire process of supersonic entry and landing took only three minutes. Out came the Mars 3 parachute, with the speed of mach 1. The heat shield, still glowing red hot, was dropped. The radio transmitter started pouring out a flood of data to Earth. But far from swinging gently beneath its canopy, the capsule was being buffeted by the ferocious winds of the planet-wide sandstorm that was roaring. Tiny grains of sand slammed into its side. 20 m above the surface, a tiny rocket pulled the parachute free so that it would not fall on top of the 450 kg landing capsule. Another rocket on its top fired briefly to lower the speed to a survivable level.

At 16.50.35, Mars 3 reached the surface. It was down in the southern hemisphere in a region called Electris. Four petals opened and the domed shape of the capsule rested there on the sands of Mars. Antennæ popped out, aerials searched skywards, TV cameras began scanning. The video came on at 16.52.05 and began to transmit a picture at once.

And then it was all over. At 16.52.25 Moscow time, Mars 3's voice disappeared in the crackle of outer space and was lost forever. We do not know if the sandstorms with their tiny but ferocious grains of sand blew it over or rendered it inoperable. Or, according to the explanation put forward many years later, the orbiting and transmitting section of the Mars 3 orbital module malfunctioned. Subsequent commentaries have gone further to suggest that the 20 s signal was an invention, devised to claim the first landing on Mars.

The experiment as a whole was far from over. The two mother ships had gone into Martian orbit, and a wide range of research began:

	Mariner 9	Mars 2	Mars 3
Apoaxis, km	17 916	24 938	190 333
Periaxis, km	1389	1380	1500
Period	12 h 34 min	18 h	11 days
Inclination	64.3 deg	48.54 deg	N.A.

The large volume of data returned from orbit partly offset the disappointment of the soft-landing failures. Both probes continued their transmissions until September 1972. They sent back 60 pictures between them: film was developed on board and then scanned by TV operating on 1000 lines, the same method as Lunik 3. The first photograph from Mars 3 showed the thin crescent shape of the planet beckoning in the far distance from the apoaxis of its orbit. The two Mars probes carried spectrometers, photometers, cosmic ray detectors and ion traps. They found mountains on Mars as high as 22 km. They found hydrogen in the atmosphere. They calculated the surface temperature on Mars as an icy minus 15°C. They found the duststorm whipped up granules of sand as high as 7 km. Both probes dipped out of their natural orbits as a result of Martian mascons.

Neither Mars 2 nor 3 was as successful as Mariner 9, whose detailed mapping photographs were spellbinding and showed the planet to be much more varied than one could ever have imagined. Mariner 9 found rilles and giant canyons. Its cameras picked out what seemed like ancient river beds. Finally it found 20 volcanoes. One, Nix Olympica, took everyone's breath away: a giant volcanic pile, it was twice the size of Earth's Everest.

THE MARS FLEET

An unparalleled assault on Mars began in 1973. No fewer than four craft were involved. Spurred on by the near-success of Mars 2 and 3, this launch window also represented the last chance that the USSR had of beating the United States to a soft-landing with prolonged transmissions from the surface. America's Voyager soft-landing project had slipped to 1971, then 1973, and now 1975. It had grown enormously complex and expensive and, as if to shake off the bad luck and difficulties with which it was associated, it was renamed Viking.

To everyone's surprise—and probably not least the Russians themselves—all four attempted launches went perfectly. They took place on 21 and 25 July and on 5 and 9 August, the last one only hours before the window closed. Never before had so many spacecraft set out for one planet at one time. Even if only half the probes worked, a real success was inevitable.

The fleet of four actually included two groups of probes. Because the launch window was not a favourable one, somewhat less than the full payload could be flown. As a result, the designers could build either landers or orbiters, but it was not possible to have both in the one probe as had been done in 1971. So Mars 4 and 5 were orbiters; 6 and 7 were landers. The orbiters would serve as relay stations for the landers. Shortly before launch, it was discovered that there was a serious flaw in the computer chips used on the Mars 4–7 probes, which would lead to their degeneration in the course of their flight; an ancestor as it were, of 1990s computer viruses. Experts were asked to predict the likelihood of the probes surviving the fault, and the chances were given as 50%. This was considered acceptable and the missions were launched regardless.

Two probes were total failures. The computer problem duly materialized: instead of firing its engines so as to enter Mars orbit, Mars 4 neglected to fire at all. It coasted past. Mars 7's landing probe separated prematurely, missing the planet altogether by 1300 km. Mars 6 underwent an experience similar to Mars 3. Its probe was successfully cast off and

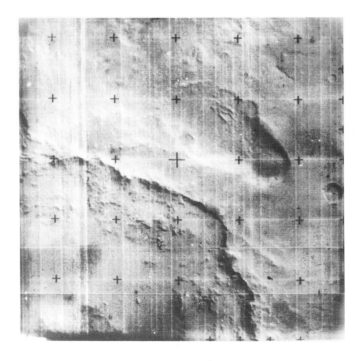

This photograph from Mars 5 shows an area of 100 km^2 of the Martian surface. It reveals the rim of a crater 3 km deep and 150 km in diameter. Near the centre-right of the picture is an irregular depression about 25 km long.

it went through the entry phase and opened a parachute. Data were returned—indeed they flooded in for a full 150 s—but, thanks to the computer virus, were quite unreadable. And then Mars 6 fell silent. 'Contact was lost', said the official sources, and that is probably all they knew.

Only Mars 5 achieved any degree of success. It entered Mars orbit with a periaxis of 1300 km and an apoaxis of 32 586 km. It sent back a modest amount of information. The photographs that it took were comparable to Mariner's, and showed volcanoes, river beds, craters and canyons. And, like Mars 3 and 2, it sampled the atmosphere.

PROJECT 5M

Both the Academy of Sciences (under Keldysh) and the Moscow Institute for Space Research (under Sagdeev) argued that the Soviet Union should not compete directly with America's Viking project in 1975. It would be wasteful, they said, and could not achieve anything the Americans would not achieve. The Soviet Union should concentrate on Venus. For once, the scientists got their way.

But not for long. A group of scientists, jealous of American achievements and concerned that Venus exploration was a dead end, persuaded Ustinov that the Soviet Union should return to Mars and take samples from its surface. The campaign was led by the elderly academician Alexander Vinogradov, the man who had processed the Luna 16, 20 and 24 samples from the Moon. In 1976, a Mars sample return mission, called project 5M, was ordered for launch in 1980.[75]

In the meantime, the American Viking project matured in 1975. Rather than releasing a probe on approach, the entire Viking entered Mars orbit. The orbiter spent a month selecting a suitable landing site—not an academic exercise since JPL's originally designated sites turned out to be dangerous and had to be altered. This period of waiting could also have been used to ride out duststorms—an option not available to the hapless Mars 3.

Viking 1 came down in a field of boulders on the seventh anniversary of the Moon landing: 20 July 1976. Viking 2 followed a month later. Both spacecraft were lucky, and had either landed just a few metres from where they did, they might have overturned, so rocky were the two landing spots. The Vikings dug for soil with mechanical scoops, sent back weather reports, analysed the soil in a small laboratory, and sent back sweeping panoramas.

The Babakin OKB, now the Lavochkin OKB, was ordered to produce the Mars sample return mission. Sergei Kryukov knew such a mission was well beyond the USSR's technical capacity, but threw his best efforts and best people into the 5M project. In the end, the mission was cancelled in December 1977; he was blamed and removed from his post.

PHOBOS

The Soviet Union did not return to Mars until the late 1980s. The first rumours of new Mars missions began in 1983 and, in the spirit of *glasnost*, the new missions were announced in 1986. Two new, large, six-tonne spacecraft were constructed at a total cost of R272 million, plus R60 million of foreign investment from 12 other nations. The lower part was called the Autonomous Propulsion System, with eight tanks carrying 3000 kg of fuel, 28 attitude control thrusters, and a rocket motor to be used for mid-course corrections, entry to Mars orbit and the distant approach to Phobos itself. The main spacecraft had two solar panels, control systems, and a high-gain antenna on top of the science package. A 30 mb computer served for navigation and onboard systems.

Following a policy of not trying to duplicate anything that the Americans had already achieved, a different and imaginative target was proposed: Mars' moon, Phobos. Mars has two moons, Deimos and Phobos, both very small, and both discovered by American astronomer Asaph Hall in 1877. Both orbit in the plane of the Martian equator, Phobos every 7 h 39 min about 6000 km out, Deimos every 30 h 18 min 23 500 km out. Phobos is 27km long on its longest axis. The new probes would enter Mars orbit, rendezvous with the little moon Phobos and land experimental packages there. A record 31 experiments were planned. These comprised a Long-term Automated Lander (LAL) and hopper. The LAL would be anchored to the surface by a harpoon, which was necessary because Phobos has a gravitational field only one thousandth that of Earth. LAL had solar panels so it could transmit from Phobos' surface for up to two months. The LAL carried a spectrometer, seismometer and solar sensor. The hopper, which had a spring to enable it to make a dozen jumps up to 20 m high, carried an X-ray fluorescent spectrometer, magnetometer, penetrometer, dynamograph and gravimeter. During a hovering manoeuvre over the moon at 50 m for 20 mins, the probes would zap the surface with a laser beam, which would vaporize the surface, the scattered ions from which would be measured by a spectrometer. Detailed photographs of the moon's surface would be taken by the Fregat system of cameras, with a resolution of 6 cm. An experiment called GRUNT was to radar-sound the surface to a depth of 2 m. Both probes came in overweight, so the hopper was dropped from Phobos 1; three experiments were left off Phobos 2.

They were given new designations—Phobos 1 and Phobos 2—distancing themselves from their ill-fated predecessors in the Mars series. Attended by a large press corps and an American military delegation, Phobos 1 lifted off on 7 July 1988, riding a blue plume of flame as its Proton rocket took it into the night sky. Two days later, mission control reported that its equipment had been turned on and was functioning flawlessly. Phobos 1 was recording Earth's receding magnetosphere. Phobos 2 followed with the same extreme precision on 12 July. Mid-course corrections took place on 16 and 21 July respectively.

MISPLACED HYPHEN

However, new name or not, the Phobos series did not shake off the ill-luck that had dogged its predecessors. On 2 September, ground control in Yevpatoria keyed up its standard command to Phobos 1. The unfortunate technician left one hyphen out of the series of keyed commands and the one which left Earth was the end-of-mission command to close down all systems. It was an embarrassing, expensive mistake—and a foolish one to have designed computer commands in such a flawed manner. The full report of the commission of inquiry was not published: there was suspicion that an operator was held responsible for a flawed computer. Many found the 'misplaced hyphen' theory unconvincing.

All was now dependent on Phobos 2. The omens were not good. In January, officials admitted that there had been 'isolated malfunctions' as the probe neared its encounter with

Mars, an impression confirmed by NASA, which was also monitoring its signals. What was happening was that the craft had three processors which between them executed the mission. There was provision for two to take a majority decision, as it were, if one failed, a system introduced by the Americans on the Voyager mission to the outer planets in 1977. On Phobos 2, one had failed and the second one was giving trouble. A programming flaw meant that the third did not have the procedural authority to continue the mission if the other two failed.

Trouble or not, Phobos 2 entered Mars orbit on schedule on 29 January 1989, 200 days into its mission, Mars then being 470 million kilometres distant from Earth. The 201 s firing of the retrorocket broke the Phobos probe into a 850–79 750 km orbit with a period of 76 h 30 min, inclination 1deg. On 10 February, it modified its orbit with a series of engine firings to place it in an orbit of 9670 km, 8 h, ½ deg. At this stage, the propulsion unit was jettisoned. A problem arose on 14 February, when there was a sudden drop in the current powering radio transmissions. By the end of the month, Phobos 2 had snapped its first pictures of Mars' little moon from a distance of 860 to 1130 km. Phobos 2 continued to close in slowly on its target. Before the mission, the precise orbit of Phobos had been known only to an approximate 150 km, so the approach to the moon involved sophisticated techniques of navigation. On 14 March, the spacecraft was only 100 km away. On 21 March, Phobos 2 entered its approach profile for the satellite. On 26 March, the probe was within 400 km of target and was preparing to send down the first of its two landers. 9 April had been set as the big day when the first spacecraft landed on the moon of another planet.

Then disaster struck! On 27 March, a mere 150 km from the moon, 57 days after entry to Mars orbit, Phobos 2 was carrying out a manoeuvre which involved taking pictures of Phobos and rotating around to transmit the pictures to Earth. The final picture-taking sequence was commanded at 3.57 p.m. Moscow time. While imaging, the craft drifted out of alignment, its transmitters turned off and signals ceased. At 7 p.m., ground control sent up urgent commands to restore communications and ordering it to use another transmitter. Phobos 2 came alive, responding by sending a stream of data at 8.50 p.m. But it shut down again after 13 min.[76] At some stage, it lost alignment with Earth. More seriously, it lost its alignment with the Sun, which meant that it lost solar power. The batteries must have drained within a few days and on 16 April the probe was finally declared abandoned.

INQUEST, RECRIMINATION

A commission of inquiry was established on 31 March. It set off an acrimonious round of recrimination within the Soviet scientific community, *glasnost* making possible the letting off of years of stored up feelings and resentments. Scientists blamed engineers, and engineers blamed scientists. The Phobos 2 postmortem, announced within a month, blamed poor computer programming, inadequate batteries (they had only five hours of power) and the orientation systems. IKI director Roald Sagdeev railed against the haste with which the project was prepared—less than 3½ years—compared to the much longer lead-in time for the successful VEGA project. However, as if to remind the world of the difficulties of planetary exploration, the Americans encountered difficulties of their own. Their Galileo four years before its encounter with the planet Jupiter. Even more frustrating was Mars Observer, which inexplicably fell silent just at the point of Mars orbit insertion in August 1993. Investigations linked the problem to a dodgy computer chip which had crippled a number of other spacecraft as well—an indication that poor quality control was not exclusively a Russian problem.

The USSR claimed that considerable scientific results were achieved with Phobos 2. En route to Mars, the Terek telescope relayed data on the solar atmosphere.[77] The probe registered a hundred bursts of hard gamma ray emissions from deep in the cosmos. An Irish instrument confirmed that radiation levels around Mars would pose no threat to cosmonauts. The Martian magnetic field was measured at one ten thousandth that of Earth. The energy and mass analyser measured the slow leaking of the thin Martian atmosphere into space. Ozone was found in the Martian atmosphere. The advanced thermoscan instrument, an infrared mapper able to see below the Martian surface, took heat maps of uplands and craters with the quality of good TV images. French and Soviet instruments measured water vapour content in the atmosphere. The cameras took 37 pictures of Phobos itself, snapping six craters and eleven hollows which the Viking missions had missed. Analysis of images of Phobos suggested that the moon was made of carbonaceous chondrites, meaning that it was a captured asteroid.

The Moscow Institute of Space Research, IKI, still hoped to send the backup model, Phobos 3, to Mars in 1992, but the proposal received no political support. Ultimately, the probe ended up going for auction in the West to raise hard currency.

Limited funding for a new mission in 1994 was made available—the project was called Mars 94, and a launch date was even set—but the project was postponed to 1996. The purpose of the Mars 96 mission, developed by the Lavochkin NPO, was to place an orbiter over Mars in September 1997, to be equipped with cameras, sensors and relay systems; to land two small 30 kg weather stations on Mars, equipped with cameras, spectrometers and meteorological sensors; and to drop two 40 kg penetrators, 1.5 m long, 12 cm in diameter, each carrying a camera and miniaturized sensors which would tunnel into the surface. The purpose of the Mars 98 mission was twofold: to land a 100 kg Mars rover (Marsokhod) in the region of Arcadia, powered by a radioisotope nuclear generator, which would explore up to 100 km from the landing site in a mission lasting a year; and to deploy a 258 kg, 42 m high, 13.2 m diameter French-made balloon. Filled with helium in an ultra-thin 6 micron envelope, this would fly over Mars by day as high as 4000 m, and as the air cooled, settle on the surface of Mars by night. The balloon's 15 kg gondola would carry an instrument package to measure temperature, pressure, humidity, dust levels and wind, as well as take photographs of the surface passing below. The Lavochkin bureau Marsokhod had six 350 mm wide-diameter wheels, which were able to cope with difficult terrain and could carry eight scientific instruments.[78] The orbiter would spend two years surveying Mars from a periapsis as low as 300 km. Its television complex was called Argus, after the mythical multi-eyed giant, and was developed at the St Petersburg Institute of Precision Mechanics and Optics. With a resolution of 10 m, it would draw up a topographical and mineralogical map of Mars. These missions would accompany a new range of small, light American and Japanese probes to the planet. By the mid-1990s, exhaustive tests of both the Marsokhod and balloons had taken place (Marsokhod had made several runs in the Mojave Desert and Death Valley in California) and the projects were awaiting the final funding necessary for them to fly.[79] Further in the distance was a plan to retrieve samples from Phobos in 2001.

Third-generation Mars probes

27 Mar 1969	Lander	Failure
2 Apr 1969	Lander	Failure
10 May 1971	Orbiter	Failure (Cosmos 419)
19 May 1971	Lander	Mars 2
28 May 1971	Lander	Mars 3
21 Jul 1973	Orbiter	Mars 4
25 Jul 1973	Orbiter	Mars 5
5 Aug 1973	Lander	Mars 6
9 Aug 1973	Lander	Mars 7
7 Jul 1988	Orbiter/lander	Phobos 1
12 Jul 1988	Orbiter/lander	Phobos 2

LURE OF VENUS

Unaffected by the problems which beset its lunar and Martian probes, the USSR developed special expertise in the exploration of Venus. Its probes were more ambitious than the American ones in the same period.

Venera 4 was put up on 12 June 1967. A companion mission, Cosmos 167, did not achieve orbit five days later, and by then the Americans had launched a rival in the form of Mariner 5. Few of the launchings were noticed; the world was then immersed in the Middle East war. This could not be said when on 18 October, Venera 4 reached Venus. Western observers had been following the mission by way of the large dish receiver at Jodrell Bank. Early that morning, Venera 4's signals had ceased on final approach. Then, as the light of dawn cleared the cold October sky, entirely new signals were picked up, coming directly from the surface of Venus. It was the first soft-landing on another planet, and the transmission lasted 93 min.

Or so it seemed. What was actually happening was more complicated. Venera 4, shaped like a milk bottle with solar wings, a dish aerial and a bucket-shaped landing capsule on one end, had sped toward Venus with extreme accuracy. Some hours before arrival the 383 kg capsule had been separated from the mother ship to begin its own descent. The atmosphere braked it, and thick parachute lines opened. The capsule swung underneath its canopy as it came down through thick layers of swirling clouds. Instruments began sending back data on temperature, pressure and the chemical composition of the atmosphere.

SUGAR LOCK

The pressure built up and up—10 atmospheres, 15, 20, until at 22 atmospheres, and still 20 km to go before the surface, the capsule cracked open like an egg and was smashed to tiny bits. Venera 4 never reached the surface; the signals heard at Jodrell Bank were those sent back during the descent only.

The data returned were invaluable, though hardly encouraging from the point of view of human habitation. Even 20 km above the surface, the temperature was 270°C, pressure 22 atmospheres, and the atmosphere was largely carbon dioxide with only 1% oxygen. If that was what it was like there, what kind of hell lay below? These pessimistic views were confirmed by Mariner 5, which passed by at 3991 km the following day. It too found high temperatures and pressures, and it was rapidly becoming clear that Venus would not be the object of early human colonization.

Even at this late stage, the Russians still believed that Venus was a watery planet, and went to some lengths to ensure that signals could still be transmitted if its spacecraft submerged. Venera 4 contained a sugar lock on its capsule. When it splashed down on the Venusian ocean, the sugar would melt, releasing the antenna.

MOUNTAIN PEAKS?

Because of the way Venera 4 had been crushed by the terrible atmospheric pressures, it was decided to reinforce the parachutes on its two successor probes, scheduled for 1969. Venera 4 had been designed to survive pressures of 18 atmospheres, not enough, so the skin of the new capsules would be strengthened. Each canopy would be much smaller—15 m^2 rather than 50 m^2 - in the hope of getting the capsule to the surface quicker before it would be either crushed or boiled. Whatever happened, it would be a race against time.

Venera 5 headed off the pad on 5 January 1969, and Venera 6 followed on 10 January. Both weighed 1130 kg and carried 405 kg descent capsules 1 m wide. Course corrections put Venera 5 on course for touchdown on 16 May and Venera 6 the following day. Alas neither of the probes was any more successful than their illustrious predecessor. Not that they did not behave any way other than their computer programme ordered. The probes duly separated 25 000 km out and crashed into the atmosphere at 11.18 km/s. By the time the atmosphere had slowed them down to 210 m/s, the parachutes had opened and their radios were hectically radioing back as much information as they could.

As they descended, the pressures and temperatures rose. The probes strained, groaned, and eventually broke up. Venera 5 was crushed 12 km above the surface and Venera 6 at 16 km. At one stage the Russians actually claimed that they had reached the surface and explained the high-altitude readings by saying that they had landed on the top of mountain peaks! But it was wishful thinking. Transmission times were 53 min and 51 min respectively. The USSR issued a list of the probes' findings: the atmosphere was 93–97% carbon dioxide, inert gases 2–5%, and oxygen a meagre 0.4%.

TWILIGHT STAR

Two probes were prepared for the 1970 launch window—on 17 and 22 August. Only the former got away (Venera 7) and the latter became known as Cosmos 359. Venera 7 went first into Earth orbit, fired its upper stage to reach escape velocity at 7.59 a.m. and by 10 a.m. Earth had receded 40 000 km in the distance. Venera 7 was due to arrive on 15 December, and on the 18th of that month, Radio Moscow reported with regret that it had not improved on the performance of its predecessors. It had parachuted down, transmitting for 35 min, and had fallen silent.

So things rested for six weeks until one of the ground controllers decided to go over the signals during the descent picked up by the receiving aerials. It must have been a tedious air-straining job, but the controller listened in patiently and with extraordinary concentration to the cosmic crackle—the squeaks, the static, the beeps and the pips. And there it was! Ever so faintly, barely discernible, was a strange signal! It started soon after Venera 7 had cut out, but it was unmistakeable. It lasted 23 minutes and it was the voice of the landing probe actually on the surface. So they had done it after all! The signals were consistent and showed the temperature constant at 475°C and the pressure constant at 90 atmospheres, so the probe could only be steady, on the surface and at rest. The 495 kg probe had sat there, cooking gradually in a temperature able to melt lead or zinc. Then it had succumbed.

It was a joyous moment, and was the first real soft-landing on another planet. Years of persistent toil had at last paid off. Since Lunokhod 1 was at the time driving on the Moon, the USSR was receiving information from two celestial bodies simultaneously. And the reason for the weak signals, it transpired, was that the antenna was out of alignment and had been pointing partly away from Earth. As a result, the signal strength actually picked up was only one hundredth of what was sent.

A repeat mission was prepared for 1972. Venera 8 was launched on 27 March 1972, and another probe was identified by some at the time as a failed pair (Cosmos 482). Venera 8's journey out went practically unremarked. After 117 days and 300 million kilometres, it approached Venus, then a slim early-morning crescent low on the eastern horizon 108 million kilometres away. The probe separated at 41 696 km/h. Aerodynamic braking reduced that to 900 km/h. When the parachute—only 2.5m in diameter this time—opened 60 km above the surface a refrigeration system was turned on to blow cold air at −8° C around the instruments so that they might survive longer.

Things could only get hotter, and they did. Venera 8 sent back readings throughout the descent, thumped down on the surface and broadcast for a full 50 minutes. A separate, deployable antenna ensured that there was no repeat of the poor signal strength of the previous mission. The main findings of Venera 8 were that the amount of light falling on the surface was similar to a cloudy and rainy day on Earth, a finding vital for the preparation of the next mission. Venera 8 represented the limit of the Korolev series of Mars and Venus spacecraft, which went back to the early 1960s. In the Babakin bureau, a new generation of Venus explorer was prepared. It could use the Proton booster. As a result, the weight of the probe could be increased from 1180 kg to five tonnes.

ROCKY SURFACE REVEALED

The preparation of a new type of Venus probe took three years, and as a result the launch window of 1973 was missed for the first time. America's Mariner 10 coincided with this gap, and it was an extraordinarily successful venture. It was a small hexagonal box with two giant TV eyes on top and two solar panel wings. Only 503 kg, it sped quickly to Venus and passed by at 5760 km in February 1974. Mariner 10 was actually en route to Mercury and was using Venus as a 'gravity assist' to get it there. Televising Venus was a major mission objective: for eight days it filmed the clouds circling around and dispersing and building up again. Because the cameras used ultraviolet filters, the cloud formations could be identified through the murky haze and the planet as a result looked much like Earth's blues and whites when viewed from half-way to the Moon.

The two new-generation probes were ready for launch in June 1975. Venera 9 got away on 8 June and Venera 10 on 14 June. The overall structure was much the same as before: a transporter and a lander. Venera 10, for example, weighed 5033 kg, including an entry probe of 1560 kg on its top. The actual lander was 660 kg. The main spacecraft was a cylinder, with an engine at the base and two solar wings, with endless pipes, rods and arms protruding. The lander looked like a mixture of a kettle and pressure cooker welded together sitting on a metallic ring. Two cameras peeped out like the periscopes of an early submarine.

Venera 9 approached Venus on 20 October. Early that morning it released the ball-shaped entry probe. Now lightened, the transporter continued on for two days, fired its engine and became the first spacecraft to orbit the planet, with a periaxis of 1500 km and apoaxis of 113 900 km. It stood by to act as a relay station.

The entry probe plunged straight into the atmosphere. At 65 km the worst was over, the protective shield was jettisoned and a metallic parachute opened. The lander fell to 50 km, when the parachute was discarded. This was the radically new design step. The lander would now fall unaided but for a disc brake—fast enough to get it to the surface quickly, yet hopefully not too fast to damage it. After 75 min the capsule was on the surface, its impact cushioned by shock absorbers. Then the real work began. Caps dropped off the camera covers. A density meter jabbed into the soil. Dr Mikhail Marov, head of the science team working on the mission, described what happened next:

> The lander touched down at 8.28 a.m. Within 15 min we had our first pictures. We were surprised at their sharpness. We expected the pictures to be dark due to the thick clouds and the dust, and we hardly expected to discern separate objects.
>
> Instead the panoramic views showed a curved horizon 300 m away with the light sky and the dark surface clearly separated.

There were rocks and rocks everywhere—sharp and round and curved on a dark black surface. They were the first pictures from the surface of another planet. Venera 10 touched down on 25 October, some 2200 km away. It too was a triumph. Venera 10 reported pressure at 92 atmospheres and temperatures at 465°C. Mission mapper Boris Nepoklonov noted:

> Venera 9 came down on a plateau 2500 m above average planet level, showing us scattered large rocks on a mountainside. Venera 10 was on an old mountain formation.

The strips of photographs were released to the press at once, unprocessed and unenhanced. They were not as good as the subsequent American pictures of Mars, but the nature of the surface was quite clear. It was an engineering achievement of major proportions.

Cutaway of the Venera lander used on the missions Venera 9–14 and VEGA.

LIGHTNING

Repeat missions were flown in 1978 by Veneras 11 and 12. They were launched in September and arrived in December. The main craft dropped the landers as they passed, not attempting to enter Venus orbit. The two craft landed 800 km apart. No TV pictures were sent back and the surface package seems to have failed entirely on both probes.

The missions were otherwise modestly successful. The atmosphere was sampled many times during the descent and quantities of inert gases were found. One instrument called Groza was designed to detect electrical activity. It found more than it bargained for: Venera 11 counted 25 lightning strikes a second and Venera 12 picked up 1200 strikes. 15 minutes after touchdown a massive thunderclap reverberated around the whole planet.

Carbon monoxide was found by the gas chromatograph. Venera 12 transmitted 110 min on the surface before succumbing to heat, pressure and the acid air, Venera 11 for 95 min. Their landings were matched by two American missions—Pioneer Venus 1 and 2. One was a lander (with three sub-probes) and the other an orbiter. A substantial amount of data was returned, and the orbiter identified canyons, craters, plateaus and mountains. So by

1979 Venus was known in some detail. It was no less hostile than originally feared. The next steps were to identify the chemical composition of the surface and to map the planet with a radar that could pierce the thick clouds.

DRILLING RIG

Venera 13 left Earth orbit on 30 October 1981 and, with what seemed like effortless ease, Venera 14 took off on a curving path to the evening star on 4 November. Venera 13 was the first to arrive. A parachute took the 760 kg craft down to 47 km and the airbrake took it the rest of the way. Venera 13 was aimed at the rolling plains of Phoebus. Somewhere near there it came to rest, raising as it did a cloud of dust. The camera lens at once fell away onto the steaming surface and the probe began work on the cauldron of the hell planet.

A mechanical ladder straightaway extended to the surface and began to analyse the rocks using screw drills. The system had to work against time, for there was the possibility that the whole probe might collapse under the pressure any time. But within minutes scientists had a read-out on the composition of the soil: 45% silica oxide, 4% potassium oxide, 7% calcium oxide. The general composition was basalt.

Remarkable though these finding were, they had none of the dramatic impact of the pictures taken by the cameras of Venera 13. They sent back eight separate panoramas, scanned in red, green and blue. The cameras revealed a rolling stony plateau and the curved horizon in the distance. Scattered on it were stones, pebbles and flat rocks. Many looked like the type of flat pebble that could be picked up off a beach and skimmed across the waves. Looking skywards, the cameras found a bright orange sky and not a blue one. By the time the experiment was over, Earthlings had a real bird's eye view of what it would be like to stand on the surface of Venus.

Venera 14 came in for landing on 5 March over a thousand kilometres away. It was just as successful and it touched down on a low-lying basaltic basin. The pictures were quite different. They showed a flat baked surface looking like icing on a chocolate cake. The more geologically professional description came from Radio Moscow, that it was 'wrinkled brownish slate like sandstone'. As on Venera 13, the mechanical drilling arm reached down for samples, scooped them into an hermetically sealed chamber and subjected them to X-ray and fluorescent analysis. The internal chamber operated at a temperature of 30°C and a pressure of 1/2000 that of the air outside. The Venera 13 and 14 missions were triumphs by any standards. The scientific data returned were unambiguous and the pictures were a feast to geologists' eyes.

	Venera 13	Venera 14
Landing	1 March 1982	5 March 1982
Pressure	84 ats	94 ats
Temperature	457°C	465°C
Transmission time	127 min	57 min
Location	7.5°S, 303 long	13.2°S, 310 long

Venera 15–16. The large Polyus radar is visible at the top.

The transmission times were better than expected, for the design life was only 32 min: all the photographic and soil analysis work had been scheduled for that period.

In the meantime, an entirely new type of Venus probe was prepared and sent on its way in summer of 1983. Venera 15 was put up on 2 June and Venera 16 on 7 June. Each weighed about 5300 kg and an ungainly looking 300 kg sideways-looking radar mapper was installed where normally a lander would be carried. The two spacecraft duly entered orbit around the planet on 10 and 14 October 1983 respectively, each 87 deg orbit taking about 1440 min, flying at an altitude of 1000 to 65 000 km.

Venera 15 and 16 each carried a Polyus-V radar which measured 6 m by 1.4 m. The solar panels were twice the size of those on previous Veneras, in order to feed the thirsty electrical demands of the radars. The communications antennæ were 1 m larger than on previous probes in order to facilitate the transmission of large amounts of data to Earth, 108 kbits a second. Each radar image measured 120 km by 7500 km, taken during the 15min of closest approach to the planet on each orbit. The resolution was about 2 km. According to American analysts, such quality can be achieved from Earth, but only at equatorial latitudes. Venera 15 and 16 concentrated on the northern latitudes. Venera 15 and 16 returned radar profiles of the two continental highlands of Venus, called the Maxwell mountains and Ishtar Terra, and measured plateaux, depressions, volcanic domes, shields, lava, plains, parallel mountains and valleys called parquet. They found 146 impact craters and volcanoes up to 200 km across with a giant 400 000 km^2 lava flood plain.

Venera 15 and 16 mapped a quarter of Venus' surface. Other instruments compiled a temperature profile of the atmosphere, reporting back on how the atmosphere conserved and redistributed its heat. The missions of Venera 15 and 16 lasted a full year, and by the time they were concluded, 120 million square kilometres had been mapped. 1000 spectrographs had been taken, and a thermal map compiled.

The large high-gain antenna used to transmit the radar images from Venus orbit to Earth.

VEGA

After the success of the radar mission, two more stations were planned to explore Venus with balloons. In the event, this was combined with a more ambitious mission to explore Comet Halley. Originally, the Soviet Union had planned to drop a lander, accompanied by a large French balloon with a 25 kg gondola to mark the 200th anniversary of the first balloon flight of the Montgolfier brothers in France in 1783. But examination of celestial mechanics suggested that by launching later, the mother spacecraft, carrying a slightly smaller balloon, could be redirected after Venus encounter, to intercept the comet—a much more exciting mission.

VEGA 1 and 2 (the acronym standing for Venus–Halley in Russian), built by the USSR with experiments from France and 13 other countries, were duly launched in December 1984. They were modelled on Venera 9 and 10. They streaked towards Venus on the most sophisticated mission to the planet ever. If they were to intercept Comet Halley two years later, all manoeuvres had to be characterized by pinpoint accuracy.

From 500 000 km above Venus on 9 June 1985, VEGA 1 released its descent module. It coasted down toward the surface, which it reached two days later. The 100 kg lander returned data throughout the descent and after touchdown. For two hours it analysed the rocks of the Mermaid plains. More spectacular was the deployment of a snow-white balloon aerostat. Released at 54 km above the surface during the descent, it had a diameter of 3.4 m and it began a 47 h journey in the Venusian atmosphere. 12 m below the balloon was a gondola, full of instruments, reporting back on temperature, winds and the composition of the atmosphere.

By all accounts the balloon had a bumpy ride. The little aerostat was caught in vortices that whirled around at 240 km/h and tossed it up and down in air pockets. Over the Aphrodite mountains, the balloon plunged a full 1400 m before steadying its fall. After two days, following a journey of 9000 km, the balloon reached the daylight side of the planet, where the heat expanded the envelope to bursting point. VEGA 2, passing Venus at 35 000 km, deployed a landing module on 14 June, which two days later came down on the dark side of Venus. The surface was like granite, according to its chemical analysis. Simultaneously, it deployed a second balloon in the atmosphere at a height of 54 km. Encountering vortices the size of hurricanes, it burst the following day when it entered the daylight zone.

Venus probes, 1967–84

12 Jun 1967	Lander	Venera 4
17 Jun 1967	Lander	Failure (Cosmos 167)
5 Jan 1969	Lander	Venera 5
10 Jan 1969	Lander	Venera 6
17 Aug 1970	Lander	Venera 7
22 Aug 1970	Lander	(Cosmos 359)
27 Mar 1972	Lander	Venera 8
31 Mar 1972	Lander	Failure (Cosmos 482)
8 Jun 1975	Lander/orbiter	Venera 9
14 Jun 1975	Lander/orbiter	Venera 10
9 Sep 1978	Lander	Venera 11
14 Sep 1978	Lander	Venera 12
30 Oct 1981	Lander	Venera 13
4 Nov 1981	Lander	Venera 14
2 Jun 1983	Orbiter	Venera 15
7 Jun 1983	Orbiter	Venera 16
15 Dec 1984	Flyby/lander/balloon	VEGA 1
21 Dec 1984	Flyby/lander/balloon	VEGA 2

Meanwhile, the two VEGA mother craft altered course for the most famous of all the comets, which visited the inner solar system every 76 years. In March 1986, the two VEGA probes intercepted the comet, passing at a distance of 9000 km and 8200 km. They sent back over 12 000 pictures of the comet's glaring red and yellow surround of gas against a blue and purple sky. VEGA carried cameras and infrared spectrometers to build up a picture of the comet. It turned out that Halley was an oblong monolith 14 km long and 7 km wide from which millions of tonnes of vapours were escaping. The surface of the comet was black and hot (100°C) with very low conductivity. From time to time the surface would burst open with active zones. The gas flows had about ten different elements—hydrogen, oxygen, carbon, carbon monoxide, carbon dioxide, hydroxyl and cyan.

ASSESSMENT

Two more Venera probes were built in the early 1980s, but they were converted instead to the observatories Astron (1983) and Granat (1989). The Venera 13–14, 15–16 and VEGA probes represented the limits of what could be achieved in the exploration of Venus. In the period 1970 to 1985 (Venera 8 to VEGA), the Soviet Union became the leaders in Venus exploration. Their landers were significant engineering achievements.

By contrast, the Mars missions exceeded the ability of Soviet long-distance communication, control and navigation. Although early American planetary probes were criticized as being over-sophisticated, the Americans were absolutely right to invest in quality electronics for their spacecraft. The momentum which Mstislav Keldysh developed in Soviet computerization in the late 1950s seems not to have been sustained. The most concentrated period of Soviet interplanetary exploration also coincided with the most difficult period of development of the Molniya rocket and the Proton.

The Soviet Moon missions of 1970–6 represented an alternative to Apollo. The Moon-scoopers and the Lunokhods were valuable contributions to the exploration of the Moon, and were engineering triumphs in their own right. The Mars rovers of the early 21st century will, ultimately, owe much to the Lunokhod experience thirty years before. Unhappily, the long-term potential of the series was not realized. As with Apollo, the political leadership of both countries lacked the appetite for long-term scientific exploration programmes. Just as both programmes were created from the political circumstances of the 1960s, changed conditions in the 1970s proved their undoing.

7

Spaceplanes and space shuttles

Look at what Valentin Petrovich has cooked up. The size difference with the American ship is about half a metre.

Vladimir Chelomei, on first seeing the plans of the Soviet space shuttle, Buran.

INDIAN OCEAN, 1982

The Cocos Islands are three tiny tropical islands off the coast of Malaysia, well out in the Indian Ocean. On 2 June 1982, Soviet ships idled offshore, waiting. Crews relaxed in the sunshine. The Australian Navy soon noticed the Soviet presence and from time to time sent over a Lockheed Orion aircraft to swoop low above the ships to snap long-range pictures. Only the drone of its propellers broke the silence of the sea lapping against the hulls.

A sonic boom crashed out. Observers anxiously scanned the skies through long-range binoculars. Then they saw it—a tiny midge-like object in the distance. It was a glider. It straightened out its flight path, and evened out for a landing. A parachute slowed its final fall until smack! It splashed into the sea. Flotation bags ballooned out to stop it sinking. One of the ships in the flotilla moved in, winched the glider out of the water, lashed it to the deck, and the flotilla sailed for home.

The Australian Navy had been there at the right time and had got the right pictures. The photographs snapped by the Orion plane were rushed to Sydney and developed. When the photographs were enlarged, no one had any doubt as to what they were looking at. It was the Soviet space shuttle.

Tass reported the flight in the normal manner as Cosmos 1374 and stated that the mission had been accomplished in one orbit. All this was perfectly true—it was a 109-min flight out of Kapustin Yar—but gave no hint was given as to its real nature. The Australian photographs showed, on deck, a small, stubby, delta-winged aeroplane, its short wings tapering upwards and a front cockpit designed for cosmonauts to fly.

Cosmos 1374 aroused world-wide interest among spacewatchers. It was one of the few launches out of the little-used base of Kapustin Yar. It followed a flight path never before used. Cosmos 1374 headed due south, passed over southeast Asia and the South Pacific, and reached an orbit of 230 by 191 km. It came back over the USSR from the northwest.

Retrofire was commanded by Yevpatoria in Crimea as it flew overhead. Cosmos 1374 went into re-entry, soaring over the Himalayas and India, and once its elevators came into play, performed a dog-leg manoeuvre of about 640 km, splashing down 560 km south of the Cocos Islands and 2250 km northwest of Australia. Upon touchdown, a 2.4 m cone ballooned out from behind the crew cabin as both a visual and a radar target.

Cosmos 1374 used the R-14 booster, whose maximum payload was 1.2 tonnes. The Orion photographs revealed that the spaceplane was not the real-life size of the spaceplane's final design, but a scaled-down model. Australian Navy analysis of the photographs, much facilitated by the presence around the craft of the men of the recovery crew (whose height could be fairly accurately guessed), gave measurements for Cosmos 1374 of 4.6 m length, 6.1 m wingspan and a weight of about 1000 kg.

A repeat was flown the following spring: again, the Australian Navy was on hand, cameras at the ready. A third test was flown in late 1983, but with some significant differences. Cosmos 1517 went up on 27 December 1983. Instead of coming down in the Indian Ocean, its splashdown point was much nearer to home—in the Black Sea. One explanation for this was the Russian desire to conduct their operations free from the prying eyes of other people's navies. More important, though, was the fact that retrofire took place automatically, way out over the Atlantic. A fourth test, Cosmos 1614, concluded the programme the following year.

Single-orbit tests of the BOR-4 spaceplane

3 Jun 1982	Cosmos 1374
26 Mar 1983	Cosmos 1445
27 Dec 1983	Cosmos 1517
19 Dec 1984	Cosmos 1614

ORIGINS OF SPACEPLANE DEVELOPMENT

The idea of a spaceplane or space shuttle was not new to Soviet space design. Far from it, for it had been part of Soviet space thinking in the 1920s. Early spaceplanes had been designed then by Friedrich Tsander. Indeed, before, during and after the Soviets raced the Americans to the Moon, a considerable part of their space effort was devoted to building and testing re-useable spaceplanes and space shuttles.

The concept of the spaceplane advanced in the 1930s thanks to Dr Eugene Sänger (1905–64), the Austrian rocket expert. With his assistant, Dr Irene Bredt, he drew up plans for the launching of high-altitude rocket planes as far back as 1933 and later at Peenemünde devised an A-4 based Raketenbomber to attack New York (a hundred copies of his designs were circulated).

Soviet engineers found three examples of Sänger's designs and they were appraised at the Kremlin meeting of 14 April 1947 which planned the USSR's post-war rocket programme. The designers, engineers and personnel from the aircraft industry present did not consider Sänger's schemes realistic, but, undeterred, Stalin ordered Colonel Tokady to further investigate the idea of an antipodal bomber. As a double measure, Stalin sent his

Friedrich Tsander, who sketched the first designs of spaceplanes in the 1920s.

agents to the West to try to persuade Sänger to defect, or, if that failed, to kidnap him, but their mission was unsuccessful. Tokady then resubmitted the ideas of the antipodal bomber to the German engineers on Seliger lake, but they criticized the designs for similar reasons. Ideas of a spaceplane rested, but not for long.

In 1958, the long-term development plan for the Red Air Force specified the development of spaceplanes (in Russian, *kosmolyot*) which could fly at ten times the speed of sound, mach 10, at altitudes of over 60 km.[80] Two were developed, the VKA-23 by Vladimir Myasishchev's OKB-23, the other by Pavel Tsybin's OKB-256, both in cooperation with Korolev's OKB-1. Both bureaux envisaged their spaceplanes flying into orbit on Korolev's R-7 rocket. The OKB-256 project designed a 9 m long, 3.5 tonne spaceplane with 8.7 m² hinged wings, able to fly a cosmonaut into 300 km high orbit for a day. For heat shielding during re-entry, it had 100 mm thick organic silicon combined with 70 mm ultrafine fibre and air ducts for cooling.[81] The OKB-23 project reached an advanced theoretical stage and much work was done on the heat-resistant materials that would be required. Both projects were cancelled in the early 1960s during a subsequent restructuring of the Air Force by General Secretary Nikita Khrushchev.

Independently, Vladimir Chelomei's OKB-52 began in 1960 to design and build a spaceplane that could intercept American spy satellites. It could fly to 290 km and stay in orbit up to a day. Interestingly, Chelomei's spaceplane had a similar brief to an American project of the same period, the Dynasoar. The United States Air Force sponsored the Dynasoar project from 1960 to 1963 as a space interceptor, when it was cancelled by President Johnson and replaced by the Manned Orbiting Laboratory (which was in turn scrapped). It was not only in the Soviet Union that designers found their plans changed and cancelled.[82]

Unlike the OKB-23 and OKB-256 projects, Chelomei's reached the flight stage. His spaceplane, called the MP-1, made a sub-orbital test on the snowy morning of 27 December 1961, when it reached a height of 405 km and flew 1760 km downrange. Engines that would have been used on his spaceplane were tested on the Polyot 1 and Polyot 2 missions in 1963 and 1964. The MP mission was repeated in March 1963 and preparations moved ahead for a crewed mission in 1965. In October 1964, the programme was cancelled.[83] The Chelomei bureau claimed that this was a fit of pique on the part of Brezhnev because Sergei Khrushchev, son of the just ousted General Secretary, was Chelomei's deputy design director for the spaceplane.

SPIRAL

The cancellation of the OKB-52 project paved the way for another competition for a spaceplane. Two bureaux bid for the contract, both being associated with aircraft rather than spacecraft. These were the Sukhoi design bureau and the MiG design bureau, OKB-155. The MiG design became famous as the project Spiral.[84] Spiral was also known as project 50/50 and VKS (Vozduzhno-Kosmichechesky Samolot, or air/spaceplane); the small spaceplane itself was also known as Lapot (the literature on the project sometimes uses the four terms interchangeably). Project 50/50 took place at a time of considerable Soviet optimism about the future of supersonic transport and hypersonic transport. The USSR became the first country to fly a supersonic transport, the Tupolev 144, though because of high costs, it never entered commercial service. Spiral's designer was Gleb Lozino-Lozhinsky.

Project Spiral received the go-ahead in June 1966. Spiral was a two-man interceptor, slightly smaller than the Dynasoar, which would be launched into orbit on the back of a hypersonic aircraft, not a conventional rocket. It was 8 m long, 7.4 m wide, 3.5 m high and weighed 10.3 tonnes. Spiral had folding wings, which came down during the gliding phase of the return. The 52 tonne, 38 m long, 16.5 m wingspan hypersonic aircraft, called EPOS (experimental manned orbital plane) was expected to fly as fast as 7300 km/h before releasing Spiral at a height of 30 km. Three men were now selected to fly Spiral on its orbital mission. By 1967, sufficient progress had been made to make three sub-orbital tests of a Spiral orbiter, at this stage called the 105.13. Half-scale models were launched from the Plesetsk cosmodrome atop ordinary rockets and recovered at the Kapustin Yar test site in southern Russia, 2000 km away, in the course of 1967–70. The tests were called BOR-1, BOR-2 and BOR-3 (Becpilotniye Orbitalnie Raketoplan, or unpiloted orbital rocketplane). By this stage, a further eight men had joined the Spiral training programme, led by veteran cosmonaut Gherman Titov.

With the Moon race at its height, Spiral was suspended for three years from 1969-72 (indeed, shortage of funds meant that one of the tests, in July 1969, was conducted with a wooden model!). Limited tests resumed during the period 1976-8, when a full-scale manned model was tested in air drops. This plane, 105.11, was called Lapot. Chief test pilot of Spiral was MiG tester Aviard Fastovets. The other test pilots were Valeri Menitski, Alexander Fedotov and Pyotr Ostapenko (all from the MiG bureau); Ministry of Aviation test pilot Igor Volk; and Air Force test pilot Vasili Uryadov. Several cosmonauts were recruited in 1978 for the project:

BOR selection, January 1979

Ivan Bachurin (transferred to Buran, 1987)
Alexei Borodai (transferred to Buran, 1987)
Viktor Chirkin
Vladimir Mosolov
Nail Sattarov
Anatoli Sokovykh

Liftoff and landing tests were conducted from May 1976. On 11 November, Lapot was carried, manned, from one test base to another. On 27 November 1976, the first air-drop test took place from a Bear Tu-95K from 5000 m. Igor Volk flew a drop test from 9000 m. Three further drop tests were made before Lapot became self-propelled with jet engines. In 1978, Pyotr Ostapenko flew the 105.11 five times. The project closed after Vasili Uryadov damaged the plane in a September 1978 test. Spiral was then cancelled. R75 million had been spent: the full-scale model is now on display at the Zhukovsky Air Museum, Moscow.[85]

'LOOK AT WHAT VALENTIN PETROVICH HAS COOKED UP...!'

When Valentin Glushko became chief designer in 1974 he cancelled Vasili Mishin's N-1 rocket and later proceeded to cancel his old colleague Vladimir Chelomei's Almaz project. To his chagrin, his own plan for a lunar colony, propelled by his own superrocket, the Vulkan, failed to win support among the military or the Academy of Sciences. The military, however, grew ever more apprehensive about the development of the American space shuttle. The political leadership within the politburo, the Commission on Military Industrial Issues and the Ministry of General Machine Building felt that the Soviet Union must match the American shuttle. Russian historians subsequently took the view that a feeling was prevalent that if the Americans, who had won the Moon race, felt that the shuttle was the wave of the future, they must be right. So the Soviet Union had to have a shuttle too. Valentin Glushko was ordered to design it. He spent several years exploring different concepts of a Soviet shuttle. Several design studies were proposed, which included wingless shuttles landing on skids, with parachutes and even versions of what would now be called single stage to orbit (SSTO). In the event, a concept close to the American shuttle model was ordered in February 1976.

The American shuttle took almost ten years to design and build. Although its first mission had been scheduled for 1978, the target date slipped and slipped. When the shuttle did appear, the main craft, the orbiter, looked like a DC-9 airliner strapped onto a zeppelin-like cylinder (the fuel tank) and two solid rocket boosters. It was to take off like a rocket, fly like a spaceship, and land like an airliner. It stood 56 m on the pad and weighed 2040 tonnes. The orbiter, which could take a crew of seven, weighed 84 tonnes and was 37 m long with a 24 m wingspan. It came down fast and landed at 335 km/h.

The shuttle—the first one was called *Columbia*—eventually flew on 12 April 1981 which, as luck or coincidence had it, was the 20th anniversary of Gagarin's historic first mission. Millions held their breath as its two-man crew of John Young and Robert Crippen reached the awesome moment when the boosters finally lit up. First came on the dull orange light of the main engine, only a small intimation of the huge power of the solid boosters which then roared to life. The shuttle shook and the solids took it away in only three-tenths of a second. The white and orange flames grew to over 1 km in length. The boosters dropped away at 40 km and the external tank took the shuttle up like a plane and it curved into orbit over Gibraltar.

Young and Crippen rolled and flew *Columbia* for two exhilarating days before hitting the re-entry button over Guam at mach 24. By the time they reached the coast of California they were down to mach 7. They were flying like a plane, head-first into re-entry, gravity pulling them forwards. Orbital thrusters soon became useless: the shuttle now responded instead to moves on the ailerons. 'What a way to come to California!' shouted Crippen as *Columbia* crossed the coast, dropping fast. It glided over the coastline, swung over the orange and wine valleys and John Young searched for the dried-up salt lake beds of Edwards Air Force Base inland. He found them, steered *Columbia* over the mountains, and floated in. It was a truly glorious moment. The reticent John Young could not restrain himself and bounded out of the hatch to tell the whole world.

Vladimir Chelomei was enraged when he first saw Valentin Glushko's design of the Soviet Union's shuttle. One of his aides coming to work one morning at his drafting table found Vladimir Chelomei already there scanning a picture of the American shuttle on the one hand, and on the other, a drawing of Glushko's shuttle:

Look at what Valentin Petrovich Glushko has cooked up. The size difference with the American ship is about half a metre.

American and Soviet shuttles compared

	US shuttle	Buran
Length	37.2 m	36.4 m
Height	17.2 m	16.5 m
Diameter	5.2 m	5.6 m
Wingspan	23.8 m	23.9 m
Surface area	295 m^2	250 m^2
Payload bay	18.3 m × 4.5 m	18.3 m × 4.7 m
Weight (dry)	68 tonnes	62 tonnes
Cabin volume	71.5 m^3	70 m^3
Tiles	34 250	38 000
Landing speed	340 km/h	340 km/h.[86]

Considering the Glushko approach to be unwieldy, expensive and in need of new and powerful boosters that did not then exist, Chelomei returned to his spaceplane studies and from 1975 to 1981 designed a small spaceplane, the LKS or light cosmic jet, which would ride into orbit on a Proton. The project borrowed liberally from his earlier MP 1960s tests.

His design was similar to the Hermes project, which arose in Europe a few years later, but it likewise failed to gain political support. It had both a manned and an unmanned version, a payload of 4–5 tonnes, would start gliding from 50 km high on its return and come into land at 300 km/h. It used a new form of heat shielding, not the tiles adopted on the American shuttle and Buran. Chelomei argued that the costs of the LKS would be small, since its booster was already proven. Chelomei deliberately bypassed the Politburo (Glushko was a member), and he appealed directly to Brezhnev to support the project. A subcommittee of the government commission appointed to evaluate the project approved it, but it was turned down by the full committee, which was chaired by army general VM Shabanov.

Undeterred, Chelomei decided that if he could not build his spaceplane with authorization, he would build it without. His designers toiled day and night, and had it ready for flight within a month. The spaceplane was decked out in Soviet war green, with 'CCCP' and the red star emblazoned on its swingback tail, and Chelomei persuaded the secretary of the central committee of the CPSU, Dmitri Ustinov, to inspect it. Chelomei and Ustinov chatted together in the cockpit for 20 min as Chelomei explained how his spaceplane could outperform the American shuttle and the Glushko plan at a fraction of their cost.

Chelomei was under no illusions about his spaceplane. He admitted to his confidants that the Glushko project was well advanced, much had already been spent, and it was too late to turn around. In the event, someone informed on Chelomei even before Ustinov could make his recommendation. Chelomei was summoned to the Ministry of General Machine Building by Sergei Afanasayev and given the sharpest possible reprimand. The oak door of Afanasayev's room cracked, so the story goes ,and Chelomei was taken to task for spending R140 000 without authorization. Chelomei returned to his bureau, gathered his workers around him for one last time, thanking them for their labours:

> I have just returned from the funeral of the light spaceplane. The grave diggers
> of progress have done their dirty deed. [87]

What was even more humiliating was that Glushko ordered the results to be transferred to his own bureau.

MILITARY SPACEPLANE

However, Spiral was to be resurrected in a different form a few years later as the American shuttle programme got into its stride. From 1985 (mission 51C) the United States began to classify a number of its shuttle missions and constructed a military shuttle launching site at Vandenberg Air Force Base in California. Although the classified shuttle missions were devoted largely to launching spy satellites and some onboard experiments, the tense atmosphere of the renewed Cold War fuelled Soviet suspicions that more offensive intentions lay behind the military shuttle programme. At one stage, a third of all shuttle flights were manifested for the Pentagon. There was the suspicion that the shuttle would practise bombing runs over Moscow, experiment with star wars weapons, and there was even talk of training a corps of space marines who, equipped with manned manoeuvring units, would jet across from their shuttle to board or inspect hostile spacecraft. Accordingly, the order was given to construct a spaceplane fighter called Uragan, the Russian word for 'hurricane', launched by Zenith, crewed by two cosmonauts and with a recoilless gun to engage the American space shuttle or any other suitable target.[88]

Cosmonaut and General Alexei Leonov watching Ronald Reagan on television at the height of the Cold War. Soviet fears of the star wars project, space marines and shuttles bombing Moscow led the USSR to develop cannon-firing spaceplane projects in the 1980s.

Several groups of cosmonauts were recruited for the project and joined the existing Spiral groups of pilots.

BOR selection, 1985

Viktor Afanasayev (transferred to Mir, 1987)
Anatoli Artsebarski (transferred to Mir, 1987)
Gennadiy Manakov (transferred to Mir, 1987)

Sub-scale models of Uragan were readied for flight and they closely resembled the Spiral design. These tests duly took place as Cosmos 1374 (June 1982), 1445 (March 1983), 1517 (December 1993) and 1614 (December 1984). The Soviets later classified these tests as BOR-4 and explained them as connected to Glushko's shuttle—unconvincingly in the event, for the Cosmos which landed in the Indian Ocean bore every resemblance to the military Spiral, and nothing whatever to Buran.

In the aftermath of America's *Challenger* disaster in January 1986, there were significant changes in American space policy. Unmanned payloads were remanifested, where possible, on expendable launch vehicles. Classified missions were finally abandoned in 1990. Owing to considerations of safety, the Vandenberg Air Force Shuttle Base was abandoned in mid-1986, even though $8 billion had been spent. With the military shuttle threat diminishing, Uragan was quietly closed down.

GLUSHKO'S SHUTTLE

Construction of Glushko's shuttle got under way in the late 1970s. Glushko awarded the Energiya project to his own design bureau without public competition: Chelomei protested, to no effect. Responsibility was given to a subsection of NPO Energiya, called NPO Molniya, directed by Spiral designer Gleb Lozino-Lozinsky (1909–).

American spy satellites picked up signs of a large amount of earth-moving at Baikonour, north of the old N-1 pads. By the summer of 1983 a runway appeared on photographs like a slash across the terrain. It was wide, big and long, and could only be a shuttle runway (a backup runway was designated in Simferopol, Crimea, and in the far east). The first shuttle orbiter, named Buran (Russian for 'snowstorm'), rolled out in 1984.

To fly Buran, a first group of cosmonauts had been recruited, led by senior test pilot Igor Volk. They were called the wolfpack (the name *volk* in Russian, means 'wolf'). No person could have been better qualified. Volk was a veteran test pilot, born in 1937, who had flown 2500 km/h in MiGs and had tested the Spiral spaceplane. For its training, the wolfpack was given Sukhoi-7 and MiG-25 fighters and two Tupolev 154s to simulate the Buran descent profile. More joined as the programme expanded. There was a high rate of attrition due to death and dismissal. No fewer than six teams were recruited to fly Buran, as follows:

Buran selection, July 1980
Oleg Kononenko
Anatoli Levchenko
Alexander Shchukhin
Rimantas Stankivicius
Igor Volk

Buran selection, March 1983
Ural Sultanov
Maghomed Tolboyev

Buran selection, February 1984
Viktor Zabolotsky

Buran selection, September 1985
Yuri Sheffer
Sergei Tresvyatsky

Buran selection, October 1988
Leonid Kadenyuk (reselection)

Buran selection, January 1989
Yuri Prikhodko

To these groups were added members of the BOR-4 squad when that programme ended. In the end, almost 20 cosmonauts trained to fly the Soviet space shuttle. Of the first group of five, four were to die in training: Anatoli Levchenko from a tumour; Oleg Kononenko when his jet crashed into the sea after taking off from an aircraft carrier; Alexander Shchukhin when his sports plane crashed; and Rimantas Stankivicius when his Sukhoi-27 went down in flames at an air show in Italy. He was buried near his home in Lithuania.

A lengthy series of tests was conducted before Buran's first flight. First, six one-eighth scale models were flown on sub-orbital tests from 4 July 1983 over five years out of Kapustin Yar, the last taking place only five months before Buran's maiden orbital flight. These tests were labelled BOR-5. The model weighed 1.4 tonnes and flew at speeds of up to mach 16 as high as 120 km.

Six full-scale analogues of Buran were built for tests on Earth. One was fitted with four engines (two jet engines, two ramjets) and used to test the shuttle's aerodynamic characteristics and landing profile. It flew 25 times. These tests took place between 10 November 1985 and April 1988, the first mission being flown by Igor Volk and Rimantas Stankivicius, who in the course of time became tipped as the likely crew for the first mission to go into space. The other pairs which flew the analogue were Anatoli Levchenko and Alexander Shchukhin; and Ivan Bachurin and Alexei Borodai.

The different parts of Buran were delivered to Baikonour by aircraft. A Myasishchev M-4 strategic bomber was adapted, called the M-3MT, one to carry Buran, the other to carry the rocket which would bring it into orbit. The rocket which was to launch Buran was an entirely new design and Valentin Glushko's final and supreme achievement. Called Energiya ('energy' in Russian) it used the one fuel that Glushko had sworn could never work and for which he had broken with Korolev and divided the Moon programme—liquid hydrogen. Energiya was ready by spring 1987.

The huge Energiya rocket in assembly.

NIGHT TURNS TO DAY: ENERGIYA–POLYUS

For the first flight of Energiya, a payload other than Buran was selected. In July 1985, the Ministry of General Machine Building ordered the Salyut design bureau to design and build a special payload, Polyus (the Russian word for a 'pole' of the Earth). Polyus was 37m long, with a diameter of 4.1 m. It comprised the Chelomei FGB service module, with a carbon-filled plastic nosecone and equipment to test radio and optical rendezvous devices—small inflatable spheres and angled reflectors; and devices to test the interaction of Polyus with natural ionospheric plasma. The chief designer was Vladimir Pallo of the Salyut KB.

The existence of Energiya was admitted for the first time during 11–14 May 1987 when communist Party General Secretary Mikhail Gorbachev made a three-day visit to Baikonour in the course of which he inspected launch pads, assembly workshops, military facilities and the administrative centre of Leninsk (the first time the town was admitted to exist). As he returned, Moscow announced that preparations were under way for the launching of a new rocket capable of putting large space modules into orbit. Gorbachev trumpeted:

Launch of Polyus prototype orbiting factory, 15 May 1987, on the Energiya rocket, the most powerful ever developed. Polyus is concealed from view.

Lenin's dream of making our State a great industrial power has come true. Everything here is Soviet-made, everything is of high quality and of modern technological standard. There is no need for us to go cap in hand to foreign lands.[89]

Night turned to day as the countdown of Energiya climaxed on 15 May. Weighing 2000 tonnes, 60 m high, with eight engines, a thrust of 170 million horsepower, the engines roared ten full seconds before Energiya lifted off the pad, illuminating gantries, observers and towers for miles around. Energiya picked up speed and headed into distant skies.

Although the launching was perfect, the outcome was not. The Polyus payload, weighing no less than 80 tonnes, had to be placed backward on the launch stack and was required to flip 180 deg so that its service module could fire to complete orbital insertion. This manoeuvre proved too complex, Polyus tumbling several times before its engines incorrectly fired the payload downward into the Pacific Ocean. Many years later, photographs of Polyus and its launch have yet to be released (photographs of Energiya's launch were released immediately, but only of the side turned away from the payload). The Salyut OKB later proposed Polyus as an alternative to Mir orbital stations, designing it as a 100 tonne space factory which could produce a tonne of processed materials a year and which could be visited by cosmonauts twice a year for ten-day periods for refurbishment. The aims of Polyus were to produce semiconductors, optical lenses, biological preparations and medicines under zero-gravity conditions. Production cycles lasting one to three months would be supervised by robots mounted on rails. Electrical power would be provided by two pairs of solar panels, one 250 m^2, the other 51 m^2, providing 56 kW.[90]

This setback did little to dampen the enthusiasm of commentators, who realized that the Soviet Union at last had the huge rocket booster it had always craved. The unhappy history of the N-1 had been put to rest; Energiya had succeeded at its first attempt. The Academy of Sciences issued a statement on 23 May, announcing that Energiya would be used to 'build cities in space, put colonists on the Moon and send cosmonauts to Mars'.

BURAN REVEALED

The existence of a Soviet space shuttle was first made public in January the following year, when Glavcosmos Soviet space agency chief Alexander Dunayev told the press conference which welcomed home cosmonaut Yuri Romanenko that a Soviet shuttle would be launched 'in the nearest future' and that preparations were being made to ready Energiya 2 for launch. In March it was confirmed that it would be quite different in design from the American shuttle (one wonders what Chelomei would have made of that, had he been alive) and that it would make two circuits of the Earth. In May it was stated that the shuttle had a payload of 29.7 tonnes and that it was intended to carry a crew of three pilots and seven researchers. The first pictures were released on 29 September, the day the American space shuttle returned to orbit after two and a half years following the *Challenger* disaster. The Soviet space shuttle indeed looked very similar to the American shuttle, with similar dimensions. However, the main differences were in the propulsion system. The space shuttle used Energiya entirely to get into orbit and was not dependent on its own engines, thus giving it a higher payload; and Energiya used liquid-fuelled engines, not the riskier solid-fuelled motors. Journalists were invited to Baikonour on 26 October and were told

Energiya–Buran heads down to the pad, October 1988.

At first sight, Buran looks very like the American space shuttle.

that the launch of the space shuttle, unmanned, had been set for three days later at 6.23 a.m. Moscow time.

The unprecedented new openness of the Soviet space programme to the media was not rewarded. First, there was a four-hour hold. Then, when the count approached the moment of reckoning, it was aborted. The waiting journalists were told that the launching was postponed 'indefinitely'. Later, it transpired that one of the swing arms had failed to retract fully and the computer had aborted the countdown. Energiya was brought back to the hanger, to re-emerge on 8 November for a second attempt. Driven by four railway cars, the horizontally stacked shuttle was pushed down to the pad, where hydraulic jacks raised it into position.

The pad for the space shuttle, adapted from the old N-1 site, had two service towers 64 m high, a traversing tower 100 m high, and was surrounded by several 225 m high lightning conductors. Embarkation and escape chutes, from the distance looking like air conditioning pipes, connected the space shuttle with an underground bunker 100 m away. In an emergency, the crew could ride a small cabin down a 4 m wide chute to safety.

A complex series of towers and escape tunnels surrounded Buran on the pad.

BURAN FLIES!

Fuelling was completed for a second time late on 14 November. Buran stood 36 m, long, 16 m high, with a fuselage diameter of 5.6 m and had a wing area of 350 m^2. Snow-white in colour, its thermally vulnerable areas were made of black ceramic tiling of extrafine quartz fibre and elastic, high-temperature organic fibres, designed to withstand 1500°C. The shuttle was equipped with MiG-25 type ejector seats, allowing cosmonauts to fire

Buran's night-time countdown, November 1988.

themselves free either up to mach 3 during the ascent or from 30 km downward during the descent.

Journalists flew back to Baikonour to cover the rescheduled 3 a.m. liftoff. As the countdown reached zero, gigantic billowing clouds erupted all around the towers. After an agonizingly long period of waiting, Buran was seen to rise slowly above the clouds of steam, dust and flame, and headed far into the night sky. Buran took eight minutes to reach orbit and then used its own engines to take it from 160 km to 260 km. The first stages impacted on the ground, the second into the Pacific Ocean.

Over Fiji, ground controllers activated the onboard television cameras which panned around the empty cabin and out the windows to mark the blue Pacific down below. At the end of its second orbit, Buran lowered its height to 100 km. Retrorockets fired. Buran came in over the Mediterranean at 25 times the speed of sound. Ground controllers and computers took Buran through a series of flying turns as the space shuttle swung toward the cosmodrome where it had started off. Baikonour radar picked up Buran at an altitude of 40 km, range 400 km.

Television picked up the shuttle as it fell gently from the early morning sky. Buran curved, rolled and aligned itself automatically with the 4.5 km long runway. Landing speed was between 310 km/h and 340 km/h. Maghomed Tolboyev, in a jet fighter, sped past Buran's tail as the wheels came down. A braking parachute of 75 m^2 area shot out to slow the space shuttle's speed. Sixteen TV cameras watched Buran come to a halt, its

Mission control as Buran nears the end of its mission.

snow-white frame standing out against the wintry russet browns of wintertime Tyuratam. Buran came to a standstill less than 2 km from its touchdown point.

The Soviet press hailed Buran as a superb technological achievement, which it was. The entire mission had been carried out entirely under automatic control. Energiya had

Buran touches down after a perfect maiden flight.

performed flawlessly. Only five of Buran's 38 000 tiles had come off. At an end-of-year press conference, Glavcosmos director Alexander Dunayev told journalists that each Soviet shuttle would make four to five flights a year. It would carry out repair work, bring up new modules to space stations and bring back unwanted space equipment, like the derelict Salyut 7 space station, he added.

At the very end of the year, a gigantic transport plane which had been adapted to transport the shuttle on its back, the Antonov 225, or Myria (the Ukrainian word for 'dream'), made its first, 76 min maiden flight near Kiev. The following summer, Myria carried Buran on its back to the Paris Air Show, where its dramatic arrival was the show-stopper. The chief designer of the Energiya–Buran system, Valentin Glushko, lived just long enough to see Energiya and Buran take to the skies. He died in Moscow on 10 January 1989, aged 81. He had been designing and building rocket engines since he was 13.

BURAN GROUNDED

But Glushko did not live to see the disappointment which followed. Buran's basic problem was that it was a spacecraft in search of a mission and a payload. Although the Krystal module on the Mir space station carried a docking module which could receive Buran, there was little Buran could do that other Soviet rockets and spacecraft did not already do. Buran still had some way to go before being man-rated: the electronics required upgrading and life-support equipment had to be installed in the cabin. The following year, touted first pilot Igor Volk gave 1990 as the date for a second, unmanned test, and 1992 as the first manned flight. But he admitted that finding a suitable payload was 'a problem'. Rumours and announcements abounded during 1989–93 of forthcoming Buran and Energiya missions.

In April 1990, Glavcosmos announced that Buran would be mothballed: it was simply too expensive to install avionics, life-support systems and fuel cells in it for manned oper-ation. The first manned shuttle would be the second one, called Pchitka (Russian for 'little bird'). The announcement took place in the context of the Soviet space budget being cut that year from R300 million to R220 million. In October that year there was the first indi-cations from Glavcosmos that the entire Energiya–Buran programme would be suspended, though as late as early 1993, there was still discussion of the possibility of a shuttle mis-sion to visit Mir and dock on Krystal. In an effort to generate fresh interest in the pro-gramme, the Energiya NPO prepared a modified version of Energiya, called Energiya-M. With two strap-on rockets (rather than four), the mission of the new rocket was to place 40 tonnes into low Earth orbit.

All this came to nothing. In June 1993, the Council of Designers formally decided to shelve the Energiya–Buran programme. The funds available were only about 1% of what was required to prepare a mission, and it was futile to carry on the pretence of preparing a flight that had no real chance of leaving the ground, they added. The following month, 52 directors of military complexes wrote a letter of protest at the closure of the shuttle programme. The cost of the programme had been R20 billion, about $30 billion in prevail-ing currency rates.

BURAN EPILOGUE

Of the shuttle hardware, two flight models had been built (Buran itself and Pchitka). They remain at Baikonour, accompanied by six complete Energiya sets and could be made man-ready should the need arise. The six analogues found homes in museums and storage sheds. One was bought by a joint stock company headed by cosmonaut Gherman Titov and was relocated in Moscow's Culture Park, where 48 visitors at a time pay R60,000 (about £12) for a two-hour multi-media space voyage in which they eat space food, travel through space and even fend off a meteor shower. Of the many cosmonauts who trained to fly Buran, only two made it into space and they flew on the venerable Soyuz cabin. The rest were disappointed.

The Energiya–Buran pads are now being reclaimed by nature. Though the programme is cited as a monument to politics and waste, it is not the only rotting shuttle launch base. On the California coast, wild flowers, desert brush and bobcats are gradually overrunning the site where the US Air Force had once planned to send military space shuttles into Polar orbit. The present booklet on the Vandenberg Air Force Base doesn't even mention that the facility exists.

Tireless Valentin Glushko's last project was the Zarya, work on which began in the mid-1980s in the Energiya NPO. Zarya was designed to replace Soyuz as the ferry for manned space stations. Zarya was a Soyuz-shaped cabin, but much larger, 13.7 tonnes in weight, 3.7 m across the base, able to ferry up five cosmonauts and 1.5 tonnes to an orbiting space station. Fitted to fly on the Zenith rocket, it had a revolutionary system of using its main propulsion system to assist soft-landing on Earth. With a mixture of parachutes, landing legs and rocket engines, its touchdown would be soft and safe, and would require the minimum of recovery crews—a step towards single stage to orbit and landing, likely to be one of the main lines of space development in the new century.

ASSESSMENT

Thus ended forty years of spaceplane development in Russia and the Soviet Union. It was an ignominious end for a series of programmes which had shown so much promise. The Russians satisfied themselves that they could build a shuttle to rival the Americans, but little else. One can only speculate on the space successes in other fields had they received the massive resources which had instead gone to Energiya and Buran.

The minuscule publicity given in the Western media to the flight of Buran meant that most people were quite unaware that the Soviet Union ever developed a space shuttle, less still matched the American space shuttle. To the contrary, the Soviet Union built up a rich tradition of spaceplane and space shuttle expertise, skills, and theoretical and practical knowledge which could provide the firm basis for exciting new, advanced projects in the early 21st century.

Part 3: Space stations

8

The first space stations

The whole idea is to move from Earth to settlements in space
Konstantin Tsiolkovsky, letter to a student

Space stations had been a central element in Konstantin Tsiolkovsky's vision of space and they were a theme of Soviet and Russian space exploration even before the Moon race was abandoned. Crews of orbiting space stations could observe Earth, distant planets and stars, and be the stepping stone for journeys to the Moon and planets. In 1962, Sergei Korolev, at the time of his first design of the Soyuz complex for translunar flight, devised a plan for a manned orbiting space station called Sibir, linking up Vostok-sized modules. Three years later, he designed a 75-tonne space station, OS-1 (Orbital Station 1), which could be launched by a version of the N-1 rocket. It had docking ports for six Soyuz spacecraft, solar panels and hatches for spacewalks. Korolev managed to build a mockup of OS-1 and for some years the mockup stood in the corner of workshop 444 of the Experimental Machinery Manufacturing Factory. OS-1 had four floors for crew quarters, storage units and scientific equipment. It was 6 m high and 2.9 m in diameter. The OS-1 was developed no further because the Moon race became the overriding priority of the space programme during this period.[91]

ALMAZ

Korolev's rival, Vladimir Chelomei, produced his first space station designs during the same period. In October 1964, Vladimir Chelomei made proposals for a space station capable of supporting two to three cosmonauts for two years. His OKB-52 accordingly came up with the Almaz (the Russian word for 'diamond') design.[92] Chelomei promoted the station to the military as the means whereby the Soviet Union could watch American aircraft carriers at sea.

Almaz and its resupply craft were both intended for separate launches on the UR-500 Proton. The Almaz space station had crew quarters, radar remote-sensing equipment, cameras, two small re-entry capsules for sending data back to Earth and even Nudelman rapid-fire cannon to defend the station against attacking American spaceplanes! Almaz was 14.55 m in length and 4.15 m in diameter. Almaz had a television observation system with a 6 m focal length which produced pictures of 50 cm by 50 cm. These were developed on board the station, scanned and relayed to Earth. The principal targets were American naval and aircraft manoeuvres. The system required that the station be pointed continuously at Earth, which was expensive on fuel supplies. The living section for the cosmonauts included sleeping and eating facilities and portholes through which to observe the Earth. Two manoeuvring engines were fitted outside the docking port. After the cosmonauts had left, additional film would be sent down by small recoverable capsules. These were bucket-shaped, 89 cm long and 91.5 cm in diameter, and were ejected from a larger capsule which was spun out of the Almaz hull, fired a small retrorocket and dropped the bucket for re-entry, parachute descent and recovery.

The crew would be ferried up in a large spacecraft called TKS, or Transport Logistics Spacecraft (in Russian, Transportniye Korabl Snabzheniye). TKS was 17.51 m long and 4.15 m in diameter. On top was a long, thin escape tower for possible use during the launch. TKS had a large service module with solar arrays and was almost as large as the space station itself. The service module was called the FGB (which translates untidily as 'universal functional block'). The FGB service module was a pressurized compartment with rendezvous and docking systems and four engines fitted on the outside of the hull. These engines, called RD-0225, were developed by the Chemical Automatics Design Bureau and had a thrust of 400 kg (or 3900 N), using UDMH and nitrogen tetroxide. The exterior fitting of the engines later caused some American analysts to misinterpret ground photographs and mistake them for cannon, and a racy report was issued in the 1980s that a Soviet 'battlestar' station was in orbit.

The cosmonauts would sit in the cabin at the top of the service module or FGB. Called Merkur (Mercury), the cabin looked more like the Apollo command module than the Soyuz's. Its cone was flatter and the cabin much larger than Soyuz. Once in orbit, to enter their service module below them, the cosmonauts would clamber through a hatch in the heat shield underneath them. It was an unorthodox arrangement, but identical to the one the Americans chose for their manned orbiting laboratory. They would dock the TKS with Almaz using through docking windows at the other end from Merkur, linking with the larger end of Almaz (Chelomei was adamant about this, fearing the ship would be otherwise unstable).

Almaz was similar in concept to the American MOL project then taking shape. In 1965, President Johnson ordered the construction of a Manned Orbiting Laboratory, MOL, based on designs for military orbiting space stations which the US Air Force had considered as far back as 1958. Two men would go into orbit on a Gemini spacecraft, which was attached to a cylindrical laboratory atop a Titan 3 rocket. They would transfer into the laboratory for two weeks or so, carry out military reconnaissance and experiments and return in Gemini. A special team of navy and air force astronauts was recruited for the missions, which were expected to start in 1968 (its members eventually flew the early shuttle missions of the early 1980s). MOL would fly out of a specially built launch centre at the Vandenberg Air Force Base in California. In the event, costs spiralled, the Vietnam war siphoned off funds, dates slipped and MOL was cancelled in 1969. New, unmanned

spy satellites were able to achieve a similar performance to what had been expected of
MOL by late 1970.

ALMAZ READY

Orders for a military space station were given in 1965 by a joint resolution of the CPSU
and the Council of Ministers. Chelomei was given the go-ahead to build the Almaz project in 1967 and told to have it ready in 1969. Station designer was VA Polyachenko. By
1970, ten Almaz space stations stood on the factory floor of the Khrunichev plant in
Moscow, almost ready to fly. The one hold-up had been the control system, which was
almost completed.

Space stations: the key government decisions

1965	Joint resolution on a military space station
1967	Chelomei OKB-52 directed to build Almaz
1969	Joint resolution laying down orbital stations as a main line of space development, confirming the Almaz project
Feb. 1970	Joint resolution directing a simplified orbital station to be built by OKB-52 and OKB-1
1979	Cancellation of the Almaz project.

By 1969–70, the Soviet Union was urgently in need of a programme to replace its failed
lunar efforts and to present a publicly credible manned alternative. The political leadership was no longer prepared to wait for Almaz. At the end of 1969, several efforts were
made to knock the heads of the different design bureaux to produce an orbital station more
quickly. In February 1970, the Council of Ministers and the Central Committee signed a
joint resolution directing a combination of the work of the Korolev OKB-1 bureau and
Chelomei's OKB-52 to build a first, simplified, experimental space station, based on
Soyuz-developed hardware and Almaz ideas. Since both Soyuz and Almaz were built in
the same sprawling Khrunichev factory, the physical effects of the directive were minimal.
It was ironic that only after losing the Moon race did the Soviet political leadership force
a level of cooperation among the rival design bureaux.

Construction of the new orbital station, called DOS-1 (Long Duration Station-1), took
only twelve months from the resolution to the point when it was sent on the train to
Baikonour. The control systems and the solar panels were taken from Soyuz and simply
installed on Almaz.

TROIKA

In the meantime, Soyuz was to be tested in a series of manoeuvres vital for successful
Earth orbit rendezvous and docking. Originally, Soyuz 6 and 7 were to link together in a

repeat of the January linkup in a final test of rendezvous and docking before such manoeuvres were carried out in lunar orbit. Now Soyuz 6 was to be outfitted as a laboratory and fly in a trio (in Russian, a *troika*) with Soyuz 7 and 8, which were to dock, while being filmed by Soyuz 6. There would be an internal crew transfer. The first indications came at the annual teach-in held in Kaluga on Tsiolkovsky's birthday (20 September) when Boris Petrov delivered the main paper. It was called 'Manned space stations: the next step'. He told his audience:

> The most efficient way to assemble space stations in orbit will be to take each part into orbit by booster rocket. Methods for mutual tracking of two such ships, put into close orbits, manoeuvring, docking, linkup and undocking, are being developed.

Soyuz 6 was fired aloft on 11 October 1969, with a two-man crew. Tass announced that its main objective would be welding in space. There were new faces aboard. Commander was Georgi Shonin, 34, who was accompanied by flight engineer Valeri Kubasov, who had worked in the Korolev design bureau where he wrote a paper called 'The correction of interplanetary trajectory using radial impulses of heliocentric velocity'. As he and Shonin boarded their spaceship it was cold and drizzly, and the two men were probably glad to get away. The USSR went to some pains to explain that Soyuz 6 was different from previous Soyuz models. It carried no docking mechanism, and no automatic rendezvous equipment: instead, it carried extra fuel for 'extensive manoeuvring'; and new means of carrying out vacuum welding.

As Soyuz 6 swung over Baikonour the following morning, Soyuz 7 streaked through cloudy autumn skies to join it. Another three, new, cosmonauts were on board: Anatoli Filipchenko, Vladislav Volkov and Viktor Gorbatko. Filipchenko was a veteran of supersonic planes; Volkov was a superb engineer from a family of aircraft designers and played ice hockey to a national standard; Viktor Gorbatko was the last of the 1960 selection to get a flight. There were now five men in orbit, and both ships were quite close to each other as they circled the globe. Vladislav Volkov spoke to Moscow television from orbit. He hinted darkly: 'I am responsible for communications and various other tasks, but I'm not going to tell you about them yet'.

'Higher and faster, up it goes!' exulted a Tass commentator, when at lunchtime the following day Soyuz 8 took off through heavy rain to join their five comrades. It was 13 October 1969. On board were two veterans of the January mission—Vladimir Shatalov and Alexei Yeliseyev. Shatalov was named as the 'commander of the space fleet'. It was a record. Never before had seven men been in orbit at once, nor three manned spaceships. They were in close orbit together. 14 October was clearly signposted to be 'the day'. Around midday, the three craft drew to within 200 m of each other. At 7 p.m. the Western radio press reported a docking between Soyuz 7 and 8, but this was quickly denied by Tass. 'Optical and signalling tests' were being carried out. Then news dried up completely. Nothing new was heard for a day. Tass announced that the Soyuz 6 and 8 had in turn been approached to 'within a few hundred metres' by Soyuz 7. They were playing a game of cosmic tag, overtaking each other in orbit, testing navigation and manoeuvring devices. 31 joint manoeuvres were completed. Later on the 15th, ground observers in

Britain spotted the three craft crossing the sky in the evening dusk. Soyuz 7 and 8 were about 11 km apart, with 6 following 450 km behind.

Then in the early afternoon of the 16th, Tass broke the desert of news by announcing that a welding operation had been concluded aboard Soyuz 6 and that the crew had returned to Earth. On its 77th orbit, Georgi Shonin and Valeri Kubasov had retreated to the descent module and Georgi Shonin had depressurized the orbital module. One entire part of it had been set aside for the experiment and Kubasov could observe what was happening on close circuit TV. Several metals were tested under three methods of automatic welding: plasma, arc and electron beam welding. While welding on Earth in a near vacuum was virtually impossible to simulate, more pure vacuum conditions could be obtained in orbit. Free of air molecules in between them, metallic parts will, provided the surfaces are clean, fuse in a vacuum. The entire device had been put together by Dr Boris Paton of the Paton Welding Institute in Kiev—probably the most advanced such laboratory in the world. It was certainly an unusual experiment, although its space station applications lay some distance in the future.

The Soyuz 7 crew of (left to right) Anatoli Filipchenko, Vladislav Volkov and Viktor Gorbatko after their return to Earth. The troika mission failed to achieve its objective of docking but built up navigation and rendezvous experience which would prove useful in the subsequent construction of orbital space stations.

Once this was done, the module was repressurized. Valeri Kubasov re-entered the orbital cabin, collected the welding samples, brought them back, and stowed them away. They fired the retrorockets and came home. Soyuz 6 was back after 81 orbits. Shonin and Kubasov came down in a field, covered in the first snow of winter and right beside a children's school. The school broke off classes at once and the children and staff ran to investigate. Soyuz 7 and 8 came down at 24 h intervals over the next two days. Within a week of the mission's brave start, they were all back on the ground.

The Soviet press hailed the heroes as 'the men who brought space down to Earth' and gave pages of details of cyclones tracked, minerals found, land masses studied, typhoons spotted and vegetation observed. Not for 20 years was it revealed that a docking between Soyuz 7 and 8 had been intended and had failed. Soyuz 6–8 was still a valuable learning experience. Launching, controlling and landing three spaceships in a week was a real achievement in coordination—and helpful practice for the space station mission.

18-DAY BARRIER

With construction of the DOS-1 orbital station under way, a long-duration mission was constructed to fill the gap until it was ready. It was a sensible move. The Soviet duration record was only five days, set by Bykovsky back in 1963, since surpassed by America's Gemini 5 (eight days) and Gemini 7 (fourteen). The later Apollo Moon missions lasted about ten days. A duration mission was necessary as a prelude to a long flight aboard an orbital station—indeed that was the whole purpose of flying orbital stations. 18 days was set as the target.

As a bonus, Soyuz 9 would test out the lunar decontamination unit. The man-on-the-Moon programme was still in existence at this stage and should it fly, some kind of decontamination would be required. The question was taken very seriously at the time. It was feared that lunar spacemen could pick up germs from the Moon, bring them back to Earth and let them loose on the unprotected population of Earthlings. When Neil Armstrong, Michael Collins and Edwin Aldrin came back from the Moon they were unceremoniously bundled into blue coveralls and gas masks and locked up in a sealed caravan for three weeks (such precautions were eventually dropped in 1971). Soyuz 9 would also develop the Earth resources observations begun by the troika. The flight would be timed for mid-summer so as to give conditions of maximum lighting over the northern regions of the USSR.

Soyuz 9 was of course limited to a crew of two, both for reasons of air supply and the amount of physical space on board. It was Vostok 3 veteran Andrian Nikolayev's last chance to get into space. Flight Engineer Vitaly Sevastianov was already known to television viewers because he had his own science programme—he was anchor-man on a Moscow television science series called *Man, the Earth and the universe*, but none of the viewers yet knew of his other identity. It was well into the night-time after a scorching hot day when the transfer van brought Andrian Nikolayev and Vitaly Sevastianov to Pad B at Baikonour. Floodlights lit up the complex as the final count began. Engines hummed and liquid oxygen boiled off in the sweltering heat.

By way of a strange counterpoint, the first man on the Moon, Neil Armstrong, was visiting Moscow that evening. He was in Star Town. Its auditorium was filled as he

Soyuz' night-time launch.

showed the audience a film of his flight to the Moon and gave his own personal commentary. The experience excited both envy and intense admiration. The film was greeted with warm applause. Georgi Beregovoi presented him with a model of Soyuz; he received a bouquet from Valentina Tereshkova. A bittersweet moment followed as he told the assembly how, on the personal request of Valentina Komarov and Valentina Gagarin, he had placed the medals of their husbands on the surface of the Sea of Tranquillity. This gesture of friendship left many tears and it seemed not to matter that it was American astronauts who put them there.

After the film show, it was time for dinner *chez* Beregovoi. Half way through, Beregovoi turned on the television and treated Armstrong to the televised liftoff of Soyuz 9. It probably occurred to Neil Armstrong at one stage that this was a Beregovoi prank, but it was not. Valentina Tereshkova, wife of the mission commander, was with them and she made it clear that it was not. By the 14th orbit on 2 June the two cosmonauts had manoeuvred into a stable orbit of 214 by 270 km, 89 min and in this pattern they remained for the full mission.

The designers of Soyuz 9 made serious efforts to provide for the material comforts of the crew. There was a sofa, a working table, a microfilm library, portholes with blinds, brass handrails and the inevitable picture of Lenin overseeing all. The men slept in sleeping bags, and were able to shave. Each man consumed 2600 calories a day: thirty types of food were stored in tubes, and an electric cooker provided hot meals and drinks. Soyuz was spun 2-and-a-half times a minute so as to distribute heat evenly over its surface. It was of course de-spun for experiments and observations of the ground, which were a major part of the mission. Vitaly Sevastianov had been specially trained to look at snow covering the mountains of the southern republics. A geological survey of Siberia was made on the 17th June, in conjunction with aircraft. On the 12th they tracked the progress of a storm over Iran. On the 16th they were able to give a storm warning to the citizens of Novosibirsk, well in advance of the local weather service.

Vitaly Sevastianov made a special project of luminous clouds and later wrote a paper about them, published in May 1971. Originally they were thought to exist only over the Arctic, but he found them over Arabia too. And on Soyuz' 188th orbit a weather profile of the Indian Ocean was made combined with sounding rockets launched from the ship *Akademik Shirmov* 230 km below and a Meteor weather satellite 370 km above. The flight was paying its own way, claimed Tass. 50 separate experiments were carried.

But the success or failure of the flight would stand or fall on the basis of the ability of the men to withstand zero gravity. At the beginning, all went well enough. Doctors insisted that they exercise at least 2 h each day on a bicycle frame and chest expander so as to build up muscles that would otherwise deteriorate. This they did, but it was not popular, particularly as there was no means of showering afterwards. Flight doctors went to some length to provide psychological comfort. Programmes were beamed up on radio and TV.

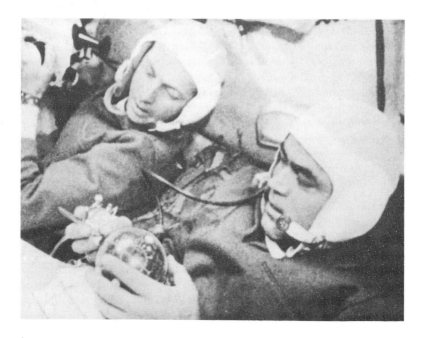

Soyuz 9 crewmen Vitaly Sevastianov (left) and Andrian Nikolayev during their 18-day mission. Information on their poor condition on return to Earth was withheld for many months.

Both cosmonauts talked to their families; Nikolayev to his daughter, Lenochka, on her birthday. The crew watched some of the World Cup soccer. They voted in the USSR General Election. They played a 35-move chess game with ground control: it was a draw.

The problems began on day 12, when fatigue began to set in. The men began to look for rest periods sooner and sooner, and once tried to dodge exercises: ground control found out when telemetry showed that carbon dioxide levels in the cabin were too low. They got eye irritation. They got so tired that ground control had to use a siren to wake them up in the morning. After 285 orbits it was decided to call it a day.

Andrian Nikolayev fired the retrorockets for 145 s over Africa. With their feet drawn together closely in the cramped cabin, they gradually felt the gentle tug of gravity begin to pull them Earthwards once more. Then stronger and stronger. They could see flames shoot past the window as they blazed in an arc over the Mediterranean. Helicopters spotted Soyuz 9 descending and followed it down for a full eight minutes. The capsule came to rest in a dusty ploughed field. It had been away for a full 17 days, 16 hours and 59 minutes—a new record. Rescue teams from four helicopters surrounded the capsule. The two men were brought out on stretchers through the top and transferred to the helicopters in a state of biological isolation. They were flown speedily to Star Town by way of Vnukuvo airport and were not let out till 2 July, two weeks later: the same period of isolation as a Moon journey would require.

Flight debriefing was carried out behind glass partitions: telephones and microphones were used. The isolation complex had probably cost a lot to build, and this was the only use it was to get. *Soviet Weekly* tried to explain:

> The isolation isn't because of fears that Nikolayev and Sevastianov may have brought back strange diseases from outer space! Indeed the precautions are for the opposite reason. Doctors consider it possible that protracted space flight may lower normal immunities and they are therefore making sure that the spacemen are protected from earthbound infection until they have acclimatized.

Although Soviet space flights grew longer and longer, the facility was never used again. The biological isolation was only one of the myths surrounding Soyuz 9. The other was the actual medical condition of the cosmonauts. First reports indicated—in fact they stated outright—that both men were well and had suffered no ill effects from the mission and were as well as previous crews:

> The condition of health, working efficiency, and the general tone of the cosmonauts are much higher than what the medical men had expected...the flight has shown that many of the worries the doctors and biologists had were unfounded.

However, observation of the cosmonauts during their isolation period showed that they were 'slow to respond', 'pale', 'their faces furrowed with wrinkles'. They tired rapidly, lost concentration, and efforts to make conversation or jokes faltered. These were the medical reports, not what readers read in their papers.

Andrian Nikolayev and Vitaly Sevastianov resurfaced publicly at an international space conference in October 1970 in Konstanz, West Germany. A new story came out there. Both men had been severely weakened by their spell in space. They could not stand for three days and their heart rates were twice the normal. They took a full month to recover. Nevertheless, these factors made Soyuz 9 a success, rather than a failure. To have proceeded directly to a space station without such a mission would have been foolhardy. The next months were quiet while Soviet engineers completed assembly of the world's first orbiting space station. It was planned to have it ready in time for the 10th anniversary of Yuri Gagarin's flight, on 12 April 1971. It was called Zarya (Russian for 'dawn').

SALUTE

Indications of an upcoming space station mission first appeared on 15 March 1971, when the unnamed chief designer told *Socialist industry*:

> It seems to me very expedient to build in the near future an orbital space station near the Earth that would operate for a very long time.

Come the Gagarin anniversary and the rumours were flowing thick and fast. Two teams of cosmonauts had already left for the pad. The tracking fleet had taken up station. The Moscow press corps was abuzz with excitement. Something big was in the air.

It happened on the 19 April. Late that morning, Moscow Radio came on air to announce the launching of the world's first orbiting space station. In the hours before launch, it was realized that Zarya was also the codename for the ground control centre, which would lead to some confusion on the airwaves when Zarya called Zarya. The station was hurriedly named Salyut (a 'salute' to the anniversary), though not in sufficient time to have the brightly painted words 'Zarya', in red, removed from its side. It had entered a low, but safe orbit, of 200 by 222 km, 88.5 min, 51.6 deg. Salyut was given a complete telecommunications checkout on its 9th orbit, and all was in order. The next day, 20 April, Leonid Brezhnev called the flight an 'important step in the conquest of space'. On the next, Georgi Beregovoi added that orbiting stations with changing crews would be the main feature of space exploration in the 1970s.

At this stage no one had a clue as to what Salyut looked like.[93] Salyut was a tapering cylinder of three different diameters—4.15 m, 2.9 m and 2.0 m. It was 14.4 m long and weighed 18.9 tonnes. At the rear was a motor and propellant so the spacecraft could change orbit, a capability that America's Skylab did not have. At the front end was the docking unit. Masts and antennæ protruded. Two solar arrays sprung out from the front and two from the rear. It might have looked like a strange aircraft of revolutionary design.

On the inside it was a real space station. Swimming into Salyut from a docked Soyuz, the visitor met a spacious control panel. It faced forwards and there were two pilot seats. Lights flashed and displays hummed and control sticks permitted the cosmonauts to control and fly the complex. The walls were full of lockers—for food, water, scientific equipment, manuals, clothes, books, hygiene and repairs. And there were handrails everywhere for the men to move about in zero gravity. Moving on to the main room of the cylinder there was a compartment filled with equipment. A telescope built into the hull allowed the men to view the stars. There were three portholes so the cosmonauts could view the Earth. Sleeping bags were slung from hooks. Several exercise devices completed the internal equipment. It provided living space on a scale never enjoyed before and a range of equipment that the small up-and-down craft could never imagine. Late on 22 April, Salyut completed its 66th orbit. The temperature at night-time Baikonour was −26°C. Three cosmonauts had just arrived at the pad. The onion-shaped Soyuz 10 rocket stood waiting, bathed in floodlight. Alexei Yeliseyev, flight engineer, was holding an impromptu press conference. In their flight coveralls alone, they would have frozen, but they wore thick leather jackets and officer caps. Yeliseyev used a twig to draw in the snow to explain the upcoming mission to journalists. With mission commander Vladimir Shatalov beside him and research engineer Nikolai Rukavishnikov—an expert in solar physics from the Korolev design bureau—alongside, Yeliseyev concluded: 'the night is cloudless, clear and starry. We are ready to go on up'. Flames licked around the base of the stand. Night turned to day as Soyuz 10 rose from the pad and sped to orbit. The chase had begun.

'LIKE A TRAIN ARRIVING...'

Soyuz 10 shot into a much higher orbit than planned, but Vladimir Shatalov at once began pursuit manoeuvres. It was the most experienced crew that could be put together for such a mission. In six hours, Soyuz 10's long-range radar had picked up Salyut. Vladimir Shatalov went through twelve complex computer manoeuvres. Soyuz 10 changed orbit three times, and Shatalov commanded Salyut through four changes. 24 h into the mission, the two ships were 11 km apart. They were closing at 98 km/h. Shatalov cut the closing speed and braked. He commanded on the navigation lights of Salyut. Now Alexei Yeliseyev could spot it through his window. With its lights flashing, the bright white cylinder, wings outstretched, was, he recalled later, 'indescribably beautiful'. The letters 'CCCP' were clearly visible on the side (and, though he did not say so, probably the station's original name, Zarya).

Shatalov moved Soyuz 10 forward till they were only 180 m apart. They lined up for docking. Then, slowly, they moved forwards at 1 m/s and cut the speed again. At 2.47 a.m. on the 24 April they had contact. The ships were coupled. Alexei Yeliseyev said it was like a 'train arriving at a railway station'. They had done it—the first linkup to an orbital station.

Or so everyone thought. The next the world knew about Soyuz 10 was that it was back on Earth. And it was not an easy re-entry either. It took place at night. Rescue teams gasped as Soyuz 10 headed straight into a lake. At the last moment a breeze blew it away and it came down on a pebble beach 44 m from the water's edge as frogmen stood ready with aqualungs. The three cosmonauts had been up for 47 h 46 min—the shortest Soyuz mission so far since Komarov's. They were flown at once by helicopter to Karaganda. Snow lay on the ground as they held a post-flight press conference.

So what happened? Soyuz 10 and Salyut had been linked for 5.5 h, or nearly four orbits. There was no suggestion that an emergency had arisen. Indeed, a telecast from Salyut showed Soyuz pulling away against a cloud-shrouded background of Earth. It was all very orderly. Soyuz, so the story went, was simply testing the docking mechanism, and it had never been intended to board the station. Not until 1993 was it revealed that there had been a gear failure in the docking unit. Soyuz 10 was ordered to fly around the station, photographing the docking joint. A number of modifications were made to strengthen the probe of Soyuz 11. On 27 April, Salyut fired its rocket motor to put it up into a much higher orbit of 251 by 277 km, 89.36 min. From there it would be in a good position, having drifted downwards once more from atmospheric drag, to receive a new crew of three men in the first week of June.

On 4 June, Valeri Kubasov failed his medical for the mission. The State Commission decided to replace the entire main crew of Valeri Kubasov, Alexei Leonov and Pyotr Kolodin with the full backup crew.

Salyut 1 flew on. Whatever the problems were with Soyuz 10 they were not so serious as to impede a new launch at the first available opportunity when Salyut was over the launch pad. The launch window began on 6 June and the most suitable landing conditions would take place from 9 to 21 July, indicating a mission of at least 34 days. Suitable landing conditions, termed 'landing windows', refer to periods when cosmonauts could make the most accurate landing in the designated area more than 3 h before sunset, thereby giving recovery crews adequate daylight to retrieve them; and when it is possible to fire the retrorockets in daylight, a procedural change introduced after Komarov's fatal re-entry.

SOYUZ 11: HEROES FOREVER

A *Pravda* interview on 3 June with Konstantin Feoktistov about the importance of space stations set the scene for the new flight. On the 24th, Tass reported Salyut's orbit as down to 212 by 250 km, 88.8 min, just in range for the Soyuz ferry. It was nearly 5 a.m. on Sunday, 6 June 1971, when Georgi Dobrovolski, 43, Vladislav Volkov, 35, and Viktor Patsayev, 37, arrived at the pad. Dawn had just broken. It was so very different from the April mission with its snowy backdrop. Now the steppes were scorched and dry and this day would be a hot one too.

Onlookers, wellwishers and launch staff pressed flowers into the hands of the departing cosmonauts. Dobrovolski was the tallest and had donned a military cap like the ones John F. Kennedy wore on wartime PT boats. Vladislav Volkov was relaxed, jaunty and cheerful as ever. Viktor Patsayev, a radio expert, was the shiest of the three and stood quietly. Then they climbed aboard.

> 5.40 a.m. From his cabin 40 m up, Georgi Dobrovolski reported: 'This is Yantar (code name) and we are ready to go on up'. The count went on automatic sequence. Fuel lines were cleared, drainage lines withdrawn.
>
> 5.45 a.m. Soyuz 11 was now on full internal power. The capsule access arm retracted.
>
> 5.50 a.m. The large squad of journalists and newsmen present trained their big cameras on the booster. They stopped talking, silent in expectation. Morning sunlight shone brightly on the white rocket.
>
> 5.55 a.m. And off it went! Soyuz 11 lifted slowly off the pad. It accelerated skywards, trailing a cottony white contrail. 'Little vibration', Georgi Dobrovolski reported back. They were soon lost to sight.
>
> 6.02 a.m. 'Temperature 22°C, pressure 840 mb, all's well.'

6.04 a.m. 'Orbital insertion', Dobrovolski reported. 'Commencing separation, stabilization, antenna and solar wing deployment'. So well was the mission going that when news of the launch was broken, it was also announced confidently that Soyuz would carry out 'comprehensive studies with the Salyut station.'

7 June, 5.26 a.m. By now, Georgi Dobrovolski had navigated Soyuz 11 across the vastness of space to within 6.5 km from Salyut. Then, using the manoeuvring stick, he closed to 100 m.

5.50 a.m. Station keeping, 100 m apart. The two spacecraft flew a full two revolutions at this distance. There may have been a fault in the automatic system, for at 8.30 he was ordered to complete the operation manually.

8.45 a.m. Linkup! Salyut had completed 794 orbits, Soyuz 18. They contacted slowly and then coupled rigidly—mechanically, electrically, hydraulically.

Then began the stage where their predecessors were cheated: climbing into the station itself. Opening up the internal hatches was not as easy as it sounded, for all the pressures and valves had to be equalized and the tunnel airtight.

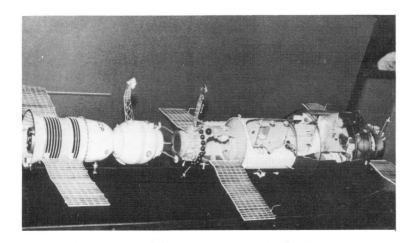

A model of Soyuz (left) linking with Salyut 1 in June 1971. A cutaway reveals some of the living quarters of the world's first orbital space station.

Eventually all was ready. Vladislav Volkov opened up and floated through. He was the world's first visitor to a space base. Gingerly he swam in, moving hand over hand on the handrails. Viktor Patsayev and Georgi Dobrovolski followed: 'the station's huge: there seems to be no end to it!', the commander exclaimed. As they floated through, they could appreciate and enjoy its size: their first task was to turn it into a real home.

And that is what they did. They unloaded their equipment from Soyuz and after two days they were able to close down Soyuz's systems. They pulled the hatch behind them and lived entirely in the station itself. Salyut was warmed up and hummed into life. Georgi Dobrovolski and Vladislav Volkov soon got used to controlling the space station from its jetliner-like flight deck. They used it to turn on Salyut's motor to raise the orbit up to 239 by 265 km, 89 min—the first time a manned space station and attached ferry flew together as one unit. The men could see a bright burst of flames through the portholes. The ship shook with vibration. Ice flakes drifted off the hull like a snow blizzard as their base swung into a higher orbit.

The three-man crew soon settled into a pattern of work. There was always at least one man on duty at a time. Breakfast happened each day at 11 a.m., after which the crew ran a comprehensive check of the station's systems. From 3 p.m. to 11 p.m. they were outside the radio range of ground control. Once back they reported in. Each day they sent in a weather report.

Starting on 9 June, the crew began transmitting a daily series of television chat shows. Each day they reported back on something new that they were doing. For the first time they appeared in strange-looking floppy tracksuits: called 'penguin suits', which were designed to stretch certain parts of the body and freshen muscles that would otherwise decay. Like Soyuz 9, exercise was the key to survival, though the roomy conditions made this infinitely easier. Each cosmonaut exercised for two hours a day on a chest expander, a bicycle and a treadmill. Although they did not like it, the astronauts knew they had to do it.

A vast programme of scientific work was begun that put previous missions in the shade. They tested radiation levels on board every day. On the 10th, Viktor Patsayev took blood samples of all three men and analysed them. They watched through the portholes regularly to see just how much the hull was being battered by micrometeorites.

11 June: a new gamma ray telescope was put into working order for the first time and they became the first space astronomers. Viktor Patsayev showed visitors his fish farm: tadpoles swam around in a jar. What they made of weightlessness we do not know, but their reactions were being tested. Biology was his speciality. Salyut had a small garden with daylight provided by fluorescent lamps and nutrition from special hydroponic solutions. He was growing kale, cress, flax, Chinese cabbage and onion. Photographs were taken each day to observe growth. Later, space food would be grown on board. As it was, Salyut had a cooker and fridge. Their food had extra quantities of calcium—essential in zero gravity, which weakened the bones.

By 15 June they had flown 134 times around the Earth in Salyut. Observations of the Earth were central to the flight. The men studied cyclones and typhoons. They fitted filters to their cameras over the USSR's ground mass, to map the snow, tree disease, crops and moisture on the ground. At one stage on 14 June, they did a coordinated sweep of an area near the Caspian sea with an Illyushin-18 flying at 8000 m and an Antonov 2 at 300 m.

On 19 June, Viktor Patsayev celebrated his 38th birthday. They had a party and ate fruit, cheeses, nuts, veal and prunes. They got down to work and used their 'Orion' telescope to track a star and its shortwave characteristics, including rays that never reached the Earth. On 23 June, they broke the Soyuz 9 record of 18 days. They were heading into the medical unknown. They saw a sandstorm start up in Africa. In the garden, flax and kale had come up.

On 26 June the men passed the three-week mark and reported fatigue for the first time. It was little wonder. The flight log had recorded a hectic round of medical checkups, astronomical studies, gardening, atmospheric observations, examinations of the Earth and charged particles. By 27 June the medical readouts suggested a continued deterioration in the cosmonauts' health. The instruments on board provided the doctors on the ground with unprecedented detail—blood pressure, heart rates, volume of breathing, speed of inhalation. Worse, there was a brief moment of real terror when a fire broke out in cables in the station, to be quickly put out by the cosmonauts. The men were simply tiring. Baikonour ordered Dobrovolski to programme Salyut's computer so the station could fly itself once they had left. On the 28th, ground control ordered the crew—then on their 342nd circuit—to pack their belongings and come down the next evening. They could have stayed up longer but the doctors did not want to take any chances. It would mean a landing outside mission rules, but a wait till 9 July was too far away.

Early or not, feelings on the ground were close to exhilaration. The three cosmonauts had smashed every record in sight. The concept of orbiting stations had been vindicated. Salyut was the first space base beyond the Earth. The scientific haul from the mission would keep the scientists busy for years. The daily telecasts had made the three personable men heroes throughout the USSR. They became the best known space fliers since Gagarin and Leonov. The nightly shows from space entertained and enthralled viewers, not to mention one demonstration after another of the value of space research. It was clear that *this* was what space flight was all about—not lunar stunt shows. And an American answer to Salyut was still some years off. It was the good old days all over again. A tremendous reception was being prepared for the three cosmonauts' return. Excitement about the flight had increased every new day they stayed up there, as the magnitude of their achievement percolated down.

They undocked at 7.28 p.m. on the 29 June. Like a pilot ship to a whale, they flew alongside Salyut for an hour. Then they drifted slowly apart. At 11.35 p.m., Georgi Dobrovolski fired the retrorockets over Madeira. They burned briefly and the spacecraft began to head home. Soon they would enter radio blackout. As they did, Vladislav Volkov peered out the window and unexpectedly caught sight of Salyut sailing past, high above. The rays of the Sun glinted on the solar panels and gleamed brightly:

> Volkov: All is well. So long. See you soon on Earth.
> Dobrovolski: See you back on Earth. We're going into orientation now... .

These were the last words spoken by the crew of Soyuz 11. Seconds later their heartbeats ceased and they were never heard again. Subsequent investigation found that the separation bolts which were used to cast off the service module jolted the valve which normally let in air to the cabin during the final stages of descent in the atmosphere. Instead, in space, the air whistled out. Patsayev unstrapped his seat belt, trying to plug the leaking valve, but the rest of the air gushed out first. They had no space suits. They died instantly.

Happier times. The crew of Soyuz 11 (left to right in cabin) Viktor Patsayev, Georgi Dobrovolski, Vladislav Volkov in training. They were not the original crew for the mission, but were substitutes at the last moment when a member of the scheduled crew failed a medical.

'AN INVESTIGATION HAS BEEN ORDERED...'

The re-entry continued automatically. The computer brought the capsule down. A helicopter saw it land. The ground control had noticed the loss of contact but had assumed only that the radio had gone wrong. The helicopter landed right beside the capsule. Its crew ran across the field to open the hatches. As the official announcement put it:

> The re-entry was entirely normal. When the recovery forces opened the hatches, they found the crew in their seats, but there were no signs of life. An investigation has been ordered.

These chilling words glossed over what must have been an appalling shock for the recovery team—seeing the capsule land intact, opening it up, to be greeted only by the stare of three dead men. It is probable no one believed their first reports. They tried desperately to revive them, to no avail.

Their shock was only an inkling of the terrible gloom that was to descend like a dark shadow on the Soviet space programme and people alike. The crew of Soyuz 11 had not just been any ordinary crew: they had done something radically new, had broken records and had vindicated Soviet science and technology. Victory had been snatched from them in their last minutes and had been transformed not merely into failure but overwhelming defeat.

From the onset the Soviet official sources were at a total loss to explain the disaster: no effort was made even to suggest an interim explanation. The effects of prolonged weightlessness were the first and most obvious culprit: the three cosmonauts had somehow passed some magic threshold beyond which the human heart could not any longer stand the forces of gravity. So their hearts had given way.

'The outlook for manned space flight is bleak' reported a leading Western paper, echoing these fears. This was only the start. The deaths of the three explorers—who Soviet citizens had grown to admire over 24 days—left the Russian public grief-stricken. There were black-bordered portraits everywhere. Chopin's funeral march played endlessly on radio and television. Tributes poured in from throughout the world, not least from NASA and the Americans.

The ashes of the three men were interred in the Kremlin wall on 2 July. Besides the leaders of State and the cosmonaut squad, the party included American astronaut Tom Stafford, representing NASA, and President Nixon. The day was hot and heavy, and blazing sunshine streamed down. The bands played to miles and miles of citizens and soldiers; portraits and banners followed the urns in solemn tribute. The endless slow pacing of shoes was broken only by the fluttering of flags, the brush of wind in the conifer trees, and from time to time by the echoing gun salute.

Shock passed: sadness set in. And on that day, a defiant note could be detected. Cosmonauts and Party leaders swore that the struggle to conquer space would go on. At no stage was the achievement of Salyut lost. Boris Petrov wrote:

> It can be said with confidence that the 1970s will be the epoch of the development and use of long-term manned orbital stations with changing crews.

The State Committee set up to investigate the accident reported quicker than anyone expected—by 7 July, in fact. The cause had nothing to do with zero gravity. It stated:

> On the ship's descent trajectory, 30 minutes before landing there occurred a rapid drop of pressure in the descent vehicle, due to a failure in the ship's sealing.

They became the first men to actually die in space.

REDESIGN

The Soyuz 12 mission to Salyut was cancelled. Salyut was abandoned, though it stayed aloft till October. The decision was taken to redesign Soyuz, a process which took a full eleven months. The Soyuz redesign was a major undertaking. At a bare minimum the Russians could simply have modified the faulty valve in question. But they went much further in order to eliminate wider risks. It was decided to put the cosmonauts into full spacesuits, which they would wear at all critical stages of the mission, such as launch, docking and landing. If for any reason there were to be a pressure loss, the crew could still survive.

Such a decision, based on conservative notions about safety, implied serious weight and space penalties. The suits, the extra life-support systems to supply them with air, power and coolant, weighed well over 100 kg for each cosmonaut, taking up critical space in the cramped cabin. Something had to give, and it was the third seat: it was simply removed. For the foreseeable future, Soyuz and space station occupancy would be based on a two-person crew, not three. This reduced all future space hours by 33% straight off, and put the USSR at an immediate disadvantage compared to America's Skylab, with its three-man Apollo—which could even take five in an emergency configuration.

The hiatus led to other design changes in Soyuz. Some fuel capacity was dropped: less fuel was needed for low Earth orbit missions compared to Soyuz' original brief. So too were the solar panels. Granted that the redesigned Soyuz ferry was supposed to fly independently for only two days, it seemed to make sense to rely on battery power alone for that period. But both decisions—the fuel reduction and the removal of the panels—turned out to be serious errors of judgement.

The work of Salyut came to an end on 11 October 1971, though not before Salyut had three times raised its orbit—on 1 July, 28 July and 10 August. Flying over the Pacific on its 2900th orbit, its engines were commanded on by signal from the ground. It was in effect a retrofire manoeuvre: and with no shielding, only one outcome was possible. It broke up and burned up. Some larger parts may not have been completely consumed by the fires of re-entry: but they were designed to fall well away from the shipping lanes. Before its fiery end, Salyut had been seen a few times by ground observers. Lit up by the setting Sun, it could be seen crossing the autumn sky, a silent, bright, fast-moving star: a symbol of things to come. Its place in space history is an honoured one: the first laboratory, the first home in space made the more poignant by the deaths of the three brave men who first flew aboard it.

FROM DISASTER TO DISASTER

The Soviet manned space programme now entered the darkest three years in its history. No cosmonaut left the ground for another two years. There was no successful round-trip space station occupation till the summer of 1974. And the first long-term space laboratory had to wait till 1977. There was to be one near-disaster to Soyuz and several linkups that failed. Three space stations were destroyed. Soviet space leaders watched helplessly as America completed its Apollo programme and, more galling still, flew a successful space station programme (Skylab)—the one area of space travel that the USSR had declared *mare nostra*. Nothing went right.

What was worse was that these mishaps had little to do with the faults related to Soyuz 11. The causes of the Soyuz 11 disaster were identified within a week and the appropriate remedies soon agreed. The repair work and modifications took less than a year, and on 26 June 1972, Cosmos 496 flew on a six-day shakedown cruise to test out the revised design. It went perfectly and the new Soyuz—with two seats, not three; with batteries, not panels; and with smaller fuel tanks—was declared operational once more. The Russians were ready to fly in space again.

A new Salyut, DOS-2, a repeat of the Salyut 1 DOS-1 design, was made fit for launch on 29 July 1972. Two cosmonauts were ready to fly in pursuit: Alexei Leonov and Valeri Kubasov. From early June 1972, the Soviet public was treated to a series of statements on the value and importance of Earth-orbiting stations. On 7 June, the anniversary of the Soyuz 11, Radio Moscow quoted scientists as saying: 'We should expect stations to be working regularly and making complex observations in the near future.' More significantly perhaps, it was announced on 22 July that the flagship of the Soviet tracking fleet, the *Yuri Gagarin* had put to sea on its first operational mission, joining the smaller

Vladimir Komarov and the *Academician Sergei Korolev*. When DOS-2 was launched on 29 July 1972, it failed to reach orbit owing to a mishap on the second stage at 162 s.

Soviet scientists could only contemplate with growing unease the impending launch of the American Skylab, then due for April 1973. Unlike the Moon race, the space station race could not be side-stepped or avoided. The USSR could not declare it was not interested—unless it wanted to pull out of space altogether.

Air Force selection, April 1970

Anatoli Berezovoi
Anatoli Dedkov
Vladimir Dzhanibekov
Yuri Isaulov
Vladimir Kozlov
Leonid Popov
Yuri Romanenko
Nikolai Fefelov
Valeri Illarianov

Civilians selected from the Korolev OKB, March 1972

Boris Andreyev
Valentin Lebedev
Yuri Ponomaryov

Civilians selected from the IMBP, March 1972

Georgi Machinski
Valeri Poliakov
Lev Smirenny

Civilians selected from Chelomei OKB-52, March 1972

Valeri Makrushin
Dmitri Yuyukov

Civilians selected from the Korolev OKB, March 1973

Vladimir Aksenov
Alexander Ivanchenkov
Valeri Ryumin
Gennadiy Strekhalov

Civilians selected from the NPO Mashinostroyeniye (OKB-52), December 1978

Vladimir Gevorkyan
Alexei Grechanik
Valeri Romanov

The Salyut 1 design, which merged Soyuz and Almaz equipment, was unique and flown only twice (Salyut 1 and the 29 July failure). In 1972, the programme re-divided into two streams: Almaz stations, designed by the Chelomei OKB-52, and a civilian programme, designed by the Korolev OKB-1 bureau. As an economy measure, Chelomei was told to use the Soyuz spacecraft to link with Almaz, rather than the larger, more ambitious TKS system which he had designed (TKS was put on hold). To fly the new space station missions in the 1970s, new groups of pilots and civilians were selected for the cosmonaut teams. This time they included cosmonauts from Chelomei's design bureau.

So the USSR had a team of about 50 cosmonauts with a wide mix of experience, age and background—from the young guards to the senior pilots, from computer specialists to designers who were to fly the ships they built.

FIRST FLIGHT OF ALMAZ

The first of Chelomei's Almaz was due to fly in April 1973. By around the same time, the first of the Korolev bureau's new civilian stations would be ready. America's Skylab was due the same month. The availability of Almaz and the new Korolev station gave the USSR the opportunity to upstage the Americans: the USSR would have two stations in orbit to America's one!

Not that the USSR was under any misapprehension as to what Skylab was all about: it was a big project. The Americans had, in an uncharacteristically crude manner, simply converted the upper stage of the Saturn V into the giant empty shell of a space station. To the front they fitted a docking adaptor and a solar observatory based on components of the old lunar module. Its weight was at least 90 tonnes, length 36 m, volume 361 m^3. It would fly nearly 400 km high. The astronauts had a wardroom, showers, even their own bedroom. The interior was so vast that it would be used to test out the Manned Manoeuvring Unit rocket backpack—which had originally been planned for use outside in open space! Three Apollo missions were set to fly up to it—one of 28 days and then two of 56 days. Both targets were way beyond the Soyuz 11 achievement. It was a dramatic and ambitious project; and the USSR felt it deserved a convincing response. Certainly the political judgement of the leadership, so often wrong, was not at fault here.

So it was that on 3 April 1973, Baikonour reverberated to the rumble of the Proton putting aloft Russia's first Almaz space station, though it was announced as Salyut 2. It soon entered orbit of 215 by 260 km, 88.9 min, 51.6 deg. During the 20th orbit, Salyut's motor fired and the station raised its perigee by 15 km, placing it in perfect orbit for a rendezvous on 9 April. Observers stood by for Soyuz 12. On 8 April, however, a further burn took place on the 83rd orbit, raising the orbit to 261 by 296 km, 89.9 min. This was high for a rendezvous, unless the Soyuz could manoeuvre to higher altitudes. The new orbit still gave rendezvous windows every five days—April 14, 19 and 25. These manoeuvres puzzled observers. Confusion was compounded by the fact that they could not pick up Salyut's signals—they had not yet realized that Salyut was transmitting on different (military) frequencies. Either way, a series of statements on Cosmonautics Day, 12 April, on the value of orbital stations, only added to the feeling that a manned launch was not far away. Two cosmonauts, Pavel Popovich and Yuri Artyukhin, were ready.

As they went through their countdown drills on Earth, disaster struck in space. An electrical fault in the engine unit caused a fire which caused the external hull to puncture and Salyut 2 to depressurize. Had Popovich and Artyukhin been on board, they might have had time to evacuate the station and reach their Soyuz ferry in time. Without its orientation system, Salyut turned end over end and within hours ground observers could spot it flashing in the sky as one side, then another, shone in the sunlight. Cosmonauts Pavel Popovich and Yuri Artyukhin climbed out of their cabin and dejectedly took off their heavy spacesuits and stood down. The *Yuri Gagarin* put in at port.

Salyut 2 crashed into the Indian Ocean on 28 May. 'The information gained will be used in creating new space vehicles', said Radio Moscow: the word 'successfully' was nowhere used in the end-of-mission statement.

FIRST KOROLEV OKB STATION

Korolev bureau's DOS-3, was much improved on the Salyut 1 design, with two large solar panels at the side and a rotating one on top. DOS-3 lifted off on 11 May, watched anxiously by its slated crew, Alexei Leonov and Valeri Kubasov. DOS-3 reached orbit—a standard civilian Salyut one of 214 by 243 km, 51.6 deg—but that was the best it could do.

The first transmissions from the craft as it sailed high over the Pacific Ocean told the ground that it had been crippled by a massive systems failure. The orientation system turned the thrusters on full immediately on entry to Earth orbit, using up all the manoeuvring fuel before it had completed even one circuit. So total was the failure, and so immediately obvious was it, that the station was hastily given a Cosmos designation (Cosmos 557). It crashed to Earth on 22 May, six days before Almaz burned too.

The appearance of Cosmos 557 did not pass unnoticed in the West, not least because of the nature of its orbit, its size when observed from the ground and its use of the traditional manned frequencies. Initially it was mistaken for an unmanned Soyuz (to inspect Salyut 2?) or a backup to Salyut 2. It was not until later, when the dual military/civilian nature of the programme was clear, that it emerged that there were two separate programmes brought together in time to upstage Skylab.

America's station nearly went the way of Salyut: one of its solar panels was ripped off in launch and the other jammed shut. It was under-powered and overheated. In a heroic mission, astronauts Conrad, Kerwin and Weitz docked with the station on 26 May, space-walked along its hull, used giant clippers to free the jammed panel and erected a protective cover over the overheating central section. The power surged in, the station cooled to the bearable, and they themselves went on to fly 28 days aboard. In the autumn, astronauts Bean, Garriott and Lousma collected tonnes of information and research on a 59-day mission. In the winter, novice astronauts Carr, Gibson and Pogue set up an 84-day record. Skylab triumphed: Almaz and Salyut were in ruins. By early June 1973 the Russians had lost three orbital stations in the space of a year, two falling out of the sky within a week. It was now two years since a Russian had even flown in space.

AIRBORNE AGAIN

It was decided to fly the Soyuz again on its own, even if a space station target were not available. The first unmanned requalification flew from 15 to 17 June 1973 and went perfectly under the cover of Cosmos 573. The manned flight was planned for a month later, and tracking ships took up position on 15 July. But there was a snag in the count-down, the mission was called off and at the end of July the fleet dispersed.

Soyuz 12 finally did lift off on 27 September. Vasily Lazarev and Oleg Makarov had been selected for this demanding mission. No man was better qualified than Lazarev—veteran of military medical school, with an aviation medicine degree, tester of Soviet Air Force jets, participant in the Volga balloon project. Oleg Makarov was a 1957 graduate from the Bauman school and had been on the Moon team. Their task was to put the redesigned Soyuz through its paces and come back alive after two days: they were to restore confidence to a faltering programme. If successful, space station flights could begin anew the next year; if not, there would be a serious question over the USSR's ability to fly manned operations around the Earth at all.

An early manned launch in the Soyuz series. The men on the clamp at the bottom give an idea of the scale of the R-7 rocket.

They boarded their capsule wearing new lightweight spacesuits, suits that were tight and stylish. Liftoff was 1.18 p.m. and Soyuz 12 went into an initial orbit of 194 by 249 km, 88.6 min, but at 7 p.m., Vasily Lazarev took the craft up to 333 by 348 km, 91 min—the highest Soyuz had ever gone. The crew spent nearly all their time testing the manoeuvring system and navigation methods, and the basic functioning of the craft. But they did have some time to run tests with cameras and spectrographic filters to look at below-ground-level ores and water, drought and disease and the maturity of crops.

In the launch announcement Tass made it clear that only a two-day flight was planned, sensibly avoiding undue speculation resulting from the flight's brevity. So it was that on 29 September Vasily Lazarev brought his craft down to a featherbed soft touchdown in a clear autumn field 400 km southwest of Karaganda.

OBSERVATORY BEYOND THE EARTH

The two men, jubilant with their modest triumph, were flown at once to Moscow to be greeted by Vladimir Shatalov. Confidence was creeping back. But it was a sorry state of affairs for the USSR when a two-day test flight of a six-year-old spacecraft was considered an achievement. Russia had at this time only 5000 man-hours in space, compared to America's 16 000. Russia had flown 34 cosmonauts on 19 missions, the Americans 64 astronauts on 29.

Still, the pace was beginning to quicken. One problem, which had to be solved if long-duration flight were to take place, was the ability of Soyuz' systems to function over long periods in orbit when linked up to an orbital station. How would the capsule endure the hot and the cold, the micrometeorites, the vacuum, and how would its stored fuels hold out? To test this out, Cosmos 613 was launched on 30 November. It was recovered on 1 March 1974 after 60 days, flying 270–385 km, the height selected for a civilian station.

Soyuz 13 soared into a wintry Kazakhstan sky on 18 December with two of Russia's youngest cosmonauts on board, designer Valentin Lebedev and young guard Pyotr Klimuk. Both were 31. Klimuk was the first of the young guard to fly: his credentials were unsurpassable and he had been one of the youngest members of the Communist Party at 20 and a cosmonaut at the tender age of 23. Pyotr Klimuk and Valentin Lebedev were not the only men in space, for they joined America's Skylab 4 crew, then a third of their way into their marathon 84-day mission. It was the first time two crews of separate nations had ever been in space at the same time, though they never had direct contact.

Soyuz 13 rapidly manoeuvred into a stable orbit of 227–273 km. It brought aloft two key experiments: Orion 2 and Oasis 2. Both were derived from Salyut 1 tests, and both were to have flown on the stations of the previous spring. Orion 2 consisted of two telescopes, one standard and one ultraviolet, and they were designed to take shortwave spectrograms of stars brighter than +9.5 magnitude (in practice they achieved +12.5). Together, said Moscow, they constituted 'a powerful observatory beyond the Earth's atmosphere'. Oasis 2 was a biological container in which chlorella and other plants were cultivated. It looked at the possibility of biological processes producing protein for a long flight. It was a closed ecosystem.

Moscow announced that the flight was completed on 25 December, though not before the cosmonauts had spent some time—without result—using their telescopes to try to pick up Comet Kohoutek as it rushed towards the Sun. They came out of orbit early on the 26th. Re-entry took place over the Caspian Sea and took 8 min. The parachute popped open on schedule and the next 14 min were the most hazardous of the flight. In the landing area, a snowstorm had been whipped up by strong 8 m/s winds. Low snow-filled clouds darkened the landing area. The blizzard meant that the ground crew could not see what it was doing, and the temperature was –8°C. Contact with the cosmonauts was lost. This ugly situation did not last long. The cone-shaped capsule came to rest in a snowdrift. Its beacon guided in the rescue crew, who airlifted out Klimuk and Lebedev. They were decorated for bravery in the Kremlin on the 29th.

ALMAZ SUCCESS

A final Cosmos mission, 638, was flown in April 1974, completing the four-stage retesting process. On 25 June, the second of Chelomei's Almaz stations reached orbit, settling into the low orbit designated for Almaz military stations at 219–270 km. Observers awaited the long-expected manned linkup. This time they were not disappointed. 'It was a soft docking!' reported back veteran Pavel Popovich early on 5 July. With fellow crew member Yuri Artyukhin he had guided his Soyuz 14 through space for 32 h with pinpoint accuracy. They had lifted off at night on the 3rd and took over a day to close in. Both Popovich, the veteran of the Vostok 4 flight of 1962, and Artyukhin, graduate of the Zhukovsky Academy in 1958 and candidate cosmonaut for ten years, were aged 43.

By 8 July Tass was able to report that Salyut 3 was in full working order. The cosmonauts were studying the Earth, solar radiation and the polarization of sunlight. Creature comforts on board included a refrigerator, TV, tape recorder, cassette library, exercise conveyor belt, and collapsible writing table. A large boom TV camera was erected outside the craft to orientate it to Earth. Apart from that, reports on what the crew was actually doing were scarce. The only experiments that were announced had to do with a solar telescope, a spectrograph to examine the effects that aerosols had on the atmosphere, bacteria cultivation and water recycling.

Early on 19 July, on day 16, Pavel Popovich and Yuri Artyukhin clambered into their Soyuz 14 ferry and at 9.03 a.m. cast off. They were back on the ground by lunchtime, only 200 m from the prearranged spot. All had gone like clockwork and it was the first time that the USSR had completed a full space station mission. The bad memories of previous years began to recede. At the time few people paid much attention to the lack of information about what the crew was doing, or why details of Salyut had not been released. Getting through an entire mission from one end to the other was considered an adequate justification in itself. The next mission was to last 25 days.

'PRACTISING NIGHT LANDINGS...'

Late on a hot and dusty summer's day, 26 August, Soyuz 15 took to the skies. The Sun was setting and the silhouette of the gantries cast long shadows across the evening Baikonour landscape. Two new cosmonauts were soon in orbit, and mission commander Gennadiy Sarafanov, 32, at once put into a chase orbit. As the pursuit got into its stride, the Soviet publicity machine pulled out all the stops. There were pictures and films galore. Pen portraits of the crew appeared all over *Izvestia* and *Pravda*. Sarafanov was the second member of the young guards to get a flight—a unit he too had joined at the age of 23. His flight engineer was, by way of contrast, 48 years old. Lev Demin, who had been a military research officer since 1956, was one of the engineering intake of 1963. He had been forced out of flying due to poor eyesight—indicating that the physical requirements for space travel had become less rigorous. At a personal level, interest focused on the fact that he was a grandfather: his married 26-year-old daughter, Natalia, had a baby boy Vladimir. He was the oldest man to fly, and after the flight he was to emerge somewhat improbably as the President of the USSR Stamp Collectors' Association. The blaze of publicity indicated a longer flight than Soyuz 14. The best conditions for landing would be from 15 to 25 September, giving a mission of 19 to 29 days.

Even as the Western press was digesting all this data, the Soyuz 15 mission was in serious trouble. As always, the main part of the mission was carried out automatically. Information on the trajectories of both Soyuz and Salyut was fed into the onboard computer: the computer then commanded the engines to fire to bring Soyuz into line for docking. However, there was a logic error. Closing commands brought the spacecraft apart and separation commands closed the distance. Lev Demin noticed them shooting past the station. Fuel was being used up fast. They made another attempt to outwit their computer. But before they had time to make a third attempt they were back in radio visibility with the ground, which told them to return to Earth at once.

Their troubles were not over yet. As they lined Soyuz 15 up for rendezvous, there was a short circuit. Hoping their gyros had been properly aligned before they cut out, Sarafanov fired the engines anyway. As they came down, the sky was lit up by a ferocious lightning storm.

Worse was to come afterwards. The State Commission felt their post-flight report was over-critical of the spacecraft computer. So the Commission blamed the crew for the loss of the mission. Even today, the Commission's report remains locked away somewhere in the vaults of NPO Energiya, despite the efforts of Sarafanov's colleagues to clear him.[94]

Various explanations for the early touchdown were given: the crew was said to be testing out a new, manual means of rendezvous. Then, later, they were said to be testing out a new automatic means of rendezvous designed to pave the way for automatic spaceship docking and refuelling! No docking had ever been intended, it was claimed. Then the purpose of the mission was to test the psychological compatibility of a 32-year-old and 48-year-old to get on in orbit. Finally, even more incredibly, they were 'testing' emergency landings by night!

On 23 September a capsule was undocked. Based on the Cosmos unmanned photoreconnaissance capsules, it returned to Earth and was recovered. On 24 October, Salyut 3 pushed its orbit back up to its operational altitude of 268–299 km. On 25 December, after 2950 orbits, *Pravda* announced that the mission had been abandoned. At the end of January 1975 the station burned up over the Pacific Ocean.

THE GREAT COMEBACK

Slowly, the Soviet space programme was finding its feet once more. The dying days of 1974 saw a new station put aloft, the Salyut 4, or DOS-4: its initial orbit was 235–270 km, but by 5 January it had lifted itself up to a circular orbit of 335–343 km. Salyut 4 carried three large solar panels on rotating levers—the third being on the top of the body like the sails on a yacht. Inside, the main control panel had one seat, not two. Salyut 4 carried a garden, an Earth-observation camera, a water recycling unit, and solar and ultraviolet telescopes. The Earth camera, set in a huge cone in the floor of the main cabin, was the bulkiest single instrument and looked not unlike a hospital scanner.

It was a full two weeks before two cosmonauts climbed aboard Soyuz 17 to set out in pursuit. No sooner were they in their cabin than fog enveloped the launch area and the rest of Baikonour. It was a thick, clammy fog and no one could see a thing. They went ahead anyway. It was 10 January. Soon they had left the mists and fogs behind and dawn greeted them as they entered orbit.

Alexei Gubarev was 43, a senior pilot from the 1963 intake. He had an explosive temper and liked to run spaceflights exactly his own way. Normally this would have disqualified him right away but he had combat experience from the Korean war and superb navigational skills, and after what happened to Soyuz 15 these were very much in demand. Georgi Grechko, also 43, was a well-built, personable man: gentle, even-tempered, humorous, smiling and a favourite with Western correspondents.

Alexei Gubarev judiciously used his thrusters to bring Soyuz 17 across 1500 km of open space into Salyut's docking nose. They nudged together and soon the crew was aboard and settling into a routine of work. In no time they had grown green peas in their garden, tracked forest fires in Africa and pointed their telescope towards the Sun, the stars and galaxies. They watched the hatching of eggs in the biological container. 100 separate experiments were planned and carried out.

By 3 February, they had broken the 24-day record of their comrades Dobrovolski, Volkov and Patsayev. Some minor medical problems had arisen. Both men suffered from colds and fatigue. Several new experiments worked out quite well. The water regeneration device meant that they needed to carry less water aloft—they simply recycled the station's moisture for their own drinking. The 250 mm telescope took views of the Crab Nebula and the star Vega. The biology experiment carried bacteria, fruit flies and frog-spawn. The final part of the flight was a survey of the land mass of the USSR, then in the grips of winter. A map of snow cover was compiled. The crew came down on 9 February after 30 days aloft. A large parachute lowered them gently onto the flat packed snow.

For Alexei Gubarev and Georgi Grechko it was a triumphant return. The jinx had been broken. Salyut 4 was the first flight for many years that actually broke new ground. They had stayed up a full month, collected a vast body of data, and done it all in rigorous winter conditions. No wonder the flight was called 'the great comeback'. And even if their condition was described only as 'quite well' when they landed, they soon recovered fully.

FALLING LIKE A STONE

After the success of Soyuz 17, the next flight was expected to double the new record. The launching of 5 April gave best landing opportunities of 26 May to 7 June (for a mission of between 51 and 63 days). It may have been in their minds to break America's second longest record, which was then 59 days. Chosen for Soyuz 18 were the veterans of Soyuz

12, Vasily Lazarev and Oleg Makarov. They surely deserved a long flight after their earlier two-day hop.

Soyuz 18 lifted off on schedule and curved over towards the northeast. The strap-ons fell away and disappeared from sight. At 120 km the time came to drop the core stage and fire the upper section. But the explosive bolts failed to fire: the whole rocket began to tumble violently end over end! Vasily Lazarev reported the problem at once, but ground control would not believe him. For some reason, telemetry did not indicate a fault. 'Abort, abort!' he screamed, 'cut us free!' Only after further pleading and swearing was Soyuz blasted free from the wildly gyrating rogue rocket. Soyuz began to fall like a stone from 192 km.

Down it came and the g forces got harder and harder. It was an almost vertical ballistic descent, quite unlike a normal re-entry. Just then, Lazarev, realizing that the craft was heading for China, began to ask for a predicted landing spot. 4 g, 5 g, 6 g. Three helicopter pilots were already in a Peking jail for a number of years for landing the wrong side of the border. 8 g, 9 g, 10 g. The cosmonauts' flesh sunk deep into their cheekbones. Each man now weighed a tonne. 11 g, 12 g, 13 g. 'We do have a treaty with China, don't we?' pleaded Lazarev. 15 g. Radio contact was lost. 16 g—past the Soyuz design limit. 17 g: each cosmonaut now weighed a tonne and a half and could no longer see. 18 g: the cosmonauts blacked out. Later, it was found that the g meter had jammed on 20.6 g.

The cosmonauts slowed down from 17 000 km/h to 200 km/h in four minutes. At last the g forces eased. The parachute popped out and filled. They were heading into the remote Altai mountains, a near-desert populated by herdsmen on horseback. The Sun had just set. Their troubles were only just beginning.

After 21 min 27 s minutes aloft, 1574 km downrange, Soyuz 18 touched down in snow—but at once began rolling down a steep mountainside. It bumped and jogged, and Lazarev and Makarov were violently thrown around. The cabin crashed and smashed over the ground, and the two men screamed as they were flung about and battered. The capsule was heading towards a precipice.

They would certainly have died if the cabin had plunged over into the valley, but the parachute lines snagged and tangled in some conifer trees and thorny bushes—and, miraculously, held. The two men, bruised and bleeding, climbed out in the darkness. What would they do? They were shaken. They lit a fire, both to keep warm and to attract rescuers. Yet the chances were that they were in the People's Republic of China. At best they faced an uncertain future. After an hour, a group of villagers who had witnessed the drama approached with torches and lights. It was bitterly cold. To the enormous relief of Lazarev and Makarov, they spoke Russian. The border was close though, 320 km distant.

Next day they were airlifted out. Lazarev came off much the worst of two—reports said that he was suffering from broken ribs, internal bleeding and concussion. He never flew again. The USSR told everyone that the crew was fine (which they were not) and explained the failure as being due to poor checking by the launch crews. Bureaucrats at the cosmodrome blamed the crew for the mishap and refused to pay them the 3000 roubles bonus for making a space flight. A squalid argument about whether they should be paid or not had eventually to be arbitrated by Leonid Brezhnev himself (they were paid). Sadly, Lazarev died of poisoning from home-brewed vodka in 1990.

The failure of Soyuz 18—later called disarmingly the 'April 5th anomaly' (one wonders what Lazarev made of that description) presented real problems. Soyuz 18 was to have come home long before the forthcoming Apollo–Soyuz flight, in fact by 7 June at the latest. The delay meant that the next mission would have to run during the Apollo–Soyuz Test Project. The Russians had never run two different missions simultaneously before.

SECOND CREW

Veterans Pyotr Klimuk and Vitaly Sevastianov were pressed into training and were in orbit on 24 May. Later that evening Salyut could be seen crossing the western sky, in a bright curving arc in the dusk. Two minutes later a dimmer faster light could be seen racing in pursuit. Later on the 25th, only one bright light could be seen: they had made it. It was the first time the Russians had ever put a second crew on an orbital station.

By 26 May, Salyut had completed 2388 orbits and its two new crew members were bringing it back to life. By the 31st, they had circularized its orbit at a steady 350 km and had got the water recycling plant going again to the extent that it was generating two to four litres a day. By early June, Klimuk and Sevastianov were fully into the mission routine. They exercised 2.5 h a day (mainly on a bicycle), sent back regular television broadcasts, tried to locate oil deposits and shot star spectrograms of Cygnus. The flight became so routine that it dropped lower and lower on the Moscow evening news, and the day's events on Salyut were only mentioned at the end. But routine was, after all, the purpose of the flight.

By 24 June they had broken the record set by Gubarev and Grechko. No fewer than 30 pea plants had sprouted in the greenhouse. By 4 July, Salyut had clocked up 3000 orbits, and Klimuk and Sevastianov were busy forecasting the summer weather. What the cheerful mission reports did not tell anyone about—and few knew about it till the flight was over—was the green mould problem. Transmissions picked up by American monitoring stations heard the two men complain from late June onwards that the station's humidity system was breaking down. What was happening was simple but unpleasant: there was too much humidity in the air. As a result, the windows fogged up (a problem known to the Americans in Apollo) and, worse still, a green mould began spreading from the floor upwards, making living and working conditions aboard quite unpleasant.

On 16 July, during a lull in the Apollo–Soyuz mission, they spoke to Alexei Leonov as Soyuz 19 crossed their path 120 km below. On 21 July the cosmonauts received permission to land. They had flown over 900 orbits and they had spent their last days looking at solar wind, the northern lights and Earth resources. They had photographed 8.5 million square kilometres of Soviet territory. So great was the volume of research that it took them three full days to pack up. Boris Petrov announced that this would be the last manned flight to Salyut 4 and if they left anything behind it would stay behind. Pyotr Klimuk, now aged 33, and Vitaly Sevastianov, now 40, (both had celebrated birthdays in orbit) eventually came down on 26 July. They had flown 63 days in a courageous mission and endured some hardship. It was the second longest space flight ever.

By the end of July, Soviet scientists could afford themselves a certain degree of self-satisfaction. Visible parity with the United States, Salyut 4 achieving all its mission objectives, and two duration flights—all in the space of six months. After four years of disasters and problems, the worst was well over. As if to underline it all, Vitaly Sevastianov was back on Moscow television with his own programme within a week of his return to Earth.

However, the flight of Salyut 4 was not yet over—indeed it was to fly in space a full 770 days or well over two years, right up to February 1977. At this stage—autumn 1975—the Soviet space programme was set to design and build its second generation of Earth-orbiting stations. It would have two docking ports. This meant that, theoretically at least, it would be possible to keep space permanently occupied. One ship could arrive at one port while another could return from the other. Equally, two ports opened up prospects for regular refuelling of the station and thereby extending its life.

UNMANNED FERRY

For this reason, an automatic, unmanned version of Soyuz was designed as a freighter which would carry fuel, water and other supplies to orbiting stations. It was to be called 'Progress'. Based explicitly on Soyuz, the orbital and command modules would be merged and the life-support systems would be removed. Progress would be dumped after it had delivered its cargo, and no return trip would be intended. A two-stage test of the elements that would be flown on Progress was commissioned. Cosmos 772 flew on 29 September 1975, on a three-day solo mission. The new Progress autopilot behaved as it

The Progress freighter used the basic Soyuz design.

should, the capsule was recovered and the data were analysed. The second test, Soyuz 20, without cosmonauts on board, was targeted for Salyut 4 itself and took off from a wintry Baikonour on 17 November 1975. Soyuz 20 was a rigorous test of the Soyuz–Progress autopilot. Two full days were devoted to the chase manoeuvres. Soyuz 20 was advertised explicitly as a cargo vehicle and the rendezvous on autopilot was, according to its designer, cosmonaut Konstantin Feoktistov, 'a great new success for Soviet space navigation'.

Soyuz 20 came down in the snow, after 91 days aloft, the following February. It was more than the test of the Progress autopilot. It did two other things: it tested the ability of the Soyuz capsule to survive 90 days in space without its fuel and thermal protection decaying. This was essential if Soyuz were to tie up at the space station so a crew could stay aboard a number of months. And second, it was a serious biological mission. Soyuz 20 carried several turtles, 20 species of higher plants, drosophila fruit flies, cacti, corn and vegetable seeds. Soyuz 20 again showed the traditional Soviet approach of not flying men until lengthy animal tests were run first.

SALYUT 5: BAD AIR

Four new cosmonauts were assigned to the second Almaz station, which reached orbit on 22 June 1976. Vitaly Zholobov was a moustached oil engineer. Zudov and Rozhdestvensky were both young guards: Vyacheslav Zudov was a highly qualified parachutist and flier of military transports. Valeri Rozhdestvensky was an expert on spacewalks, something probably related to his experience as commander of the Baltic Sea fleet's diving rescue service. And Yuri Glazhkov, engineer and young guard, had a candidate of science degree for a thesis on spacewalking.

Soyuz 21 was planned as a 66-day mission, starting on 6 July and coming down on 10 September. Boris Volynov and Vitaly Zholobov were in orbit on schedule and by midday on 7 July they had brought their Soyuz ferry to within 400 m of their twinkling target. 'Hard dock!', Boris Volynov reported on a crystal-clear radio line as the two ships clunked together 40 minutes later.

As with the earlier Almaz, there was noticeably little public information available on what the crew was doing. There were some major Soviet military manoeuvres in eastern Siberia in late July, and spotting them could have been an important part of their work. There were scientific experiments. The cosmonauts had a guppy fish on board in a tank and they spent much of their time observing how it reacted to zero gravity.They had fish eggs in another aquarium. They tried to assess pollution in the atmosphere and whether aerosols destroyed ozone. They forecast the weather, and their advice was eagerly awaited, for Europe was in the throes of a severe drought all summer. Farmers scanned the skies in vain searching for signs of relief.

More significantly, Salyut 5 carried the first full battery of materials processing equipment into orbit—a prototype of the first space factory. Zero gravity and the exterior vacuum of space between them provided an ideal environment for testing out pharmaceuticals, magnets, electronics, optical glasses, tools and ceramics. A processing plant could manufacture specialized industrial equipment to a standard not possible on the ground. To operate it, the crew simply swung particular items for testing out through an airlock on the side of the main cabin. Salyut 5 carried four such experiments—Sfera (for melting lead, tin and cadmium); Krystall (growth experiments with potash); Diffusia (for making alloys); and Reaction (which melted nickel and manganese). The two cosmonauts soldered 15 mm wide stainless steel tubes.

SUDDEN RETURN

Then suddenly Radio Moscow announced that the cosmonauts were preparing to return to Earth. Normally this announcement is the prelude to six days of packing up and switching the station to automatic operation. But Boris Volynov and Vitaly Zholobov were on the ground no more than two hours later—near Baikonour itself (most unusual) and at night (like Soyuz 15). They had been up 48 days.

Boris Volynov and Vitaly Zholobov held their post-flight press conference at Baikonour next morning. They reported that their flight had been 'interesting but complicated', the normal codeword to indicate that problems had arisen. Then *Izvestia* reported that they had suffered 'sensory deprivation'. And there was none of the usual fanfare that normally greeted returning cosmonauts after completing a successful mission. It was low down in the news reports and received little mention. Years later, the early return was explained by a combination of acrid odours in the station and Zholobov falling ill and suffering acute fatigue.

NORTHERN AUTUMN

Even as this work went on, an independent manned flight was in preparation. A backup spacecraft had been left over from the three allocated to the Apollo–Soyuz test project. It had waited on the pad in case Soyuz 19 had not been up to expectations. Now it was decided to fly it on a solo, once-off Earth resources mission. The docking apparatus was removed and replaced by a massive, purpose-built camera from the GDR. The camera, known as MKF-6, weighing 204 kg, was the most advanced of its type in the world and was built by the Carl Zeiss Factory in Germany, which had been manufacturing high-quality optical equipment since the nineteenth century. During the Second World War, no self-respecting field-marshal or U-Boat captain was seen without Zeiss binoculars around his neck.

The MKF-6 was to take pictures of the ground in strips 120 by 180 km wide in six light-bands, using colours that could be stereoed together. Each cassette of film could take 16 million square metres. The pictures were to be analysed by cartographers, by river engineers, by geologists and by agricultural experts to assess the autumn crops. If the MKF-6 worked well, then it could be used on the next orbital station, Salyut 6.

It was the first time that foreign equipment had flown on a Soviet manned spaceflight, and only a day before it took off, the Soviet government announced that it was inviting the other socialist countries to send cosmonauts to the USSR for training. This decision was one that produced mixed feelings. Those favouring an expansion of international space links supported it, as did those who wished that the benefits of Soviet technology should be more widely available. There were views against it. For the trainers it would mean training a whole series of cosmonauts, only half of whom would fly (each country sent two for one flight) and they would only fly once. For mission planners it meant running a succession of visiting missions up to Salyut that had no engineering justification. Space-flight planning was once again determined by political considerations. Soon after, air force officers from Czechoslovakia, Poland and the German Democratic Republic appeared for training; and Vladimir Shatalov, now responsible for crew assignments, put them in place for a series of flights due from 1978 on.

The Soyuz 22 flight took place against the background of quiet, warm autumn weather with abundant sunshine and excellent lighting conditions. The commander was Valeri Bykovsky, on his first flight since Vostok 5, and the engineer was Vladimir Aksenov. They flew into orbit on 15 September and rapidly manoeuvred into a circular orbit of 250 by 281 km, 65 deg, 89.6 min. It was the first time that the 65 deg pattern had been used since Voskhod 2, and it brought Soyuz over northern latitudes for the first time. It also overflew NATO's 'Operation Teamwork' in Norway at the same time (64°N), but that may have been coincidental.

Once in orbit, Vladimir Shatalov announced that it would be a short, solo mission—conscious that unless this were said, there would be speculation that it was supposed to have some relationship with Salyut 5. Experiments began soon after arrival in orbit. Bykovsky and Aksenov turned their camera eyes on the Baikal–Amur railway in eastern Siberia and forests near the Yenisei. They looked at tidal zones in the Sea of Okhotsk; the salinity of the Caspian Sea; and acid rain in the GDR. They came down on 23 September after eight days and with 2400 photographs. The fine weather held, clear skies had prevailed, and it had been an 'Indian summer' across the Soviet Union. Lengthening autumn shadows could be seen around the Soyuz 22 capsule when it came to rest on a field in the steppe.

BLIZZARD!

Salyut 5 remained aloft. Analysis of Soyuz 21 data suggested that the fault in the air regeneration system could be dealt with. There were compelling reasons to return to the station; the onboard camera was continuing to take film of military value and it was desirable to process it.

The next launch window opened late at night on 14 October, with landing windows scheduled for 28 October to 9 November (for a short mission) or 27 December to 8 January (for a longer one). Floodlights bathed the Baikonour cosmodrome in creamy light when Soyuz 23 went aloft and shot through the darkness. Watching cosmonauts shielded their eyes against the glare. A bad omen for the flight was that the transfer van carrying the crew, Vyacheslav Zudov and Valeri Rozhdestvensky, broke down during the trip down to the pad.

Worse followed. The R-7 launcher deviated off course during the ascent, nearly forcing an abort. The orbit was far from perfect, being lower than planned. The igla rendezvous system failed, forcing additional fuel consumption. By the time the cosmonauts had closed in on Salyut 5, Zudov and Rozhdestvensky had fuel for only one ballistic de-orbit burn, not the two more gentle firings planned. This violated mission rules, so the crew was ordered to return to Earth, despite pleas to be allowed to continue. Moscow fell silent and bulletins on the two men dried up.

Zudov and Rozhdestvensky knew that they would be coming in for a night landing, but they had no idea just how dangerous it would be. All during the day the weather had worsened in the recovery area. Snow began to fall, gales whipped up the snow and temperatures plummeted. Late on the 16th, temperatures were down to −17°C and falling.

The heat shield of Soyuz 23 was still red hot when parachute lines came open and beacons began flashing. But the six Mil helicopters already up the air could not see a thing. They bucked the winds but despite full searchlights all they could see were flurries of snow. The winds whistled as Soyuz 23 was blown downwards—crashing right down into a salt lake! It was Russia's first splashdown and it could not have taken place in more atrocious conditions. It was now −22°C.

Zudov and Rozhdestvensky must have realized quickly that they were not in a snowdrift but adrift on a turbulent, choppy lake. The main parachute filled in the blizzard and began to drag the cabin across the lake. Then salt water corroded electrical lines, causing a short, which prompted the reserve parachute to pop out. The reserve chute filled with water and sank, dragging the Soyuz cabin downward. Had the lake been any deeper, it would have pulled the cabin to the bottom and drowned the cosmonauts. In the event, the reserve parachute hatch filled with water, depressing the cabin even further. The situation of Zudov and Rozhdestvensky was precarious and deteriorating. The cabin was now so low in the water that the crew exit hatch was covered. The communications antennæ were under water, preventing transmissions. Zudov and Rozhdestvensky could not climb out of their watertight cabin: but they had air for only two hours and an emergency supply for another five only. They could hear the communication signals of the prowling Mil helicopters but could not transmit to them. And the winds howled on and on. Memories of the Soyuz 11 disaster must have flashed through their minds: would they die from lack of air—but on Earth?

The situation became ever more desperate. Ice began to form on the inside of the cabin. The frozen cosmonauts stopped moving, to conserve air. At daybreak, a Mil helicopter managed to attach a line to the cabin. So filled with water was the cabin that the Mil could not lift it free of the lake. Instead, the Mil crew tried to drag the Soyuz across the lake toward the shore. At this stage, the Mil crew advised the commander of the recovery forces that there was no response from the crew, who must now be presumed dead.

Finally, the Mil managed to reach the shore line and righted the cabin. Valeri Rozhdestvensky climbed through the top, opened the hatch, gulped in fresh air and with his companion fell into the arms of the rescue crew, who wrapped them in warm blankets. Eleven hours after splashdown, flight control heard that the two men were safe. Zudov and Rozhdestvensky were decorated for bravery—as were the crews who rescued them. They deserved their medals.

SOYUZ 24

Recovery of film cartridges from Salyut 5 was obviously an important mission objective, for Soyuz 24 was launched on 7 February 1977. Weather conditions had improved compared to the recent ill-starred flight. Patches of snow lay on the ground around the pad as Viktor Gorbatko and Yuri Glazhkov went aloft. They docked smoothly on revolution 19 the next day.

Soyuz 24 was limited to an 18-day tour. Western suspicions that bad air had caused problems the previous summer were confirmed when the new cosmonauts failed to board Salyut 5 straight away. They spent a whole day in Soyuz 24 before heading down the tunnel. This had never happened before nor has happened since. Then, on the 21st, they carried out an entirely novel exercise—they completely renewed the air supply by dumping all the existing air out one end of the station and flooding in fresh air from the other.

Not that Soyuz 24 was all about bad air and film cartridges: the cosmonauts repaired the computer on board. They grew mushrooms. They photographed glaciers. The metallurgical experiments started by Zholobov and Volynov were pressed back into use. Steel pipes were soldered, which later withstood pressures of 500 atmospheres. Seeds left behind during the summer were watered, and duly sprouted. Fungus was grown on board: strangely it grew into the most unpredictable of shapes rather than the normal. Gorbatko and Glazhkov used the onboard telescope; and they tracked atmospheric pollution.

Soyuz 24 made an uneventful return to Earth on 25 February. Victor Gorbatko and Yuri Glazhkov came down in cloudy weather, strong winds, and subzero temperatures, but they were quickly spotted and recovered. On the following day, Salyut 5 ejected its military film capsule.

A further visit was scheduled for July 1977: slated for what would have been the Soyuz 25 mission were Anatoli Berezovoi and Mikhail Lisun. However, by that time Salyut 5's fuel reserves began to reach a critically low point and the mission was cancelled. In the event, Salyut 5 burned up on 28 August 1977 after 14 months aloft. For the first time in many years, the skies were now empty of Soviet space stations. But the experience learned during the period of 1971–7 had been put to good use and the next civilian Salyut would be a radically new step forwards. With a five-year life, two docking ports and provision for unmanned resupply by the Progress freighter, it would take space development into new areas not before considered imaginable.

END OF ALMAZ PROGRAMME

The next Almaz manned space station—it would have been the fourth to reach orbit—was scheduled for 1979. Four crews were in training, under mission commanders Anatoli Berezovoi, Vladimir Kozelsky, Gennadiy Sarafanov and Vladimir Vasyutin; and four Chelomei bureau engineers were ready to fly with them—Valeri Makrushin, Valeri Romanov, Dmitri Yuyukov and Alexei Grechanik. Chelomei later hoped to launch a 35 tonne version of the Almaz on an uprated Proton rocket.

However, the civilian Salyut programme run by the Energiya OKB began to command the increasing share of resources. Almaz was also a victim of the changing political order since 1974. Chief Designer Glushko and secretary of the Central Committee, now defence minster, Dmitri Ustinov, ordered the cancellation of the Almaz programme in 1979 and, either for security considerations or spite, the destruction of its hardware.

In response to a military specification, the Chelomei bureau had already modified a version of the Almaz station to an unmanned version carrying a large side-imaging radar. Following Glushko's destruction order, the bureau concealed it under covers in a distant workshop. Prying eyes were kept away by 'Danger! Radiation!' notices plastered over it.

With the change in government in 1985, it was possible to launch the unmanned radar Almaz, but it crashed owing to a failure of the Proton carrier rocket.

The first successful unmanned Almaz was Cosmos 1870, launched 25 July 1987 into a high-inclination, 71.9 deg orbit, at 168–282 km, carrying a 10 m side-looking radar and other equipment for hydrology, remote sensing, cartography and meteorology. It later manoeuvred upward into a stable orbit of 245–259 km. It was de-orbited two years later on 30 July 1989. It was able to see through clouds and returned images to Earth with a resolution of 10–15 m.

The first publicly identified Almaz was eventually launched on 31 March 1991. Almaz weighed 18.5 tonnes and entered orbit of 170 by 280 km, 72.7 deg. It incorporated two 15 m long radar antennæ. 12 min after orbital insertion, its two solar panels sprang out. On its third orbit, it deployed its radar array. On 4 April, Almaz maneouvred to a circular orbit of 275 km, one raised every 24 days. Almaz was intended to return 100 images a day which would sell for $1600 each. Each image was to cover an area of 40 km^2 as it snapped the ground below between latitude 78°N and 78°S. The resolution was 10 m and the radar could map the ocean floor. Indeed, when an American company (the Space Commerce Corp.) first marketed Almaz images showing the 200 m-down sea floor in Puget Sound, military analysts quickly realized how difficult it would be for submarines to hide from such high-quality space surveillance. Almaz burned up on 17 October 1992. The Chelomei design bureau, by then Mashinostroyeniye NPO, sold about $100 000 worth of Almaz images to the West, recovering some of the costs of launching the platform. A second Almaz mission, labelled Almaz 1B, was set for the 1997–8, to be run by a joint Russian–American company called SAR, comprising the American Sokol Group Inc and the Russian Rosvooruzheniye.

ALMAZ POSTSCRIPT

Although the Almaz manned programme effectively ended in 1977 and was cancelled in 1979, Vladimir Chelomei's 1965 design saw a new lease of life later in the 1980s and 1990s. The TKS transport system, with its Merkur capsule, although it was never used in connection with Almaz, became the basis of a series of operations with Salyut 6, Salyut 7, Mir and, later, the International Space Station.

Chelomei's TKS system had been suspended, not cancelled. In the mid-1970s, Chelomei received permission to test out the Merkur capsule, which was designed to fly cosmonauts on the TKS. On 15 December 1976, two Merkur capsules were stacked together to test their re-entry capabilities. Both capsules, named Cosmos 881-2, made pre-dawn entries into the Earth's atmosphere. These tests were repeated by Cosmos 997-8 (30 March 1978) and Cosmos 1101-2 (22 May 1979) (there was a failure on 5 January 1979). The first full-up test of the TKS came with Cosmos 929.

Cosmos 929 went up at 9 a.m. on 17 July 1977. It went into an orbit of 221 by 298 km, 51.6 deg. Ground trackers at once identified it as of space station class, weighing at least 16 000 kg and with solar panels. During one pass in the evening twilight it was seen to flash brightly, its panels glinting in the Sun as it turned over. During the first month of its flight, Cosmos 929 fired its engine four times. By 17 August its orbit was so low that it was skimming the upper layers of the atmosphere. Then on 16 August a recoverable capsule, the Merkur, was sent down. Two days later, as if to confound everyone, the main spacecraft blasted itself into a high orbit of 314–329 km. There it stayed for some time. Suddenly on 19 December a blast of the motors sent the craft up to an unprecedented 440–448 km altitude. On 2 February 1978 it was de-orbited over the Pacific away from the shipping lanes.

Cosmos 929 was a first, exhaustive test of the TKS. Later versions were modified as specialized modules for Salyut 6 (Cosmos 1267) and Salyut 7 (Cosmos 1686); as space tugs (Kvant 1, Polyus) and as large modules for Mir (Kvant 2, 3, Spektr and Priroda); and finally as the FGB for the International Space Station (1997–2010). So Chelomei's forbidden creations survived Glushko's grasp to outlive both of them.

First-generation Soviet orbital space stations

DOS-1	Salyut 1	19 Apr 1971	Occupied by Soyuz 11 crew
DOS-2		29 July 1972	Failed to reach orbit
Almaz	Salyut 2	3 Apr 1973	Depressurized, abandoned
DOS-3	Cosmos 557	11 May 1973	Failed on first orbit
Almaz	Salyut 3	25 Jun 1974	Occupied by Soyuz 14 crew
DOS-4	Salyut 4	26 Dec 1974	Occupied by Soyuz 17, 18B crews
Almaz	Salyut 5	22 Jun 1976	Occupied by Soyuz 21, 24 crews

ASSESSMENT

Although space stations had been at the heart of cosmonautics since the 1920s and had been the subject of designs by Korolev and Chelomei in the early 1960s, the introduction of orbital stations was delayed by the Moon race, which diverted attention, energy and resources for several years. When the first space stations flew, two entirely different designs were developed, following distinct purposes and principles. The early years of space station development were dogged by systems failure, emergencies, teething troubles in a diverse range of equipment and one fatal accident. However, by the late 1970s, persistence with the problems and difficulties had paid off, and the basis had been laid for a second generation of orbiting stations. The soundness of their design was confirmed by the continued use of Almaz -based equipment into the twenty-first century.

9

Living in space

It is a world without reference points: there is no horizontal, no vertical and the sensation of weight is lacking.

Konstantin Tsiolkovsky, *Free space*, 1883.

SECOND-GENERATION SPACE STATION

The flight of Salyut 5 over 1976–7 marked the end of the first phase of the manned orbital space station programme. Historically too it marked the end of Russia's first twenty years in space, for 1977 was the 20th anniversary of the first Sputnik launching. The next stage was the establishment of a semi-permanent orbiting space station, with two docking ports, regularly resupplied by unmanned Progress cargo craft.

The introduction of Progress was to be matched by an improvement in the manned ferry craft. The reduction of crew size from three to two had produced its own problems in performance, compounded by the repeated docking problems. Happily the advent of microelectronics offered a solution to both. Lightweight electronics saved space and gave the Soyuz computerized controls. The new model was called Soyuz 'T'—T for transporter. Solar panels were introduced with an area of 11.5 m². There was a unified propulsion system, meaning that fuel could be transferred from the main engine to the attitude control jets and vice versa, thus providing better margins for difficult manoeuvres. The orbital module was to be cast off in orbit before retrofire, reducing the re-entry thrust required. The onboard propellant was increased from 500 kg to 700 kg, giving an extra margin.

Ideas to improve the Soyuz model dated as far back as December 1967. Vasili Mishin gave permission for preliminary design to begin in June 1968, and the new design was approved in October 1968. Initially, Soyuz T was to be a two-man craft but it was redesigned as a three-man spacecraft in February 1976. The tests of Soyuz T were Cosmos 670, 772, 869, 1001 and 1074. The extreme caution shown in introducing this model of Soyuz again showed the extent to which the USSR was anxious to make safe its new spacecraft.

New cosmonauts were recruited in anticipation of the second-generation station. They were:

Air Force selection, August 1976

Leonid Ivanov
Leonid Kadenyuk
Nikolai Moskalenko
Sergei Protchenko
Yevgeni Salei
Anatoli Soloviev
Vladimir Titov
Vladimir Vasyutin
Alexander Volkov

Air Force selection, May 1978

Nikolai Grekov
Alexander Viktorenko

Civilians selected from NPO Energiya, December 1978

Alexander Alexandrov
Alexander Balandin
Alexander Laveikin
Musa Manarov
Viktor Savinyikh
Alexander Serebrov
Vladimir Solovyov

Civilians selected from the IMBP, December 1978

Gherman Arzarmarov
Alexander Borodin
Mikhail Potapov

Civilian selected from IMBP, March 1983

Oleg Atkov

Civilian selected from IMBP, September 1985

Yuri Stepanov

At last, the new space second-generation station was ready. On 29 September 1977 a Proton rocket put Salyut 6 into orbit. It manoeuvred to its operational attitude of 336 by 352 km on 7 October. Two days later the two cosmonauts selected for the first mission arrived at the pad. It was still dark and liftoff was scheduled for 5.40 a.m. Fully helmeted and suited they clambered out of the transfer van and, carrying their life-support boxes, walked gingerly across the concrete apron like scuba divers about to take the plunge.

Both the commander, Vladimir Kovalyonok, and the engineer, Valeri Ryumin, were aware of the importance of their mission. Valeri Ryumin was tall and barely fitted into the cramped Soyuz cabin. With a big mop of steely black hair, he had trained as a Red Army tank commander and was well used to small spaces. Yet it was his experience as a communications officer on one of the comships that led him into the Salyut design office first and the cosmonaut squad soon after. The crew chatted to the pressmen and drew their attention to the fact that this was the same pad from where Sputnik 1 had been launched twenty years earlier. Nor were these historic parallels lost on the Soviet media. Moscow television showed the cosmonauts heading skywards in their Soyuz rocket with hammer and sickle flags flying proudly on the apron. Soyuz 25 headed into orbit 27 minutes behind Salyut. After course adjustments on orbits 3 and 5 it was below and behind Soyuz and closing fast. The crew rested that night and prepared for docking.

Down on the ground, Kettering Grammar had picked up Soyuz on the standard frequency and listened to the voice exchanges between Soyuz and the ground. They were glad they did. On revolution 17 they heard Kovalyonok call off 'three metres a second and closing fast', and then 'two metres a second'. They waited for the next pass, in which they were expecting to hear the pressures between Soyuz and Salyut had been equalized. But they picked up no such reports on revolution 18. What was going on? At the same time—though Kettering could not know it—American ground trackers measured Soyuz and Salyut so close as to be indistinguishable.

But far from having docked, they were still on their own. A silence descended on the mission in Moscow. Eventually after 14 hours it was announced that the docking had been cancelled and the crew was returning to Earth. The craft was powered down to conserve energy. Kovalyonok and Ryumin were down the following morning near Tselinograd, having been in space two days and 46 minutes. They were exhausted, frustrated and depressed. They were at once flown off to Baikonour to begin the process of finding out what had gone wrong. Whatever it was, the men themselves were not to blame. They had rendezvoused perfectly—and indeed had spent revolutions 18 to 24 only a few hundred metres from the station. Four times they had closed in to dock. Four times they had failed to get a connection. Each time they had operated all the mechanisms, but there was still no capture.

It was an experience identical to what American astronauts had found on Apollo 14 and Skylab 2: a stubborn refusal of the mechanisms to couple. On both occasions the Americans had simply rammed their ships together and it had eventually worked. Kovalyonok tried this again and again, but to no avail. So the big question was: did the fault lie on Soyuz or the station? They hoped the former and feared the latter. If Salyut's docking port was faulty, the Russians had just launched another defective orbiting station.

RESCUE JOB

Mid-November: a contingency plan had been prepared. They would fly the next Soyuz up to the other docking port. They would then send a cosmonaut spacewalking to inspect the other docking port and try to locate the fault in the course of the first Soviet spacewalk in eight years. The backup spaceship was made ready. It would be the first Soviet repair mission in space. Cosmonaut squad commander Vladimir Shatalov pulled the original flight engineer from the flight and substituted the more experienced Soyuz 17 veteran Georgi Grechko. Older, longer in the business, a spaceship designer himself, better he do the spacewalking than a novice, even if he had only four weeks in which to get ready. Georgi Grechko and his commander, Yuri Romanenko, must have worked flat out for the next four weeks to prepare their mission, upon which the future of Salyut depended. For the first time they were able to use a huge new hydrotank in Star City for their spacewalk training. Like a giant swimming pool, it contained full-scale mockups of the Soyuz and Salyut which were placed on the bottom before the tank was filled with water. It had glass sides so that observers could see everything that was going on. Romanenko and Grechko donned scuba suits built to the same size as their spacesuits and repeatedly practised exiting from the hatch, inspecting the faulty docking drogue and returning. The tank had its limitations but it was the nearest that they could approximate to zero gravity on Earth.

It had always been intended to resume spacewalks on Salyut 6. For the second generation Salyut, a new spacesuit had been introduced, a radical advance on the Leonov suit (1965) and the Moon suit tested by Yeliseyev and Khrunov (1969). The new suit had a metal upper torso, and cosmonauts entered it through the swing-open backpack. It was liquid-cooled and designed to keep cosmonauts at a comfortable 20°C.

They blasted off on 10 December. It was a night-time launch and they met the dawn as they came over the Pacific Ocean. They settled in for the day-long chase of their target. Ground control was crowded early the following morning as former fighter pilot Yuri Romanenko steered Soyuz 26 in for docking at the second port. Konstantin Feoktistov stood behind the control consoles, checking each one in turn. Engineers, frowning and anxious, studied incoming data. Large wall displays charted the main information. The cameras were switched on to show the gull-shaped Salyut in the middle of the screen, becoming larger each minute. Mission director Alexei Yeliseyev had his earphones on and listened to the crew's every report.

Automatic control brought the two craft waiting 10 m from each other. Yuri Romanenko then took over and, wasting no time at all, nudged Soyuz forward for the last little bit. 'Full pressure...full electrical coupling!' he reported. They had done it! There were sighs and signs of relief all round and ground control emptied out like a parliament once a crucial vote is taken.

Within hours an exuberant Yuri Romanenko and Georgi Grechko were aboard the Salyut, crawling through the rear end. Salyut 6 was no bigger than its predecessors, but the internal design was much improved and Georgi Grechko must have been struck by the changes of design that had taken place since his sojourn aboard Salyut 4. Dominating the large equipment module was the cone-shaped BST1M telescope located on the floor and, also recessed into the floor, was the MKF6M multi-spectral camera. Storage tanks and food lockers were recessed into the walls. So too were a treadmill and sleeping bags. As they moved into the forward part of the station the cosmonauts found the large control console with displays and blinking lights.

There was a water recycling plant, full of pipes, blocks, and cylinders; a barrel arm for rotating the solar panel on the roof; and finally in the airlock hatch were stowage containers for the spacesuits that they would soon need. Salyut 6 on its own was 15 m long, 4.15 m in diameter at its widest, weighed 18.9 tonnes and the solar panels had an area of 60 m^2. The manoeuvring engine had a thrust of 300 kg. Habitable volume was 90 m^3, nine times more than their Soyuz ferry. A multi-layer blanket had been put on to protect the skin. Radiators had been added to disperse the heat. The small portholes had been sealed by rubber. The only other breaks in the structure were an electric welding furnace called Splav-01 and a refuse hatch.

For Yuri Romanenko and Georgi Grechko it was to be their home and the designers had made some efforts to improve creature comforts. One such device was a shower made out of collapsible polythene. A pump would be used to squirt in water at one end and extract it at the other. The American Skylab shower had been an all-round disaster, taking one-and-a-half hours to erect. The astronauts hated it: there was never enough water and it left them covered in soap bubbles.

For their first week on board, Yuri Romanenko and Georgi Grechko settled in, turning all the systems on till they were humming. They evacuated and mothballed their old Soyuz. They took viewers on tour of the station, with their colour camera. They tested the Delta navigation system and swung the station through different attitudes.

Perhaps the most important change compared to the previous missions was in the length of the working day. On earlier missions there was a constant need for contact with the ground. This meant that one cosmonaut had always to be up and this proved to be very tiring. Now there were teleprinters on board, which meant that there could be an automatic telexing of information from Earth up to the station and vice versa. As a result, the crew worked Moscow time, like the ground, and the telexing could be taking place when the crew was asleep. This made the work much easier, and after a week in space the crew was in a position to carry out the vital spacewalk that would determine the entire future of the mission.

'NO SCRATCHES!'

They went into the airlock hatch and got into their new spacesuits. It was midnight early on 20 December by the time they were ready and had tested their suits for faults and leaks. Grechko emerged first; Romanenko was to remain behind in a depressurized airlock to monitor readings from Grechko's suit. At least that was the idea.

Grechko emerged when Salyut was cruising over the Cook Islands in the Pacific. He was nearly blinded by the sunlight. Gingerly he grasped the handrails alongside the hull and edged his way along to the docking port. By the time he got there the Sun had gone down. It was pitch black. He looked down and he could see the pin-prick lights of African and European cities glowing in the dark. The Moon was setting and he could see the stars. From the inside of the station it was simply impossible to comprehend the vastness of a sky like this.

Soon he was over the USSR and in contact with the ground. He set up a bright arc lamp so that he could inspect the docking unit. With him was an equipment box of tools and spanners. And in no time he could see that there was little visibly wrong with Salyut's docking port:

> The butt end is brand new—just as when it was machine-tooled. There are no scratches or dents or traces. The cone is clear: not a scratch. The lamps, sockets and latches are in order.

He tested all the plugs, sockets and rods, and they all worked perfectly. It must have been the Soyuz that had been at fault. Grechko beamed the camera onto the docking system so that the images could be transmitted to the ground for them to see. They were in a state of exhilaration. 'Come back in!' Grechko was ordered. He grabbed the handrails and headed back—and got the fright of his life.

Yuri Romanenko had spent the past hour in the airlock, suited up and watching instruments, and seeing none of the action. Curiosity got the better of him. He poked his head out of the hatchway and pushed himself gently out just for a look at the view. He expected his tether to pull him back—but it did not. He must have never attached it! He was heading rapidly into open space, on the verge of becoming his own one-man satellite of the Earth. His air might last an hour or two. He began thrashing wildly to try to attach his tether somewhere, just anywhere.

Georgi Grechko had just reached the main part of the airlock module to see his comrade in dire distress. 'Yuri, Yuri, where do you think you are going?', he called. He pushed off from the hull, floated towards him, judging his movement ever so carefully, reached out and grabbed his line and pulled him in. Seconds later and it might have been too late. Sweating madly and their hearts pumping, they climbed in. Never again!

They were debating about whether to tell ground control about this *faux pas* when they were confronted by a more serious crisis. They ordered the valve which depressurized the airlock to close—but it would not. The instrument panel showed it as open and jammed open. They could repressurize the airlock as much as they wanted but the air would still go gushing out into space through the valve. They were stuck in the vacuum and their spacesuit air was running out even as they discussed what they could do next.

Flight control was shocked to hear of this development: the cosmonauts should have been back in Salyut long ago. They talked and argued and decided that they simply had to repressurize and hope that the instrument reading was wrong. The pressure held. They climbed back into the main part of Salyut, took off their suits, headed for their sleeping bags and slept for ten hours. The worst was over. The mission was saved.

DOUBLE LINKUP

Ground control was not told of Romanenko's little adventure until they were back on Earth. He made his confession to the post-flight press conference and did so in such a charming and disarming way that no one felt they could reprimand him.

The successful spacewalk paved the way for a linkup with the front docking port which now had a clean bill of health. The Czechoslovakian visiting mission was not yet ready, so the first visiting crew would be an all-Soviet one. Vladimir Dzhanibekov and Oleg Makarov were selected. Vladimir Dzhanibekov was a tall, big, sandy-haired fighter pilot who had trained pilots of the Indian Air Force through English. He was in fact a skilled English speaker and a Shakespeare lover and expert. In his spare time he was a hi-fi builder, radio ham and electronics expert.

Having recovered from their EVA, Romanenko and Grechko got on with their more routine work. They exercised regularly. They checked each other medically each day. They watched forest fires in Africa. On 26 December, two supertankers collided off Africa and they reported on the resultant oil slick. The cosmonauts worked six days a week and established a pattern of Sundays off. They played chess, using magnetic counters. They read books, and Georgi Grechko kept up his English. They had video cassettes if these diversions were not enough.

They needed their recreation. They found it hard to sleep at night with the relentless noises of an orbiting station. In daytime the humming and clicking of the motors, relays, equipment and filters did not matter; but at night it kept them awake and they were always alert for the sound that might tell them something more serious had happened. Keeping the station in order used up much of the time. Every five days they had to replace the air units, which were chemical and soaked up carbon dioxide, eventually becoming saturated. The water regeneration systems had to be renewed, and each cosmonaut needed about two litres of water each day. As for food, they ate mainly from cans. There were ten dehydrated items which they could put into hot water. A typical day's menu was:

> Lunch: vegetable soup; canned chicken; plums; nuts; biscuits and cheese.
> Evening dinner: black bread; canned steak; fruit juice; cocoa.

Vitamin pills were obligatory. But the food tasted blander than on the ground—somehow there was a difference. The crew craved items like honey and spices. Above all they desired onions, garlic, horseradish and mustard.

On 1 January they became the first Soviet crew to move from the old year to the new while in orbit. They crossed the time zones fifteen times in one day. They were never far from the twenty portholes on board. Georgi Grechko gazed down on the icy peaks of the Himalayas, and this is what he told the ground :

> Our cities in the northern hemisphere are snow-clad but their outline can be clearly seen. In the south, hot summer has set in. Snow has melted in the mountains and the rivers have dried.

Four days later, tadpoles hatched in the fish containers brought on board. Unlike Earthly tadpoles, they swam in spirals. On the biological front they grew chlorella, which could serve as a source of food. On 6 January as they flew over Japan they spotted Mt. Fujiyama, 3.7 km high, rising through the clouds. Two days later they activated an experiment called Medusa. Two sets of containers were set up, one outside the station and one inside. Each contained amino acids and the other basic building blocks of life. The two would be retrieved and repaired, the external one being particularly interesting from having been exposed to the rawness of space.

Meanwhile preparations had continued at rapid speed on the ground for the first-ever double space linkup—joining two manned craft to one orbital station. If successful it would mark a landmark in the development of orbital stations. On 10 January, cosmonauts Vladimir Dzhanibekov and Oleg Makarov arrived at the launching pad. It was a clear winter's day and very cold when they lifted off on Soyuz 27. The final part of the chase was in darkness. Vladimir Dzhanibekov picked up the space station visually at 1500 m and saw its docking light blinking at 300 m. He went in automatically and the two ships clunked together. The mishap of the previous October might never have happened.

Romanenko and Grechko had retreated to their own Soyuz 26 and battened down the hatches, just in case the docking was violent and pressure was lost. They need not have worried. Dzhanibekov and Makarov were on board within hours and it was a cheerful reunion. And why not, for the suspect docking port was now operational and the first ever three-ship linkup was now history. Tass crowed:

> For the first time in history of astronautics a manned scientific research station has been created in terrestrial orbit consisting of an orbiting station and two spacecraft.

The complex weighed 32 tonnes and was 30 m long. The process was not as easy as it looked, for the engineers were afraid of structural strain. Unanticipated metal fatigue had, after all, destroyed the career of the Comet 1 civil airliner in the 1950s. So in an experiment aptly named Resonance the crew had to jump up and down to a metronome beat relayed up from the ground, to see if they set up any unanticipated strains. They did not.

On 15 January, Dzhanibekov warmed up the old Soyuz 26 to prepare to bring it home. They swopped their own custom-built couches from Soyuz 27 into 26 and vice versa. Several televised broadcasts showed them happily at work in the main cabin, clipboards in hand and communications cords snaking all about.

On the 16th they undocked from Salyut 6 and pulled slowly away. Dzhanibekov and Makarov circled the Earth twice, blasted the retrorockets and went into blackout over the Caucasus mountains. They touched down in the snow 20 min later. Their six-day mission had proved conclusively that manned orbiting stations could be met in space, crews put on and taken off, all with the efficiency of a train timetable.

FERRY AHOY!

Dzhanibekov and Makarov, flush with their triumph, arrived in Star Town on 20 January to be greeted by Konstantin Feoktistov. Only hours before, television pictures relayed on Moscow television had showed a new R-7 Soyuz rocket on its way to Salyut. Early that morning the first of the Progress ferry craft had set off in pursuit of the orbital station.

This was a critical moment. Progress had been tested only twice before. There was a danger of collision if Progress came in too fast. For this reason, two precautions had to be taken. First, two external camera trackers had been installed on the outside of Salyut. Second, data from Progress read out automatically on Salyut's TV. That way the crew would know if something was wrong and they could intervene.

Progress' slow pursuit took two full days, and Romanenko and Grechko eventually picked it up against the background of the Earth when it was 10 km away. It was moving rapidly against clouds. Soon its contours came sharply into focus. It moved in and docked smoothly. Within hours, Romanenko and Grechko had opened the transfer hatch and were unpacking the robot visitor.

First, and always first, came the personal items. The families of cosmonauts used these opportunities to write to their away-from-home fathers and husbands. Families could now send up letters and even small parcels. It did wonders for morale and with visiting crews, return letters were now possible as well. This did much to break down the psychological isolation of orbit. Newspapers helped too.

Not the least welcome of the Progress cargo were underwear, fresh clothes and bed linen. The ferry also carried bread, fruit, more film, seat straps and medicine. There was a small electrical glass furnace experiment. To help with Earth observations was something so basic that no one had thought of putting it in Salyut in the first place—an atlas.

PUMPING UNDER PRESSURE

But that was the easy part of the Progress operation. The more difficult part—refuelling—lay ahead. On 30 January the cosmonauts pumped air on board from Progress into Salyut's air tanks, under pressure. Transferring volatile fuel around under pressure in zero gravity was tricky, dangerous and difficult. Still, it had to be done. Salyut's own fuel, used to boost its orbit whenever it fell low, was nearly used up. The craft was frequently reorientated for observations, and these manoeuvres were dear on fuel too.

Salyut had six fuel tanks—three of them hydrazine and three of them nitrogen tetroxide, pressurized by nitrogen at 220 atmospheres. This nitrogen had to be pumped out so as to let the new fuel in. All this required a formidable amount of electrical power—in fact 1kW—or most of the station's available energy. So that this could happen, the station was powered down and all the other experiments were turned off. Romanenko and Grechko took up position at the control panel. They had to be ready to respond to any problems that might arise, such as leaks or airlocks.

First they brought pressure inside Salyut's fuel system down to 3 atmospheres. Then they purged the system with helium. Finally, the new fuel was pumped aboard aided by the 8 atmosphere pressure in Progress. They could hear it gurgling and flowing in. After six shifts, the operation was complete. It had gone perfectly and on 5 February a last purge was carried out to prevent Progress spraying Salyut when it undocked. Finally on the same day, and noting that there was still a fair amount of Progress' own fuel still aboard, flight director Alexei Yeliseyev blasted Progress' engine to push the whole complex into a higher orbit. It was the first-ever use of a space tug.

They were not finished with Progress yet. They loaded it up with rubbish, such as leftovers from food, containers, boxes, paper, in fact anything they no longer needed. Then they sealed the hatch and commanded Progress 1 to undock. Progress withdrew to 16 km. Then ground control activated its backup rendezvous system and commanded it to return to the station, which it obediently did.

Finally on 8 February its engines lit up for the last time and it was de-orbited into the North Pacific Ocean, away from shipping lanes. It had passed all its tests with flying colours and vindicated its designers. In the space of three weeks, Progress 1 and Soyuz 27 between them had given the USSR an operational space station. The failures of earlier flights receded.

Until Progress, the disposal of rubbish was indeed a problem. America's Skylab astronauts expressed the view that unless special measures were taken, astronauts were in danger of circling the Earth in the polluted debris of their own rubbish. Salyut cosmonauts also dumped rubbish out of their airlock hatch. At one stage ground control told Grechko that they could see flying saucers closing in on the station. He looked out, and found the station was being enveloped in plastic bags which they had dumped overboard just a few orbits before. They only got away from them when they changed orbit.

On 11 February they had spent two months in space, and with still a month to go they broke the 63-day record of Pyotr Klimuk and Vitaly Sevastianov, set in 1975. The previous day had been the 150th anniversary of the birth of Jules Verne, and Georgi Grechko hosted a special press conference to mark the occasion:

> Hello, everyone. Today is Jules Verne's anniversary. There's hardly anyone who hasn't read his books, at least among the cosmonauts. He was a dreamer and a visionary who foretold flights into space. I'd say this flight was predicted by Jules Verne.

Like Leonov, Georgi Grechko brought his drawing block with him into space. With coloured pencils, he made drawings of clouds in the upper atmosphere, of auroræ and Venus rising over the horizon.

SPACE HORIZON

The USSR had paved the way for welding experiments in space, starting with Soyuz and continuing on board Salyut 5. After Progress 1's arrival the cosmonauts were able to complete assembling an electric furnace hailing under the name of Splav-01. Once all the components had been put together, they were placed in the airlock. Splav-01 weighed 23 kg and could heat metals up to temperatures of 1100°C, with a computer controlling accuracy to within 5°C. For the first experiment, which lasted 14 hours, the station was powered down and allowed to drift, both to save energy and so as not to disrupt the work of the furnace. Capsules of copper, indium, aluminium and magnesium were put into the furnace and crystallized. The airlock was then repressurized and the samples were recovered. A second experiment was then run in soldering and welding aluminium and tungsten. The samples were retrieved and placed in containers for later recovery on Earth. The great advantage of the new manned ferry and automatic cargo ship system was that the scientists could examine the results and then send up new materials in the next ferry.

On 20 February, Romanenko and Grechko brought their large telescope into action for the first time. It was the largest telescope of its kind ever flown in space—indeed it used up a substantial proportion of the equipment module. Its detector crystals were cooled by liquid to a temperature of −269°C. Like any Earth-bound astronomer they sighted it with a small built-in telescope sight. And it opened up the universe to them. Through it they could spot and photograph Mars and Jupiter, the star Sirius, the Orion nebula and interstellar gas clouds. Using it to look towards Earth gave even more spectacular vistas.

Things did go wrong from time to time. At one stage the radio broke down and they lost the sound channel completely. They had to turn on the television and use gestures and drawings to explain what was going on! And then there was the great fly escape. Fruit flies escaped from their container. Romanenko and Grechko spent hours chasing them around trying to catch up with them and mop them up with a vacuum cleaner. They got most of them, but a few would still come out to buzz around their ears whilst they slept.

By now they were well into a routine. Relaxing each seventh day. Sleeping, eating, housekeeping. They hated the mandatory two hours' exercise each day. It cut down on the time for experiments, which was why the reason they had gone up there in the first place. It was uncomfortable and left them sweaty and tired. The shower took hours to erect and take down, and there was not enough water. But they also knew that their bodies could never return to Earth unless they exercised. By the time they received their second set of visitors to the station on 3 March, they were not in the best of humour.

COMRADES ABOARD

Now it was time for the first of the international missions, Soyuz 28, with a Czechoslovak flight engineer, Vladimir Remek. There was no engineering justification for these missions, since the crews often returned on the same spacecraft as the one which brought them there for their week-long visit. The purpose was essentially political—to reward socialist allies and to upstage the Americans, who also had an international manned programme in the pipeline. Spacelab was a small manned laboratory to be flown in the cargo bay of the shuttle, and the first Spacelab mission had been set for 1980. Spacelab was built by the European Space Agency, ESA, partly because NASA could not get the funds for Spacelab on its own. But part of the deal was that ESA could nominate astronauts for NASA to fly aboard Spacelab. The manned Intercosmos missions meant beating Spacelab. Eight Intercosmos flights were slated for Salyut 6, departing in order of political loyalty. The Romanians, the most disloyal of all the eastern bloc countries, had to wait till last. The Americans were not beyond reproach either, and in 1983 President Reagan magnanimously offered seats on the shuttle to Brazil, Mexico and Canada. A Saudi Arabian prince even got to fly. A share of the space action was fast becoming part of the superpower game.

On board Salyut 6, four cosmonauts open a commemorative post office to mark the first Intercosmos mission. Left to right: Vladimir Remek (Czechoslovakia), Alexei Gubarev, Georgi Grechko and Yuri Romanenko.

Soyuz 28 docked with Salyut's rear docking port on the evening of 3 March. Vladimir Remek and Alexei Gubarev were given a warm welcome aboard and they celebrated through the night. Georgi Grechko spent much time comparing notes with Alexei Gubarev, with whom he had flown on Salyut 4 four years earlier. Pictures of Leonid Brezhnev and Gustav Husak were sticky-taped to the walls before the TV cameras. Fraternal greetings flowed to and fro.

A number of joint Soviet–Czechoslovakian experiments were devised for the mission. Chlorella investigated how seaweed could be used to develop a closed ecological system. They used the Splav-01 furnace to smelt glass, silver and copper for the Academy of Sciences in Prague. There were eight other experiments, whose strategic value was uncertain.

Alexei Gubarev and Vladimir Remek undocked over Lake Baikal on 20 March. Retrofire was over the South Atlantic and they were down near Arkalyk within half an hour. In weeks they were feted as heroes throughout Czechoslovakia. Streets were named in their honour and they opened schools and talked to youth groups and factory workers throughout the summer. Remek, single at the time, married twice after his return and became director of the Aviation and Space Museum in Prague.

Their return gave Romanenko and Grechko the breathing space they needed to reorganize Salyut and prepare for their own return. Tension rose—they would be returning after being aloft longer than anyone before them. Exercise periods were doubled for their last week in space. They used their penguin suits all the time.

Closing down the orbiting station sounded simpler than it was. A precise inventory had to be made of what was still on board. Systems had to be turned on automatic. All research results had to be stowed carefully on Soyuz 27. On the 15 March they fired the Soyuz engine for a quarter of a second to check that it was still operational. The two men rose early on 16 March, had breakfast and surveyed the interior of Salyut for the last time. It had been their home for three months and it had served them well. They scribbled a note for the next crew, slammed the hatch and strapped themselves into the descent cabin.

CARRIED AWAY

Their blackened capsule, beacon flashing, was spotted coming down under its single parachute. It was on time and in the right place. Shadows of the ground crews and the helicopters stood out in the spring snow. The five Mil helicopters, their engines roaring as they raced their throttles, their blades whirring, closed in and landed a safe distance away. They turned off their engines. Calm returned to the snowscape. There was only the crunching of boots on the snow.

They placed ladders against the capsule. Doctors raced to the top and opened up. They were greeted by two grinning faces. Romanenko and Grechko were eased up, put onto stretchers and carried into the waiting helicopters. Their smiles and grins stretched from ear to ear. Relieved and elated, they were breathing real fresh air for the first time in a quarter of a year. How wholesome it was, how natural in its coldness! The quiet words of welcome were muffled in the snow. The Mil engines roared and they were carried away. They were someone else's business now.

They had good reason to celebrate. The flight was 96 days and 10 hours, no less, twelve days beyond the Skylab 4 record. Grechko had reached a personal record of 124 days in space. But in one sense the experiment was only just beginning. How would they readapt to our heavy planet? The men were forbidden to walk unaided, not that they could not have done so, but for fear of in some way straining their hearts. They found everything heavy. Their beds were heavy. Lifting a cup of tea was a challenge akin to weightlifting. Sudden movements brought nausea. This might have caused worry, except that there was nothing wrong with their sleep nor their appetites.

By 20 March they were able to go for a walk together. Soon they were talking to the different scientific groups that had prepared and followed their flight—the engineers, the spacesuit designers, the astrophysicists. By early April they had put back the weight they had lost in orbit and had shaken off the sensations of the flight. They eventually rid themselves of the tendency of trying to 'swim' out of their beds in the middle of the night!

The head of the Medical Team, Dr. Anatoli Yegorov, attributed the medical success of the mission to their ability to go on working, to regular exercise, the size of Salyut itself and psychological compatibility. Yuri Romanenko and Georgi Grechko became good friends during the flight and their friendship was to endure. Grechko's humour probably kept things going when times got hard. On 10 April, they returned to Star Town. There was a reception in the Kremlin, medals, speeches and toasts. A large press conference followed, attended by experts from different aspects of the flight. Early in May they joined the Soyuz 28 crew then touring Prague and Bratislava.

By early 1978, Soviet cosmonauts had spent 600 days in space aboard the six Salyuts, compared to the 500 days of Skylab. But the achievement of Georgi Grechko and Yuri Romanenko was more than the number of hours flown: they had demonstrated the ability to live and work in space, to refuel, to take on visiting ships and crews, to inspect damage, to weld materials in the vacuum and take Salyut to its limits. There had been problems, but the systems had passed their tests. The bad old days seemed behind them at last. So they were. Soyuz 26 began a period of virtually unbroken success in which one record was broken after another and one frontier after another pushed back. The years of persistence were paying off.

OFF AGAIN!

Evaluation of the first set of missions was complete by mid-May and the decision was taken to proceed with the next long-duration mission. An added incentive was the long summer evenings because they gave good lighting conditions in the more northerly parts of the USSR.

The crew commander selected was Vladimir Kovalyonok, Soyuz 25 commander, and the flight engineer was Alexander Ivanchenkov, a computer expert from the Moscow Aviation Institute. The challenge they faced was to extend the last mission by 50%, to around 140 days. Kovalyonok and Ivanchenkov took off on a warm summer's evening, only a week before the longest day in the year. It was 15 June. A new navigation system had been installed on Soyuz 29 called igla, the Russian for 'needle'. It was switched on 22 km from Salyut and took care of the final phase of the rendezvous.

It took them a week to get Salyut back into shape again and operational once more. They worked a more relaxed schedule than their predecessors—a five-day week rather than a six-day week; nine hours sleep a night rather than eight; and a schedule from 8 a.m.

The crew of Soyuz 29, Vladimir Kovalyonok (left) and Alexander Ivanchenkov, reading *Pravda* over a glass of tea.

to 11 p.m. From 23 to 26 June they ran a three-day smelting experiment on mercury and cadmium. They closed the Soyuz, turned off the thrusters and let the station drift to prevent irregularities in the metals. It so happened that they found themselves in an orbit in which the Sun simply rolled low on the northern horizon and never set and they could look at it without the need for filters.

On 27 June, Polish strongman General Woicech Jaruzelsi went to Baikonour to bid goodbye to Poland's first cosmonaut, Miroslav Hermaciewski, who had been teamed up with Pyotr Klimuk. The general must have been well satisfied with what he saw: Soyuz 30 lifted off smoothly and on 28 June its crew was boarding Salyut through its rear port. A batch of experiments was put together by the Polish Academy of Sciences and the Warsaw Institute of Air Medicine. The most important, called Sirena, involved 14 hours of smelting pure glass. The experiment was to be run at night, so that the process of development would not be interfered with by wakened cosmonauts moving around the station. But Miroslav Hermaciewski was so worried the equipment was working that he got up several times during the night to check, with the result that he may have ruined the outcome! They were back on the ground after a week on board, coming down inconsiderately on a field of maize on a State farm. Hermaciewski was franker about his feelings during re-entry than his Soviet colleagues normally were:

> You sit in the landing capsule and you see nothing but flames all around...you trust the machines, you trust the technology, but in your heart of hearts you still have that nagging doubt.

On his return to Poland he became director of a military air force school.

MEDUSA

Progress 2 rose to join them on July 7 and was alongside a day later. It brought 50 days' worth of supplies of food, water and air, as well as letters and, for Ivanchenkov, his guitar which he had requested. At this stage, new advantages of the Progress began to show up. Salyut 6 had run out of film: Progress 2 brought up 100 kg of new film. One of the main instrument panels had blown: Progress brought up a replacement. And a new internal furnace, Krystall, was sent up. Propellant was transferred, almost as a matter of routine at this stage.

By 29 July they were ready for a spacewalk to retrieve the Medusa experiment. Medusa consisted of living tissues and organisms left in capsules on the outside of Salyut. It was the role of cosmonauts to retrieve the experimental container and see if life had survived or not. The two cosmonauts emerged in pitch blackness over the Pacific. The sky rolled around their heads like the dome of a planetarium. Alexander Ivanchenkov turned off his miner's style lamp so as to get used to the darkness. He could see the stars march through the heavens, the lights of Earth's cities below, and the flash of fireballs and meteors crashing into the atmosphere. Turning on his lamp, Ivanchenkov, with his companion beside him, removed all the samples from the side of Salyut's hull and replaced them with new samples. As well as Medusa there were radio-sensitive plates to register micrometeorites. The two cosmonauts had worked hard by night and day, and after 45 minutes ground control told them to come in when they were ready.

They did not. There was simply too much to watch and see—the grandeur of their space island floating over the oceans, rich blue seas and rugged brown mountains. Out there they had the whole universe at their feet. They could turn and fly and somersault as free as a bird and there were no walls to collide with. They made the most of it and came in just in time before their next pass over a ground station.

The spacewalk was a great morale boost and it lifted their spirits no end. There had been no problems, no dangers and it had gone like clockwork. Soon it was back to work. The furnace burned away and by 2 August they could display a beautifully finished 12-faced crystal to the ground.

2 August was also a red-letter: Russian cosmonauts finally overtook America's grand total of 937 days in space. The same day, Progress 2 was released and sent crashing into the Pacific. No sooner had this happened than Progress 3 was on its way, arriving 10 August. Its manifest declared its contents as 280 kg food, 1901kg water and 450 kg oxygen.

Unloading Progress and keeping the systems going used up much of their time. Despite that, Kovalyonok and Ivanchenkov had difficulty getting to sleep at night and had to resort to drugs. Other problems tended to be minor. Ivanchenkov lost weight until supplies of cheese arrived on Progress: he had earache, cured by an alcoholic drink; and both had headaches until they spring-cleaned the air purifiers.

When the Americans designed Skylab they planned a wardroom for eating and recreation that did not have a porthole. The astronauts rebelled and insisted one be cut into the hull. They never regretted it and the three crews spent hours in fascination watching the ground pass below them. They were never far from it. Salyut was no different. Kovalyonok and Ivanchenkov spent hours simply gazing at typhoons, the seas and the underwater sea beds, glaciers and mountains. Kovalyonok spotted a big iceberg drifting north from Antarctica, trailing clear fresh water against the blue green sea. He noted the gradual advance of desert land in Africa. The crew never tired of their global geography lesson every 92 minutes, all in the richest of colours. Indeed the onboard 192-grade colour chart was not subtle enough for the variety of shades they encountered.

CLEAN SHEETS

Progress 4 improved on their comforts. It arrived on 6 October with sausages, fresh milk and chocolate; boots and slippers; electric razors; clean sheets; and partitions so they could make their own bedrooms. Their station in the sky became more of a home each day.

A second international crew came aboard at the end of August. Soyuz 31 took off on 26 August, carrying Valeri Bykovsky and Sigmund Jaehn of the German Democratic Republic. Sigmund Jaehn brought Practika cameras up with him: it was no coincidence that the best pictures of the Salyut 6 missions date to the Soyuz 31 flight. Jaehn took some memorable pictures of the delicate shades of orbital sunset gently bathing Salyut as he and Bykovsky slowly drew away for their return. Antennæ sparkled in the soft sunlight.

Bykovsky, riding his third mission home, took the old Soyuz 29 cabin down on 3 September, leaving Kovalyonok and Ivanchenkov a new capsule, their Soyuz 31. Jaehn returned to the GDR, was temporarily unemployed after German reunification, but was able to advise in the German–Russian mission of 1992.

Valeri Bykovsky and Sigmund Jaehn return to Earth, 3 September 1978.

140 DAYS

Kovalyonok and Ivanchenkov now faced the final stage of their flight on their own and they still had two months to go. Their first task was to take advantage of the fact that they had a fresh Soyuz on board. However it was attached to the rear docking unit, which they needed for the next Progress. It had to be moved. So on 7 September, they climbed into Soyuz 31 and undocked.

They backed 200 m away from Salyut and began a careful aerial ballet. They commanded Salyut 6 to turn through 180 deg. Slowly the giant station swung around in its path, nudged along with little orange thruster bursts. With the forward port now facing them, Kovalyonok eased Soyuz back towards the station. It was the first time a ferry craft had undocked and redocked: yet another display of its capabilities. This was to become a standard procedure. Not long afterwards they heard that the 'Medusa' spacewalk had been a success. Feoktistov called up to tell the how the meteorite plate they had brought in (and which Bykovsky had carried down) was covered in tiny microscopic craters: it was as if it had been raining, he said.

By the end of October 1978 it was time to come home. By all accounts the humour of the crew was good and morale was high. Kovalyonok commented on relationships between the two crew members:

> Heated discussions are unavoidable—a space flight is not a society reception and we all have our points of view, so there are disputes. But during the 140 days we never took breakfast or dinner or supper separately—that fact tells a great deal.

On 2 November they plunged through the atmosphere and floated down to Earth. Kovalyonok climbed out unaided, picked up a handful of soil, stood up and waved it in the air—and promptly fell back into doctors' arms and they put him into special restraining couches. But he showed them that gravity had not beaten him and their grins showed just how pleased they were with their 139 days, 14 hours and 48 minutes. A plane brought them to Baikonour and lunch of tomatoes, bread and grapes, and a cup of tea. But more than anything else, said Ivanchenkov, they loved the intoxicating fresh air of mother Earth and the breeze of wind in their faces.

By 4 November they were walking and the next day the doctors told them there would be no breakfast in bed—they could find their own way to the canteen. They had some weight to make up: Kovalyonok had lost 1 kg and Ivanchenkov 1.8 kg. They were then sent to a resort in the Caucasus mountains to write a full mission report.

HALF-YEAR BARRIER

The fact that Kovalyonok and Ivanchenkov were in better condition than Grechko or Romanenko showed that the measures taken to combat weightlessness were working. The key was pacing the flight—neither overworking the crew nor leaving them unoccupied, but finding the right balance between work and leisure. So it was that in late 1978 consideration began of a third and last mission to Salyut 6. The aim would be to take a mission to 175 days, a full month further. There would be two Intercosmos linkups, from Bulgaria and Hungary. The crew chosen was Vladimir Lyakhov and Valeri Ryumin. It was to be an epic mission—but not in the way the designers had intended.

The two cosmonauts boarded the Soyuz 32 on 25 February. Ground control played music over the loudspeakers to the crew as they counted down. 'Yest Stikovka!' ('we have docking') reported Vladimir Lyakhov a day later as the Soyuz probe snapped into place in Salyut's docking tunnel. They had made it and after floating down the tunnel the first thing they did was turn on the lights because everything inside was pitch blackness.

The smell of pine forest had been stacked in air containers. The cosmonauts turned on Salyut's venting system and soon they had freshened up the whole interior. They soon got into the swing of things and established the patterns of a working week. They planted cucumbers, onions and parsley in the garden.

REPAIRS AND LEAKS

Repair work was the first priority and the new crew were sent up with screwdrivers, vices and pliers. It was not as easy as it sounded and the first attempt to unscrew a panel went badly wrong: Lyakhov spun round and round, not the screw! An attempt to fix their broken tape-recorder was more successful, using a fitter's soldering iron.

Progress 5 came up with 2300 kg of cargo and arrived on 14 March with rocket propellant, fresh water, a fire-warning system, a new teletype unit and a walkie-talkie unit so that they could communicate with each other while at other ends of the station. The fire alarm was sensitive enough to be set off by cigarette smoke. Lyakhov had been a heavy smoker until he entered cosmonaut training and if he resumed his former bad habits he would be found out. Unloading Progress took four days: there were 300 separate items to be taken out of 27 containers. For personal interest there was a 9 kg parcel of letters, newspapers and gifts from home, family and friends. Then the problems began: the Western press suddenly began to report that there were fuel leaks on board. Alarms sounded.

In fact there was a fuel leak. A membrane had broken and had been contaminated with nitrogen. As a result, pressurization of the Salyut system had been partly lost. They could not fire the main engine. There was only one thing for it: the errant tank had to be isolated. So on 16 March, they spun Salyut round and round to force out the fuel, and the contaminated fuel was forced into an empty tank. Once done, the valve was then closed and purified for new fuel. The contaminated tank was then opened at the other end to vent into open space to shake out the bad fuel.

Progress brought a television for the crew and as a result they were able to pick up direct broadcasts from the ground. First of all they were sent up a video of their own launching. In fact the principal value of the onboard TV was psychological, for it enabled the crew to talk direct to their families and vice versa. But there were many other practical benefits: on the planning side there could be teleconferences with the mission directors; and statistical and computer data could be gone over together. In addition, they had 50 video cassettes on board, including films, concerts and cartoons.

After a month, the crewmen took their first shower. There was a new ring to collect stray water, so the overall process was better than the earlier attempts. Several days later, Progress 5 was cast off and de-orbited. Before it left, it burned its engine to leave the complex in its ideal orbit of 91.4 min, which was ideal for the upcoming launch window.

BURN OUT

Bulgaria was one of the smallest of the East European socialist countries. The most loyal to the USSR of the States in the block, the flight of Soyuz 33 was set to be of tremendous symbolic importance, rather than as some Poles and Czechs had made it, the subject of underground jokes. Accompanying Soviet commander was Bulgarian flight engineer Georgi 'Gosho' Ivanov—a tough moustached aviator.

Surrounded by a gaggle of Bulgarian officials, politicians and functionaries, Nikolai Rukavishnikov and Gosho Ivanov arrived at the launch pad at 6 p.m. on 10 April 1979. It was a fresh, blustery day with winds gusting at 18 km/h. After that, things got worse and the wind speed picked up to 40km /h. No spaceship had ever been launched from there in such bad conditions before. The Soyuz swayed back and forth, the crew on top sensing the gusting, but the launch went ahead anyway and it was dark when they took off. After ten minutes they had left the Earth's unpredictable weather behind. Mass rallies were held throughout Bulgaria to celebrate. Pavel Popovich spoke to crowds on the streets in Sofia. A special song was composed. Bulgaria, tiny Bulgaria, was the sixth of the world's nations to have a man in space.

Docking was due at 9.15 p.m. on 11 April. At 8.30 p.m. the two spaceships were so close together that they were in the same time zone and Yeliseyev—who was directing the mission—could talk to both crews simultaneously. On the display screen the scarlet (33) and blue (Salyut) lights had nearly joined. Rukavishnikov fired the engine for a final, closing 8 s. It burned for four seconds—and then flickered and died. It just spluttered out. The propulsion system suffered a total failure. Soyuz 33 whizzed past the space station. 'Something's gone badly wrong !' whispered Ryumin to Lyakhov—they had both been watching through the portholes. Soyuz 33 disappeared from sight.

Fortunately, Soyuz had a reserve system, otherwise they would have been truly marooned. Yeliseyev ordered them to come home at the first available opportunity. He had no choice but to do so. And if the fuel tanks were at fault, then the reserve system might not function either. Lyakhov and Ryumin could not sleep that night for they were thinking how they could somehow set out in their own Soyuz 32 to rescue their comrades. A complication was that they could trust the reserve system for only one firing. Normally a Soyuz coming home from the space station would be expected to de-orbit in two burns—the first one at 350 km, and the second at 220 km. Soyuz then goes into a gentle, sliding re-entry. But one burn only and at 350 km meant a plunging vertical descent. But there was no other way.

On their 31st orbit, Rukavishnikov fired the backup motor. It should have run for 213 seconds but it did not shut down. He had to turn it off himself. Soyuz 33 plunged earthwards. G forces built up—4 g, 8 g, 10 g. Contact with ground control was lost. Inside, it was 'like being in a blowtorch' said Rukavishnikov as Soyuz was subjected to the full ballistic descent. 'The capsule shook and shook around: there was the roar of a burning chimney fire', he recalled. But they made it and were coming home under a cloudless sky with a blazing full Moon. It was now mild and calm, unlike the previous day. An aeroplane pilot spotted the glowing red of the heatshield underneath the capsule and a flashing beacon on top. Flight control relaxed when the crew reported and told them the parachute was out and that they were alive and well. They were a little distance from the recovery area—not surprising considering the type of descent—and the aircraft pilot directed the helicopters to the site. Soyuz 33 touched down and rolled over onto its side. The two men lost no time in getting out.

They were whisked away to the 'Hotel Cosmonaut' in Baikonour. They were quite exhausted. All Rukavishnikov could manage was to comment that the flight seemed like it had lasted a month. The next day he told a press conference that their situation had been much too much like America's Apollo 13 near-disaster for their comfort. He was probably right. Soyuz 33 was the closest that the Russians had come to a disaster since the launch abort of April 1975 and the nearest they had ever come to getting a crew stranded in orbit. Years later, Rukavishnikov still shuddered when thinking of the close call: 'I was scared as hell', he admitted.

PROBLEMS

The failure of Soyuz 33 created all kinds of problems. There was the fault in the engine itself, which was serious enough, made worse by the fact that the guilty parts had burnt up on re-entry and could not be examined. Analysis of the fault would have to be based on telemetry alone. Second, Soyuz 32's own safe on-orbit lifetime would expire in June. So they would have to either bring the crew back then, thus cutting short the mission, or send up a replacement Soyuz by then. This could be either manned (if the fault had been isolated) or unmanned if it had not. Third, there was the political issue. The Bulgarian had not reached the space station, so should the unfortunate Bulgarians have a second shot at it? Would they relaunch the same crew, or their backups (Yuri Romanenko and Alexander Alexandrov)? If they did, would there be repercussions from other Eastern European countries?

By mid-May it was clear that work on the faulty engine would take some time yet. The controllers felt sufficiently confident that they could keep Lyakhov and Ryumin up there, but not confident enough to fly a new crew as well. So they would replace the ageing Soyuz 32 with an unmanned Soyuz 34, even though this laid them open to criticism that it might have the same flaws as the hapless Soyuz 33.

As for the Bulgarians, they were sent home. They must have been disappointed. And the Hungarians, next in line, had to wait a full year. Ivanov later became a deputy in the post-revolutionary Bulgarian parliament; Alexandrov did get the chance to fly (Soyuz TM5) though his subsequent efforts to enter politics were less successful and he wrote a doctorate on cosmonautics instead.

On 6 June, Soyuz 34 was launched—with no one on board. It closed in on the station and docked on 8 June. Lyakhov and Ryumin more and more took the view that the Soyuz 33 engine failure was one of those occasional random and worrying failures that do arise from time to time. The engine was traditionally extremely reliable, and this was the first such failure in 4000 firings. Neither the recently arrived Progress 6 nor Soyuz 34, which had identical designs to the faulty engines, showed any indication of the problem, whatever it was.

As it was, the cosmonauts decided to use the situation to best advantage. The old Soyuz 32 would become the first cargo ship to return from the station to the ground, unlike the Progress ferries which burned up. So they packed it with 180 kg of the results of their experiments—29 welding samples and 50 canisters of film and biological specimens. Soyuz 32's capsule was back on the ground on 13 June. This hectic pace continued. The next day the crew climbed into Soyuz 34, undocked, and flew it around to the main docking port. This left the rear port free for Progress 7, which went up on 28 June with fuel, freight, a radio telescope, a political briefing on the SALT-2 Treaty and a book on the history and geography of Moscow city. The Progress 7 engine then fired a total of 191 s to boost the complex to an all-time high of 411 km.

SEARCHING THE UNIVERSE

Ever since Galileo, humans have relied on the eye to scan the heavens, using eyepieces and telescopes as the principal means of increasing the sum knowledge of the skies. After Galileo had come Herschell in Germany and Rosse in Ireland. They had noted planets, mapped nebulæ and glimpsed distant galaxies. But in the 1950s, scientists realized how the visual world was only a tiny fraction of the universe. Radio signals, invisible to the eye but audible to the electronic world, could tell infinitely more. So giant radio dishes such as Jodrell Bank in the 1950s were built.

The next task of Lyakhov and Ryumin was to assemble the first radio telescope in space, called the cosmic radio telescope (KRT-10), given the title '10' because it was 10 m in diameter. They assembled its component parts like a model aircraft to fit through the central line of Progress, like a closed umbrella. The base was attached to Salyut's rear docking port. Together with the 70 m dish of the Deep Space Communications Centre it was possible to create a very long base-line for radio-interferometry experiments.

On 18 July 1979, Progress 7 drifted away, careful not to brush against the radio telescope in its tunnel like a dipstick in a car oil filter. No sooner had Progress disappeared from sight than the telescope was commanded to unfurl, which it did just like an umbrella popping open. So from the rear port could now be seen a wire mesh not unlike a spider's web.

KRT-10 worked together with the 70 m dish in Crimea. By doing so the combined systems used a base-line which could be as wide as the diameter of the Earth itself. It went into action at once and homed in on pulsar PL0329, the Sun and the Milky Way. It was an innovation of great significance. The only snag was that it gobbled up so much electric power that it could be used only on alternate days.

The radio telescope experiment was completed on 9 August. It was cast off so as to free the rear port for future dockings. Lyakhov and Ryumin had now been up for nearly six months and their return had been fixed for some ten days later. They had, after all, been in orbit since February and had watched the seasons turn and warmth and greenness spread over the northern hemisphere for a spring and summer.

KRT-10 cast off all right—and promptly snagged in the optical sighting device on Salyut's rear. The station was now pulling along in its wake a wobbling, useless metallic wire mesh. Salyut was shaken around by its manoeuvring jets to jolt it free. It remained stubbornly stuck. There was only one thing for it—and that was to spacewalk and cut it free. But it was late in the mission and the cosmonauts were very tired. The radio in the airlock was broken. The telescope was at the far end of the station, away from the airlock. But in the meantime some other cosmonauts tested out the idea of a spacewalk in the hydrotank in Star Town and said that it could be done.

Lyakhov and Ryumin were not so sure. They loaded all their research results into Soyuz 34 so it could return without them if need be. Each man wrote a last letter to his family and put it on board. The spacewalk was agreed for 15 August. All the work would have to be carried out away from ground contact because of the broken radio. But out they went. They ran into a problem right away: the airlock hatch jammed. It took twenty minutes to open. By the time they got it open it was night, and they had to wait another half hour, for mission rules forbade any night-time work.

They waited and rested—Ryumin outside the hatch, Lyakhov just inside. Weightless or not, Valeri Ryumin admitted that he was scared as he contemplated the drop 300 km below. So he took his mind off a potential phobia by watching the pinpricks of stars in the night sky. Then dawn marched over the horizon and he could get to work.

He clambered down the hull of Salyut and played out the 20 m safety line to its limit. He reached the far end. Sunshine glared directly into his eyes. It got hotter and hotter. Condensation steamed. But he reached the snag and cut away with his clippers. It cleared and he gave it a final adieu with his boot. Success! The radio telescope drifted slowly away. Soon it was hundreds of metres off. As he returned to the airlock he picked up the cassettes left by Kovalyonok and Ivanchenkov a year before. After an hour and a half, Ryumin struggled back in alive, exhausted and elated. He reported his success to ground control. They stood in applause, so loud that it deafened his earphones. Yet another in-flight problem had been dealt with in real time.

The spacewalk was the last major activity of the mission. The next few days were centred on closing the station down. 19 August was the 175th day of the mission and Soyuz undocked at 11.08 a.m. Alexei Leonov was in charge of recovery operations. He ordered all air corridors in the area closed. All electricity lines were disconnected. As retrofire was reported; he scrambled 15 helicopters and 11 aircraft. They waited. It was not to be long. The TV helicopter spotted the capsule coming down under a red and white parachute. The bottom was blackened and the windows covered in soot. The capsule came down in flat, harvested cornfields and at once rolled on sharp stubble. Ground crews were beside the capsule three minutes later and helped Lyakhov and Ryumin into flat lounge chairs. Ryumin was in the better shape and was able to walk. A doctor pressed flowers into his hands, but he could barely find the strength to hold them though he loved the smells and adored the fresh scent of the harvest air. His friend Lyakhov was dazed and could not balance. They were both carried to a giant inflated tent which was quickly erected behind the capsule. It looked like one of those Antarctic cabins and was ideal for medical examinations.

The full medical report on the mission was made available in April 1980 and was written by mission doctor Robert Dyakonov and senior medical expert Oleg Gazenko. The two cosmonauts were in no worse condition than the first Salyut 6 crews. Bone calcium loss was 8%, compared to 6.8% on Skylab, and was well within safety limits (20%).

Lyakhov and Ryumin were, meanwhile, guinea-pigs for new measures of readaptation. They were encouraged to swim in the pool of the Hotel Cosmonaut at Baikonour. They underwent massage to rebuild their muscles. Within four days they were jogging and playing tennis. On 9 September they were allowed rejoin their families for holidays in the Crimea. The six-month barrier was down.

After their record half-year in space, Vladimir Lyakhov and Valeri Ryumin are tended by doctors. On the right is their Soyuz cabin, which has rolled over. In the background on the left is the medical recovery tent.

SOYUZ TRANSPORT

Salyut 6 flew directly over the Baikonour cosmodrome on 16 December. If a Soyuz launching is planned, it normally takes place 30 min after the flyover, or 60 min later in the case of Progress. But not this time. No less than 73 minutes later, a Soyuz rocket headed off the pad into the wintry skies. This was something different. The new spaceship entered orbit, shot ahead of Salyut and three days later, approaching from up front, slid into dock. No one was aboard. This was Soyuz T.

At first glance, Soyuz T looked similar enough to the old Soyuz. The solar panels were back, which was the most obvious change. But once the observer looked inside, there the resemblance ended. First of all there were three seats. Life-support systems were miniaturized. Second, the control panel was quite different. It had computer displays and the whole system was geared to operation via computer. Soyuz T used all the microchip technology that came in during the 1970s and which could not have been envisaged in Korolev's time. Soyuz T was the first to fly the new 'Argon' computer with a 16 K capability—it was able to fly the mission on its own and provide instant readouts to both the crew and the ground. Overall, Soyuz T was 200 kg heavier. It was designed to be faster, more efficient, safer than the old Soyuz, and not least of all was designed to eliminate the type of faults that had prevented four previous dockings.

Soyuz T's search, rendezvous and docking went flawlessly and the manoeuvre stretched over three days. Soyuz T undocked on 23 March 1980 and then went through two days of tests on its own. It was back on the ground in a night-time landing on the 25th. Flight time was 100 days 9 hours. It went so well that it could now be considered operational.

But what was going on with Salyut itself? Only three resident missions had been planned for the station, and these had now been carried out. The next Salyut would not be ready till 1981, so a fourth resident mission was planned, to fly a similar length to the last. A crew was selected—newcomer Leonid Popov and designer Valentin Lebedev of Soyuz 13. Launch was set for 9 April 1980.

In preparation for the new mission, a Progress freighter was sent up in advance. This was new. Progress 8 went up on 27 March and docked at the rear end two days later. Soon after, its engine trimmed Salyut's orbit to await the new crew. But there was turmoil in the training centre. In mid-March, Valentin Lebedev was exercising on a trampoline in Star Town to keep up his fitness. Something went wrong: he smashed his knee and was rushed to hospital. He must have known at this stage that he would be grounded, and he was. The State Commission had a problem in finding a replacement. The new mission had no backups because it was an unplanned bonus mission. It needed the most experienced person available. That was Valeri Ryumin—just back from half a year in space. He was asked. He agreed. We do not know how he felt, nor his family, nor his fellow cosmonauts. But on 9 April he was back in orbit on Soyuz 35 and en route to Salyut once more.

RUBBER BOTTLES

Jet pilot Leonid Popov guided Soyuz into Salyut 6 and they docked solidly. They picked up a message left for them by the previous crew. Ryumin had never dreamed that he would be leaving himself his own note! A TV broadcast to Earth was transmitted. Ryumin produced an enormous cucumber which he said he had found in the station's garden. It had grown during their absence. The biologists were stunned. How could such phenomenal growth take place? Then Ryumin coyly admitted it was a plastic imitation. The biologists were furious at being taken in, but the doctors were delighted at Ryumin's high spirits.

It took two weeks to get Salyut ship-shape again. Clocks and light-bulbs had to be fixed; new batteries were needed; water tanks were changed. Air and fuel were pumped aboard from Progress 8. It was then sent spinning away to a fiery end on 25 April. The next six weeks were to be frantic—like a train schedule, according to *Pravda*. Progress 9 set off on 27 April bringing a biological centrifuge, air filters and a system for pumping water directly on board. Called Rodnik, all drinking water (180 kg) was now transferred in pipes, instead of in 5 kg rubber bottles, bottle by bottle. Again, this was another example of step-by-step improvements on each new flight, improvements not conceived when the flight began. Progress 9 left on 20 May.

The next Soyuz was already flat on its rail-transporter being pulled along to the pad. This was the long-awaited Hungarian flight: Valeri Kubasov and Bartalan Farkas. Launch was on 26 May. The visitors spent seven days aboard Salyut and carried up a record 21 experiments, though for Popov and Ryumin the highlight may well have been cans of Hungarian goulash. Some of the 21 experiments were out of the usual. One was an electronic aptitude test to measure reaction times and fatigue in orbit. Another was for the manufacture of interferon. It was thought to hold the key to a cure for cancer: extremely expensive to produce on Earth, the process was easier in zero gravity. They smelted copper, aluminium and arsenide.

Kubasov and Farkas returned in the old Soyuz 35 on 3 June. They had already unloaded most of their equipment by the time the helicopter crews arrived. And in the now-familiar game of cosmic musical chairs, Ryumin and Popov above them brought the new Soyuz 36 around to the main docking port. Farkas returned to Hungary and became an ecological research scientist.

In a well-established tradition among cosmonauts, Bartalan Farkas (left) and Valeri Kubasov autograph their cabin with chalk after their return.

'Soviet space crew heads for docking' flashed the newspapers from Moscow on 5 June. Someone was a bit late with the previous week's news, was the first reaction. A new Soyuz was up in space—the first manned version of the Soyuz T. The new launching—the second manned flight in ten days—took everyone by surprise. Aboard Soyuz T2 were Yuri Malashev and Vladimir Aksenov. They kitted up in new lightweight suits with zips, elbow and knee joints, and individually fingered gloves that could, at least according to the designers, pick out a match from a pack.

It was the first operational test of the Soyuz T. It was not all plain sailing either. The brand-new Argon computer brought Soyuz T2 to within 180 m of Salyut's rear port and then promptly broke down! Once again, Soviet cosmonauts faced failure, and, with the station still in sight, Malashev's pulse shot up to 130/min, with Aksenov's not far behind at 97. But Malashev was not contemplating failure. Without asking, or indeed telling anyone, he took over manual control and pressed Soyuz T2's nose into its port. They had made it.

Malashev and Aksenov spent three days on the Salyut. More was not considered necessary at this stage since it was a test of the Soyuz T's systems first and foremost. They left on 9 June and spent a couple of hours on a photographic flyaround of the ageing station. They then came out of orbit, touching down at local midday. In a small but important move to improve visibility, the exterior cabin windows, soot-blackened after re-entry, were dropped off, thus enabling the crew to see properly as they came in.

Soyuz T was now operational and the order was given to put it into production. Meanwhile, aboard Salyut, Popov and Ryumin settled down into a quieter period. They smelted materials, turned their telescope on the stars, and they used the long daylight conditions to make observations of the northern parts of the USSR.

A happy Viktor Gorbatko (right) and Pham Tuan chat with the press on their return to Earth.

They had two visitors. Vietnamese jet pilot Pham Tuan, 33, was launched on Soyuz 37 with Soviet commander Viktor Gorbatko on 23 July. For the Vietnamese the main mission objective was to map tidal areas of Vietnam, silting and flooding and the wartime effects of defoliation on the jungle. After the mission, Tuan went back to his job in the Vietnamese Air Force. On Soyuz 38 were Yuri Romanenko and Arnaldo Tamayo Mendez of Cuba, who flew up to Salyut on 18 September. Mendez became the first black person in space. He spent some time conducting 27 Cuban-designed experiments, some of which involved the behaviour of sugar in the weightless environment. Sugar was central to the Cuban economy. And whenever he could, he went sightseeing at the portholes to try to spot his home country in the midst of the blue Caribbean Sea. The Soyuz 38 cabin was later presented to the people of Cuba and became a permanent exhibit in the museum in Havana. Mendez became head of civil defence in Cuba after his return.

Arnaldo Tamayo Mendez (left)—orphan, shoeshine boy, vegetable seller, rebel for Castro and cosmonaut, with his Soviet commander, Yuri Romanenko.

MOST TRAVELLED MAN IN HISTORY

Ryumin celebrated his 41st birthday in orbit on 16 August—the second time he had been away from Earth for the occasion. Leonid Popov and Valeri Ryumin came home on 11 October after 185 days—over 6 months. It was a triumph. Ryumin pulled himself out of the cabin, strolled across to the reclining chairs and declared that he was ready to fly to Mars! He, at least, had banished weightlessness with a vengeance. Of the past 18 months of his life, he had spent less than 6 months on Earth. He was the most travelled man in history, and the accolades heaped on him in the months that followed were richly deserved.

This time, Ryumin gained weight on board—3.5 kg. The two cosmonauts also gained height as their spinal fluids expanded: Ryumin grew from an already tall 184 cm to 187 cm. And, thanks to Einstein's law of relativity which said that the faster you travelled, the slower you aged, both men came back 4.5 milliseconds younger than all the earthlings they had left behind on our planet when they were away!

The scientific results of the flight, published in 1981, were also excellent. The volume terms alone were impressive. They welded 196 samples, took 5500 photographs, recorded 40 000 spectrograms and spent hundreds of hours on astronomy. They had replaced 50 items of equipment. Even the plants had done better: orchids had bloomed and an arabdopsis plant had flowered. Like Captain Nemo's ship *Nautilus* from Jules Verne, future space crews would live in a green world that they would harvest themselves. And by doing their own repairs, growing their own food, recycling their own air and water, the space station would be less and less dependent on the Earth for its existence. And that was what living in space was supposed to be all about.

NEW COSMONAUTS

At around this time, the USSR extended its programme of manned international cooperation outside the socialist block. France was the Western country with the most long-lasting scientific contacts with the USSR. De Gaulle had visited Baikonour (1966); French equipment had flown on Lunokhod (1970), Mars 3 (1971) and subsequent Venera craft. The arrangement suited both sides well. From the Soviet point of view, it provided access to Western technology and, particularly, French expertise in cryogenics. From the French point of view, it demonstrated French independence and the ability to choose partners at will and pick between the two superpowers. Not only that—and France kept close links with NASA throughout—France also became the driving force behind the European space effort. It was the main supporter of the European Space Agency (ESA) and the principal funder of the all-European rocket, Ariane. In 1980 two French cosmonauts arrived at Star Town, both air force pilots. They were Patrick Baudry and Jean-Loup Chrétien.

By 1980, French candidate cosmonauts were in training.

In late 1980, the first flight of the American space shuttle was now close and listed for spring. NASA had adopted affirmative action policies, encouraging women and minorities to apply for astronaut training. It was only a question of time before a woman flew on the shuttle: no Russian women had flown since Valentina Tereshkova in 1963. In Russia, women were still not wanted and in March 1980, cosmonaut Yuri Glazhkov told readers of *Soviet Weekly*:

> Cosmonautics is still in its infancy and life aboard spacecraft is extremely wearing, demanding and physically difficult...including perhaps dangerous situations. That being so, we feel the time is not yet right to impose such a strain on women.

But, with NASA prepared to impose such strains on American womanhood, the time suddenly became right again. Four months later, the call went out for more women cosmonauts.

Civilians selected from NPO Energiya, July 1980

Natalia Kuleshova
Irina Pronina
Svetlana Savitskaya

Civilians selected from IMBP, July 1980

Galina Amelkina
Elena Dobrovashkina
Tamara Zakharova
Olga Klyushnikova
Larisa Pozharskaya

Civilians selected from Academy of Sciences, 1980

Ekaterina Ivanova
Irina Latysheva

REPAIRING THE STATION

The return of Popov and Ryumin meant that Salyut 6 had accomplished not only the three basic missions that had been planned, but a lengthy bonus flight. The next space station, Salyut 7, was still at least a year off. Two groups of Intercosmos cosmonauts remained to fly: Mongolia and Romania. Could they be flown before Salyut 7?

Many parts of Salyut 6 had worn out and needed repair. Based on the reports of Popov and Ryumin, Salyut 6 would not be able to support a full further 6-month flight. So a compromise was worked out. A two-week repair mission would be flown up to Salyut in late 1980, and it could also be the first operational three-man Soyuz T mission. Then in March 1981 there would be a medium-length resident crew on Salyut, with the last two Intercosmos visitors. Once again, these decisions were the product of operational planning, with the planners responding to changed circumstances as the needs arose.

On 16 November, Progress 11 refuelled Salyut entirely under automatic control. Chosen for the new mission were Leonid Kizim, Gennadiy Strekhalov and three-times veteran

Oleg Makarov. Kizim was a short, businesslike young guard commander. Strekhalov, a coppersmith by trade, had been with the Korolev bureau since 1965 and was one of the designers of Soyuz T. The crew of three reached Salyut on schedule on 28 November and the computer worked faultlessly. They quickly boarded the station and began work. It was the first three-man launch since Soyuz 11 in 1971 and the first time the USSR had three people on a station on a resident basis since Skylab.

The first problem they tackled was the hydropump which circulated antifreeze to keep up the temperature on board. It had simply given out and had never been designed with repair in mind. They had to take the whole system out, which meant using a metal saw to cut it free. The most important thing was to ensure that the antifreeze did not spill out and deluge the station. It did not, and the replacement job worked. The hydropump was not the only problem. Kizim, Strekhalov and Makarov repaired an electricity commutator and the electronic telemetry system; onboard timers; and a refuelling system transformer. The two engineers then spent a full week inspecting every nook and cranny of the station to prepare a full report on its flightworthiness. The work completed, the three men spent their second week in space on a total of ten experiments. They brought up the first holographic camera to be used in space to produce three-dimensional images.

Kizim, Strekhalov and Makarov dropped away from Salyut in the early morning of 10 December. By mid-morning they were parachuting down to a Kazakhstan snowscape. First to spot the craft was a group of Cossack horsemen. They galloped across the snow to meet the crew. The old and the new stood together: the tiny capsule that had whirled around the world at 8 km/s, and the horse, transporter of humans for four thousand years. The three men were in far worse shape than the long-duration crews: they had worked non-stop on board and had failed to exercise. But on a two-week mission they suffered little harm. Progress 11 undocked the next day and burned up after 70 days in space, the longest time any Progress was in space.

FINAL VISIT

Soyuz T3's crew gave Salyut 6 a clean bill of health for a final visit and preparations began immediately in the New Year. Progress 12 went aloft on 24 January and refuelled the Salyut automatically. Soon after, problems developed. One of the solar panels stuck, thus reducing the electricity available inside Salyut. Temperatures fell to 10°C from the normal 21°C. The new crew would have to fix this problem.

Chosen for the last resident mission were veteran Vladimir Kovalyonok, and 41-year-old geodesist Viktor Savinyikh. Winter had thawed out at Baikonour when, on 12 March, Vladimir Kovalyonok and Viktor Savinyikh rode the elevator to climb aboard Soyuz T4. It soared skyward and an evening later they were aboard. Within hours they had fixed the solar battery and temperatures aboard were once more comfortable. They unloaded Progress 12, but by the time they finished they had run into the problem of where to store all the equipment that was now aboard.

The remainder of the flight of Soyuz T4 went smoothly. The Mongolian crew went up from 22 to 30 March on Soyuz 39. The commander was Vladimir Dzhanibekov and his copilot was 34-year-old Jugderdemidiyn Gurragcha, an army captain. The Russians in Star Town never mastered his name and nicknamed him 'Gurr'. The crew brought up a record

30 experiments, several of which concentrated on mapping the deserted and inaccessible regions of Mongolia. Gurragcha returned to the Mongolian army. The last of the old Soyuz—number 40—flew up to Salyut 6 on 14–22 May. Commander was Leonid Popov, who flew with 28-year-old Romanian Dimitru Prunariu. Their most interesting experiment was an attempt to produce solar cells in orbit using silicon monocrystals. Prunariu became a director of the Romanian Civil Aviation Agency after the revolution of 1989.

Mongolia's Jugderdemidiyn Gurragcha (right) with his commander, Vladimir Dzhanibekov, before they flew to Salyut 6 in March 1981.

Vladimir Kovalyonok and Viktor Savinyikh came down on 26 May after 75 days, the shortest resident Salyut 6 mission. When a few days later President Leonid Brezhnev gave them their awards at a ceremony in the Kremlin, he told them:

> Now we will have to embark on the next step—to put into orbit permanent orbital research stations with changing shifts of crews. Cosmonautics will be busy: there is fascinating and vital work to be done.

Their return marked the end of the Salyut 6 manned programme, but an important test lay ahead. The Soviet Union used the opportunity to carry out an exhaustive test of Vladimir Chelomei's TKS, not independently, as had been done with Cosmos 929, but attached to the Salyut. Cosmos 1267 was launched from Baikonour on 25 April 1981, just before local dawn. It followed a two-month-long rendezvous pattern as it closed on Salyut. It released its Merkur cabin on 24 May and docked with Salyut's forward port on 19 June. Only then did the Soviet press announce the nature of the mission. A prolonged test of the module's systems began, with the complex kept in a constant orbit of 350 by 380 km. Salyut 6, with the TKS still attached, was de-orbited a year later on 28 July 1982. The Soviet press gave it a perfunctory obituary and much less than it deserved. 'Salyut 6 says goodbye' was the best headline it could muster.

Salyut 6's record had been impressive by any standards: there had been five main expeditions, 11 visiting missions and 12 Progress supply flights. This accounted for 27 dockings. Salyut 6 was manned for 676 days. 1330 separate experiments had been carried out. Three crews had made spacewalks. 15 000 photographs had been taken. The BST1M telescope had been kept at subzero temperatures for the duration of the flight. Emergencies had been faced, fought and dealt with. Controllers had adapted to new circumstances as they arose, continuously modifying the flight plan. All the years before Salyut 6 could now be put down to a learning experience, and the space programme had at last come of age.

SALYUT 7

Salyut 7 was off the pad on 19 April 1982, eleven years to the day since Salyut 1. By late April it had reached operational height. Salyut 7 was little different from its predecessor, at least externally. Two rendezvous antennæ were added. Three furnaces were put on board—Kristall, Magma F and Korund. The BST1M telescope was replaced by the SKR-02M spectrometer and an X-ray telescope called RT4M. In the first phase of Salyut 7, there would be a series of long flights after which the crews would return to the Earth. In the second phase, some stage later, the new crew would already have been on board when the resident crew left. Such a handover was the basis of permanently manned orbiting stations.

As Salyut 7 orbited, crew members Anatoli Berezovoi and Valentin Lebedev waited for their moment to come. We know quite a lot about how they felt, not only before their flight but during it, because Valentin Lebedev kept a diary. Cosmonauts were required to surrender all their logs after their flight and that was the last they ever saw of them. Valentin Lebedev broke the rules, not so much by keeping a personal diary, but by not surrendering it afterwards. When this became known, there were moves to drum him out of the cosmonaut squad. The diary was published in *samizdat* form initially, then officially but selectively in the Soviet press, and finally in an unedited version. The problems were procedural, disciplinary and political, for the diary spilled few secrets. But it was the first bird's eye view by a cosmonaut that had been written.

Valentin Lebedev left Moscow on 28 April:

> When we were driving off I looked at the balcony and saw my mother wiping her eyes. I waved but she didn't see.

11 May. Valentin Lebedev confided to himself that he feared the 200-day flight, not because of its dangers or hardships, but because of:

> Sudden doubts you might have that you might not be able to live and work alone with a colleague for so long—what if you show some weakness of character or stroke of bad temper?

They went up on 13 May. After their first day they went asleep—Lebedev in the descent module and Berezovoi in the orbital module. When they awoke early on the 14th, Lebedev could not find his colleague—all there was in the module were two hang-up spacesuits on the walls. But Berezovoi had taken refuge in one, so cold was the night.

They docked on 14 May. Lebedev, who had flown before, had great difficulty in keeping his commander away from sight-seeing at the windows. Nausea afflicted them, like any new crew, and Berezovoi kept talking in his sleep. Berezovoi and Lebedev spent some time getting Salyut into order. On 17 May they launched a small subsatellite, Iskra 2, through the airlock. It was a bit of one-upmanship on the shuttle, which was specifically designed to launch satellites from orbit, but had not yet done so. Progress 13 came up to the station on 23 May. When it left it used its motor to lower Salyut's orbit, as the upcoming three-man mission could not travel up as high as the two-man crews.

Lebedev and Berezovoi had meanwhile been weather forecasting and mapping cotton and grain fields around the Volga. They were into a work pattern and began to resent the thought of new arrivals which included the first French cosmonaut. Lebedev's diary tells it best:

> We're waiting for our guests nervously. Our relationship has settled. What impact will the new people have on us? The two of us have got used to each other and we're getting along well in our work. Now it's as though we'll have to start all over again. We've eaten all our soups. All we have now is porridge, wheats and canned food. The bread is inedible. There's nothing left to feed the Frenchman—we'll hope they bring up something themselves.

HAUTE CUISINE

'Polyot normalyo!' reported Vladimir Dzhanibekov as Soyuz T6 lifted off the pad just after midsummer's day. It was 24 June. T6 was alongside next day. Then the gyro broke down. Soyuz was still 900 m from Salyut. Dzhanibekov seized manual control. Perhaps he was afraid that he would be ordered home, because he wasted no time manoeuvring T6 forwards and did not even turn the TV system on. They docked over Africa, 14 min early and well outside ground control.

Vladimir Dzhanibekov, Alexander Ivanchenkov and Jean-Loup Chrétien clambered on board—the Frenchman bringing up crab soup, lobster, hare and cheese, with orange and strawberry lollies. He wanted to bring wine and garlic as well. The former was forbidden (though strangely Salyut 7 did carry vodka for medicinal purposes) and the latter was disallowed because the air purifiers could not cope with it. Lebedev:

> Everyone then went to bed except me. I took a thick mail envelope and hid away in the transfer compartment reading my mail. I had a great time...Lyusha and Vitalik had written lots of letters.

The French visit lightened the atmosphere:

> Jean is a funny man. He brought a quasimodo face mask up with him and when I approached the instrument panel a hairy image came out at me. I screamed! There was laughter all round.

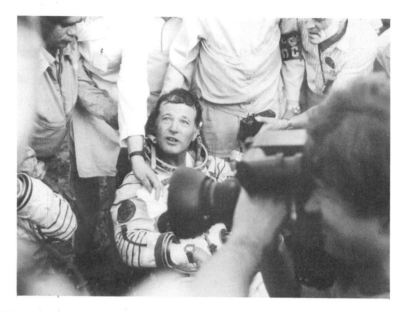

The first Frenchman in space, Jean-Loup Chrétien. France flew its spacemen (in French, *spacio-nautes*) on both American and Soviet spaceships.

Soyuz T6 brought up several experiments. An ecograph was used to get TV images of the inside of the heart, like a scanner. Cytos-2 looked at bacteria. There were three welding sessions: the thrusters were turned off and the crew took long-duration photographs of the Earth and the sky during orbital night-time.

Dzhanibekov, Ivanchenkov, and Chrétien returned to Arkalyk on 2 July. Progress 14 came up to the station on 12 July and stayed till 10 August. During its visit the cosmonauts spacewalked 2.5 h to inspect the exterior of the station:

> The night before I did not sleep at all. I kept thinking of my home, of the flight, of my friends, of my work. I should have dozed off a little, but I did not. Tolya (Anatoli) did not sleep well either.
>
> I turned the lock handle and bright sunlight flooded in. Space began to suck everything out like a giant vacuum cleaner. There were washers and nuts and a pencil. My first impression was that of a huge Earth and the real unreality of everything that was going on. There was the dark velvet of the sky, the blue halo of the Earth, lakes, rivers, fields and cloud clusters. It was dead silence all around. Nothing to indicate speed. No wind whistling in your ears. No pressure. It was serene and majestic.

AROUND THE WORLD FOR 200 DAYS

By mid-July fatigue had set in. Lebedev told his diary that the most difficult thing was not to lose one's temper either with one's colleague or with the ground. You have to keep calm because if there is a row, any crack in the relationship between crewmen can only grow wider. Even still, the strain was growing:

> 16 July. It is more and more difficult to fly on. But watching the Earth calms you.
> 26 July. The days are harder to bear.
> 6 September. Will I ever be back on Earth, with my own people? I find it harder and harder to fall asleep. I am lying like a young girl, dreaming of all and sundry. I fall asleep after midnight.

The image of the long-distance space traveller was the fearless forty-niner, the let's-stay-up-and-fly-further hero. But the reality was a story of loneliness, of fear and homesickness. Either way, however, the sheer routine of running a station diverted their attention from these problems for the rest of the time:

> A pair of scissors is the most indispensable thing on board. Each of us has one tied by a long cord to his pocket and uses it every minute, preparing the food or doing the repairs—the first need everywhere is to open packages or tapes.

Routine used up so much of the time that even some scientific work became wearying:

> 6 September. Today I at last finished plotting the fracture of the geological feature from the Caspian Sea to Lake Balkash.

Four days later, sprouts began to shoot up in the garden: there were cucumber, radish, peas and wheat. Then in late summer came the second visiting team, the first flight of a Soviet woman for 19 years, just in time to beat America's first spacewoman, Sally Ride.

The only real contender for the mission was 32-year-old Svetlana Savitskaya. Her credentials were better than most of her male colleagues. Svetlana Savitskaya was a skydiver at 16, she had three world parachute records at 17 and she was world aerobatic champion at 22. She was dubbed "Miss Sensation" by the British press after a display she gave in England. She went on to fly planes at four times the speed of sound, did design work and made one terrifying parachute drop from 14 252 m (44 000 ft), only opening the ripcord 500 m above ground. To add to all this, this cheerful daredevil had a father who was an Air Marshal of the Soviet Union.

> 20 August. At last we see the transport ship (Soyuz T7) 5 km away, coming towards us like a bright star. The Sun lit it up from underneath. Next to it I saw a tiny star—a real one. It was all very beautiful.

Leonid Popov, Svetlana Savitskaya and Alexander Serebrov spent a week aboard Salyut 7. Svetlana was the star of the show, and the mission even received modest coverage in the Western press. There were regular telecasts of the five cosmonauts swimming around in weightlessness.

> 26 August. They are going to land tomorrow. I'm not at all upset, but we stay. We have our own job to get on with—the earliest we can hope for a landing is in two months.

Break time on Salyut 7—Svetlana Savitskaya manoeuvres for a biscuit.

Popov, Savitskaya and Serebrov returned in Soyuz T5, leaving them the fresher T7. They then left the station and took T7 round to the front docking port. They took Salyut 7 back to its operational altitude of 350 km. Two more cargo ships resupplied them—Progress 15 which arrived on 20 September and Progress 16 on 2 November. On 18 November they launched another Iskra subsatellite through the airlock.

WILTING

The next landing window was early January, but by early December it was clear that the crew would not last that long—at least not psychologically. Despite exercise and a five-days-on, two-off routine, they needed no less than 12 hours' sleep each night. Berezovoi and Lebedev expressed a strong wish to be with their families by the New Year, which meant a return at least two weeks before. They requested a night landing on 10 December, and the doctors and flight directors approved. The men's humour perked up at once.

> 10 December. I wonder how things are down below? We've got so used to being here in this little island in space—just think of going back into the real world again.

Soyuz T7 came down at 00.03 Kazakhstan time. That was when the trouble started. The Soyuz rolled over: Lebedev crashed out of his seat belt onto Berezovoi. When the battered men crawled out it was freezing cold. They were rapidly enveloped in thick bands of fog.

Visibility was about 1000 m and closing rapidly. They heard the search helicopter hovering somewhere overhead. Its pilot picked up the Soyuz beacon and tried to land. It came down nearby but it was a heavy landing in a dried-up river bed and it lost a main wheel. It guided in the medical helicopter to a safe landing. Now snow was falling. Things could only get worse. They did. Temperatures fell to −15°C. It was a recipe for disaster and the pilot of the wrecked command helicopter ordered the other helicopters to scatter. The press helicopter was blown 150 km off course by high winds and had to wait 10 h to be rescued. The journalists missed their story.

Back at the Soyuz, Berezovoi and Lebedev—who were theoretically supposed to be under the most intensive and delicate medical care—were huddling together to keep warm. They had wisely kept their spacesuits on. The medical team found them in an hour, but conditions were so atrocious that the medical helicopter could not fly them out. A big transporter was summoned from 50 km away. It had huge wheels for heavy cross-country work and a rear section originally designed to carry a platoon of soldiers.

Post-flight debriefing had long since gone by the board as the rescue team battled blizzard, fog and a penetrating icy wind all in the dark. Only the radio kept the operation together at all. After hours of waiting, the cross-country teams eventually arrived. Berezovoi and Lebedev spent their first night back on Earth in the bumpy rear cabin of a troop transporter. But they were too tired to care. It was all over now. Getting the rest of the way back to base was someone else's responsibility.

Berezovoi and Lebedev were with their families by New Year's eve as promised. Flight control was now beginning to analyse the results of the experiment and the 211 days aloft. There were 20 000 photographic plates to examine. Pictures from Salyut 7 helped to locate oil and gas fields. They guided the route for the transcontinental gas pipeline and the Baikal–Amur railway. The cosmonauts' weather forecasting alone saved a billion roubles a year in advance warning.

RADAR TROUBLE

Four months were to elapse before the next mission got under way. The crew comprised Vladimir Titov, 36, a new pilot selected in 1976; and veterans Gennadiy Strekhalov and Alexander Serebrov. It was by any standards a strong team. Vladimir Titov was no relation to Gherman Titov—they are not uncommon Russian names. Longer periods of occupancy would be facilitated by using Chelomei's TKS spacecraft, which would provide additional space and supplies. A Proton booster carried the TKS aloft on 2 March 1983. It was labelled Cosmos 1443. The Russians were coy about its purpose and said nothing further until it had docked with Salyut 7 on 10 March. Details of its design were not released until the late summer and only then in one of the less well known Soviet technical periodicals.

Very early on 21 April, the Novosti press agency in London published pictures of the Soyuz T8 crew. It was all a terrible mistake, for, far from being in orbit as Novosti thought, they were still asleep at the cosmodrome! They did not fly till lunchtime. Spring was at an advanced stage and Soyuz T8 took to the skies in bright warm and sunny weather freshened by gusting winds. A blaze of publicity greeted the new flight. Moscow TV ran a 20-minute special programme from Baikonour and captured the tension of a difficult and challenging mission.

Though they did not know it, Titov, Strekhalov and Serebrov were up to their heads in trouble. The rendezvous radar, which swings out of the side of the craft, simply failed to deploy. It stuck stubbornly in. No radar and the crew was flying blind. Titov, however, was not the kind of man to let this ruin the mission. He asked and received permission to fly the first-ever all-manual chase and rendezvous through space. This seemed to work, for by orbit 17, Titov was able to bring Soyuz T8 to within 80 km of Salyut 7. Flight control remained nervous about the idea, but so far so good.

Soviet media coverage had, meanwhile, stopped abruptly. The flight disappeared from the news. In hours everyone realized it was in trouble. Titov flew on. He burned the motor for 50 s on orbit 17 and by orbit 19 he had Salyut in sight. Nearly there! Could he pull it off again against all the odds—a space rendezvous without radar? Final approach. He nudged Soyuz forwards. Just then, Soyuz went into darkness. Pitch black enveloped the Soyuz and the Salyut/TKS complex. Titov commanded on the searchlights to illuminate the target. Soyuz T8 was drifting in towards the Salyut. But Titov found it harder and harder to get his bearings and estimate his distance in the dark. He could see he was getting closer and closer, but how close? There was a danger of collision and impact. 300 m, 200 m. Too fast, too fast. Titov fired his motor once more, to pull away just for the moment. He had got as close as 160 m to Salyut.

By the time they emerged into light they were a full 4 km away. Titov then reported back on the fuel situation. The gauges indicated the tanks were nearly dry. They soft-landed safely on 22 April. The Politburo was hosting a reception in the Kremlin at the time, and Defence Minister Dmitri Ustinov was handed a note to tell him of the safe soft-landing. He squeezed past shoulders to tell everyone: the relief was visible to all.

This setback was a bitter disappointment. It was the fifth such rendezvous or docking failure, and the whole purpose behind Soyuz T was to eliminate the possibility of these failures. But there was nothing for it but to press on. The backup crew was pressed into service and launched on 27 June. There were no hitches this time and the crew of Vladimir Lyakhov and Alexander Alexandrov was aboard the next day.

It took them three weeks to unload Cosmos 1443. There were 600 items to be unloaded with a total weight of four tonnes. To speed up the process, the module was fitted with mechanical railcars, so unloading scenes must have made the men look like coal miners. The TKS stayed attached until on 14 August Cosmos 1443 was undocked to free the docking port for fresh Progress spacecraft. The Merkur capsule separated and was recovered near Arkalyk on 23 August; the main spacecraft was de-orbited on 19 September.

Lyakhov and Alexandrov had a busy summer. They photographed nearly a million square metres of land. 4000 photographs were taken in the first eight weeks alone and were processed by over 700 institutions. They located shoals of fish as their station swung over the oceans.

FIREBALL!

Then things began to go badly wrong. During refuelling by Progress 17 in the second week of September, the oxidizer line sprang a leak. Lyakhov and Alexandrov speedily evacuated the station, sealed themselves inside Soyuz and closed the hatches. They pre-pared for an emergency return, but after a number of hours, flight control had managed to reassess the situation. Only one oxidizer line had gone; there was no danger of an explo-sion; at worst the station would lose 50% of its manoeuvring ability. They climbed back in.

The cosmonauts had barely recovered from this episode when one of the three solar panels went out of action completely, for a reason then unknown. But the consequences became obvious soon enough. The internal temperature fell to 10°C and, more seriously, the humidity level rocketed to near 100%. Besides being unpleasant, the damp conditions made the electrical systems prone to shorting.

These two incidents forced an abrupt change of plan to the next mission due on 27 September with Vladimir Titov and Gennadiy Strekhalov. Two weeks were set aside for what promised to be a risky and dangerous operation. Not only would Titov and Strekhalov be required to attach new solar panels, but they would inspect the damaged oxidizer line at Salyut's rear. Spacewalking was and is a dangerous exercise, and as is known from both Ryumin and Lebedev, the cosmonauts feared it.

Titov and Strekhalov were aboard Soyuz T10 two hours before the scheduled liftoff at 0.37a.m. local time. It had been a hot autumn day, the temperature reaching 27°C. Now it had fallen to 10°C, with winds gusting at 12 m/s. At T–2 minutes the main gantries had fallen back. There was full pressure in all tanks. Only the sounds of 'everything normal'' broke the static of the airwaves.

T–25 seconds. Fire on the pad! A valve jammed at the base of the R-7 rocket. A small fire had broken out and more fuel gushed out of the lines, spreading the flames even fur-ther. It was only a question of time before the whole explosive rocket would go up in a bang. Black smoke curled around the rocket.

At this stage the emergency rocket on top of Soyuz should have fired the Soyuz craft free of the about-to-explode inferno. But it stayed there, unmoving. Were the cosmonauts aware of what was going on? No one knew. Unless they got them out of there at once, it would be too late. Still nothing happened. The yellow and brown fires began to roar and flash and had now reached the top of the rocket. The device which normally activated the escape system clearly had not yet sensed the problem. There was only one resort left, which was for ground control to activate the launch escape system.

Whoom! A gigantic bang engulfed the whole launch site. The ground just shook and shook. Flaming debris careered through the air. Controllers underground felt as if they had received a direct bomb hit. Hearts raced...they must have been too late to save the cosmonauts. Yellow, orange, red flames could be spotted through billowing black, grey and white clouds that mushroomed and swelled outwards and upwards. Hot air was blown outwards into the night and the charcoal smell of burning metal. Wreckage was still falling. Huge billows of smoke arose from the furnace centre of the inferno and the inten-sity of its violence.

And above all the smoke shot a pinprick of light! It trailed tiny flames and was lost in the clouds. The escape tower! The system had worked and worked when it mattered. The tiny rockets on the tower hurled the capsule free, every hundredth of a second bringing it further from the violence of the explosion, every instant nearer safety. The cosmonauts hit 15, then 17 g. It fired for only five seconds, but that was enough to get it clear of the fireball. At 1 km altitude, four petals unfolded from the base of the Soyuz. The tower took the orbital module away. The equipment module was hurled free by explosive bolts. The Soyuz heat shield was shot free. The air pressure system registered low altitude. Those parachutes had to come out fast for they had no altitude to play around with.

The system was designed only to be survivable, not for comfort. Titov and Strekhalov had about five seconds worth of air out of the parachutes before the capsule hit the ground. Despite cushioning by the Soyuz landing rockets, they were bruised all over from the bumpy impact. A rescue team pulled them out. They were too shaken to talk and were given vodka to restore their nerves. Titov later joked that his main memory of the flight was not the escape, but his headache the next morning. They were bundled off in an ambulance which sped past what was left of the burning launch site 4000 m away. Their spaceflight had lasted about 20 s. The launch pad was utterly wrecked. They were lucky to be alive.[95]

A successful daytime Soyuz liftoff. On what should have been Soyuz T10, the pencil-tip escape tower at the top fired to lift the Soyuz cabin clear of the inferno below. By contrast, the Americans had no launch escape system for their space shuttle.

DEAD IN THE WATER

Flight control advised Vladimir Lyakhov at once about what had happened and that he and Alexandrov would have to stay up there while the problems were sorted out. This might take some time. The inside of Salyut was more and more uncomfortable, and oxidizer was spilling out into space. Salyut 7 was 'dead in the water' according to the Western press, aware not only of the problems on Salyut but that the rescue crew had nearly had been killed trying to go into orbit to make repairs.

The *New York Post* ran a sensational story called 'Trapped in Space'. The British *Sunday Express* said Lyakhov and Alexandrov were stranded and 'in a precarious state.' Their only hope was rescue by the American shuttle: but the Russians were too proud to ask for help, preferring that their men die. The truth was, as ever, more mundane. Kettering Grammar, still on the job, used its shortwave radio to pick up the crew chattering away. They did not know Russian but they could tell by the tone of their voices that they were not listening in to the desperate or the dying.

Flight control worked flat out to get the flight back on a level keel. The cosmonauts were given a new programme of work with the emphasis on technological experiments. On 9 October they spotted the first snowfall sprinkling the terrain of the USSR. The work programme in fact gave the cosmonauts a new sense of purpose and, according to official sources, stopped and reversed their psychological decline. By 12 October, Moscow felt confident enough to announce details of a Soviet–Indian flight planned for the spring. The USSR had already launched an Indian Earth satellite, so an Intercosmos flight was a logical sequel.

The future of the existing mission was decided on during a ground-to-air teleconference held on 16 October by mission director Viktor Blagov. He told the crew that they would not be in a position to launch another Soyuz. Could they stay up another month? Would they risk flying home a 150-day-old Soyuz? And last, would they be able to attach the two spare solar panels themselves, even without the specialized training?

'LOOKING LIKE STARS...'

The cosmonauts prepared for their spacewalk and repair mission. They were tired, at the end of an exhausting vigil in orbit, one that had encountered snag after snag. But they rose to the challenge. Alexander Alexandrov opened the hatch:

> It was a tense, emotionally charged experience. Only a thin suit separated you from the rawness of outer space. The Earth below was dark, like a shadow play. If we dropped small objects like nuts or bolts they looked like stars.

The spacewalk took 2 hr 50 min and they returned two days later for another of 2 h 55 min. Vladimir Lyakhov became the first Russian to make three spacewalks. They had to pull the 1.5 m by 5 m panels out by means of a winch and attach them to the existing panels and then ensure that current was connected. The adding on of the solar panels increased the amount of power available to Salyut by 50%.

Vladimir Lyakhov and Alexander Alexandrov undocked on 23 November after 150 days in orbit. Salyut's new panels glinted brightly in the glow of Soyuz' searchlights. The landing was at night and in fog: no pictures were available, but the crew was in good condition and taking walks in the woods around Baikonour a week later, wrapped up in fur coats and Astrakhan hats.

DOCTOR ABOARD

Salyut 7 was not to remain unoccupied for long. On 8 February 1984, Soyuz T10 arrived, crewed by Leonid Kizim, Vladimir Solovyov and Oleg Atkov. The most significant crew member was Oleg Atkov: a medical doctor, he was the first Soviet physician in orbit for twenty years. Soon after they had manned the station it was announced that the mission target would be a new record of 240 days. The presence of Dr Atkov meant that the response of the crew to long-term weightlessness could be monitored on a daily basis by a medical expert on site. From reports reaching the ground, Atkov was quite insistent on running a full medical check each day.

The new crew inherited at least some of the problems of its predecessors. The most serious of these was the oxidizer fuel leak. In late April 1984, Kizim and Solovyov began a series of spacewalks to inspect the faulty line with a view to drawing up a repair programme. Five spacewalks were made that April and May, but the decisive one came in early August when, using tools which had been designed in the interim and flown up to them, they eventually isolated the fault and completed a full repair.

Two visiting missions were flown up to Salyut 7 during their occupation. The first, Soyuz T11, was from 3 to 11 April and was the Indian Intercosmos mission. The cosmonauts who took part were Yuri Malashev, Rakesh Sharma and Gennadiy Strekhalov. Sharma was chosen because of his quick ability to master Russian, but the selectors should not have been surprised for he arrived for training with a full command already of Punjabi, Hindi, English and Telagu! There were eleven passes over India itself, which made possible Earth resources surveys of the Himalayas, mainland India and the islands off its coast. Sharma experimented with yoga to combat weightlessness; and brought up to his colleagues mango bars and curry. Sharma returned to India to be a test pilot.

The second visit, Soyuz T12, was more spectacular and lasted from 19 to 31 July, a full twelve days. Aboard were Vladimir Dzhanibekov, spaceplane engineer Igor Volk and Svetlana Savitskaya. This was Savitskaya's second space flight. Late on 25 July Radio Moscow announced that the crew was on the verge of new experiments and promised tantalizingly that they would 'give listeners full details in the morning'. So they did. Vladimir Dzhanibekov and Svetlana Savitskaya went out to walk in space for 3.5 h. It was the first spacewalk by a woman, and Svetlana Savitskaya was assigned the task of testing out the first electron hand welder in outer space. The equipment weighed 30 kg and had a full console. With the welder she cut, welded and soldered metal plates and then, to finish off, applied a coating. It was nothing less than the full-scale welding task of the type that would be used in the future to cement together the different parts of an orbital complex.

Svetlana Savitskaya clearly relished the work and returned to the cabin exhausted but jubilant. Her success came hard on the Americans, who had been readying Kathryn Sullivan for what they had hoped would be the first spacewalk by a woman. At the time the American shuttle was temporarily grounded owing to trouble in the main engines. Immediately on his return to Earth, Igor Volk was bundled first into a helicopter, then into a

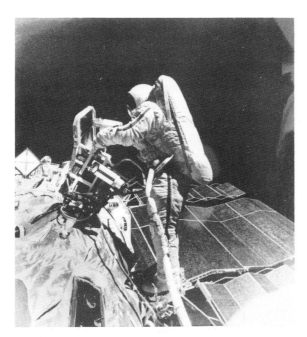

Svetlana Savitskaya makes the first spacewalk by a woman. This was the second time major welding experiments were carried out in orbit by the Soviet Union.

Tupolev-154 airliner to fly to Moscow; immediately afterwards he was rushed into a MiG, which he had to fly 21 km high and then return with an engines-dead landing, in a practice to test piloting skills immediately after weightlessness.

The Salyut 7 crew of Kizim, Solovyov and Atkov came back to an autumn Earth on 2 October 1984. They had flown over 237 days, 110 million kilometres, spent 22 h space-walking, and accepted two manned and five unmanned visiting Progress craft. More important than the statistics was the sheer ability of the men to endure such a lengthy mission, function effectively and carry out difficult repairs. Within a few days the cosmonauts were walking again and at the end of October they returned to Moscow. Next to fly would be an all-women crew: Svetlana Savitskaya, Ekaterina Ivanova and Yelena Do-brovashkina.

SKYWRECK

Then out of the blue came the announcement on 2 March 1985 that Salyut 7 had been abandoned. It was made on just one broadcast on the North American service of Radio Moscow and not repeated elsewhere.

Salyut 7 was in serious trouble. In early January, the solar panels had lost their lock on the Sun and the station had drifted hopelessly out of alignment. Simultaneously the water system had sprung a leak, flooding the station and shorting some of the electrical circuits. With the loss of solar energy, the station lost heat. The leaked water froze to ice. The batteries went flat. Radio contact was lost. Salyut 7 was a ghostly wreck. The new Soviet leader, Mikhail Gorbachev, had made it clear that technology was one of his top priorities. The next space station would not be ready for a year, so a rescue mission was ordered. Two crew members were selected: four-times veteran Vladimir Dzhanibekov and Soyuz T4 veteran Viktor Savinyikh. Their names were announced long before the flight, the first evidence of Gorbachev's policy of openness (*glasnost*) at work in the space programme. The duo had only a month's training, much of it spent in the hydrotank in Star Town, practising spacewalks. They were launched on Soyuz T13 on the 57th Russian spaceflight on 6 June 1985. The all-women mission was cancelled.[96]

Vladimir Dzhanibekov (left) with Viktor Savinyikh (right) and an instructor as they prepare the rescue mission. It was the first time cosmonauts were ever called on to link up with a derelict space station.

Two days were taken to close in on and dock with the dead space station. Rendezvous was accomplished entirely manually, using computers linked to laser optical devices. The two cosmonauts clambered into the station. It was the first docking with a derelict space object. Inside, it was dark and frozen. The air stank and there was a strong smell of damp. Every few minutes they had to retreat into Soyuz to warm up. Ground control could hardly hear what they said, for their breath froze on the grills of the microphones. A stalactite grew from one of the frozen water pipes.

It took Dzhanibekov and Savinyikh a full ten days to get the station back into basic order. They wore furs, gloves, hunting boots and woolly hats. Savinyikh rotated the panels back into position, thawed the station out and reconnected the electrical systems. Batteries were replaced. Radio and TV contact with the ground was restored. The gamble paid off and on 2 August the two cosmonauts went on a five-hour spacewalk to recharge the solar panels. Salyut 7 was shipshape once more.[97]

The two cosmonauts spent the summer on a series of Earth-observation experiments and providing a weather observation service. They unloaded the Progress 24 freighter which arrived on 23 June, and a second freighter which arrived on 22 July. It was called Cosmos 1669 when it entered what at first appeared to be an unsatisfactory orbit. Anxious to avoid a potential public Progress failure, the Cosmos cover name was used and the mission was explained away as a new type of 'support satellite'.

PERMANENT OCCUPANCY

Phase two of the Salyut 7 station had, as its goal, the permanent occupancy of space. The intention was that a new resident crew would be settled in by the time the old one flew home from the other docking port. To fulfil this objective, Soyuz T14 flew up to the station on 17 September, carrying 54-year-old Georgi Grechko, the oldest Russian in space, and two new crew members, Vladimir Vasyutin, the commander, and Alexander Volkov. They spent a week on board, carrying out experiments into materials processing, astrophysics and Earth studies.

This was the prelude to the first ever replacement of the crew of an orbital station. Soyuz T13 came back to Earth on 26 September with Georgi Grechko, but bringing back Vladimir Dzhanibekov, who had been 112 days in orbit. His colleague, Viktor Savinyikh, was left on board to continue his long orbital flight, now accompanied by Alexander Volkov and Vladimir Vasyutin, the last-mentioned now commanding the station. The crew replacement operation made the concept of the permanent orbiting station with changing crews a reality at last.

The crew of Salyut 7 from late September to end November 1985: (left to right) Viktor Savinyikh, Vladimir Vasyutin, Alexander Volkov, before Vasyutin's collapse forced a sudden return to Earth.

Barely was Soyuz T13 back on Earth than the Soviet Union launched its second Chelomei-designed TKS module to the station. Cosmos 1686 docked with Salyut 7 on 3 October. It was a modified version of the TKS, with a battery of scientific instruments replacing the Merkur cabin. Cosmos 1686 was a multipurpose laboratory combining an astronomical observatory, a greenhouse of biological experiments and a technological workshop for the manufacture of semiconductors and extra-pure medicines. Its arrival doubled the size of the station and the equipment available to the cosmonauts. The entire complex was 35 m long and nearly 50 tonnes in weight.

However, celebrations of the achievement were dampened by worrying developments in the new crew. The new station commander, Vladimir Vasyutin, was noticed by his colleagues to be listless, fatigued, uninterested in his work and to spend long hours simply gazing out the window. This was the very stuff of the science fiction writer: the mission commander collapsing under a nervous breakdown. Viktor Savinyikh and Alexander Volkov reluctantly reported his deteriorating psychological condition to the ground. For several days, exchanges with the ground took place over scrambled, military circuits. Mission control ordered the mission to be terminated. The three cosmonauts evacuated the station and parachuted into the winter snow on 21 November. Vasyutin was rushed to hospital: it was the first time a mission had been cut short due to illness.

Second-generation orbital space stations

DOS-5	Salyut 6	29 Sep 1977	Occupied by crews of Soyuz 26, 27, 28, 29, 30 31, 32, 35,36, T2, 37, 38, T3, T4, 39, 40. Received TKS module Cosmos 1267.
DOS-6	Salyut 7	19 Apr 1982	Occupied by crews of Soyuz T5, T6, T7, T9, T10, T11, T12, T13, T14, T15. Received TKS module Cosmos 1443, 1686.

Salyut 6 resident crews

1	Soyuz 26	10 Dec 1977	Yuri Romanenko, Georgi Grechko
2	Soyuz 29	15 Jun 1978	Vladimir Kovalyonok, Alexander Ivanchenkov
3	Soyuz 32	25 Feb 1979	Vladimir Lyakhov, Valeri Ryumin
4	Soyuz 35	9 Apr 1980	Leonid Popov, Valeri Ryumin
5	Soyuz T3	27 Nov 1980	Leonid Kizim, Oleg Makarov, Gennadiy Strekhalov
6	Soyuz T4	12 Mar 1981	Vladimir Kovalyonok, Viktor Savinyikh

Salyut 6 visiting missions

1	Soyuz 27	10 Jan 1978	Vladimir Dzhanibekov, Oleg Makarov
2	Soyuz 28	2 Mar 1978	Alexei Gubarev, Vladimir Remek (Czechoslovakia)
3	Soyuz 30	27 Jun 1978	Pyotr Klimuk, Miroslav Hermaciewski (Poland)
4	Soyuz 31	26 Aug 1978	Valeri Bykovsky, Sigmund Jaehn (GDR)
5	Soyuz 36	26 May 1980	Valeri Kubasov, Bartalan Farkas (Hungary)
6	Soyuz T2	5 Jun 1980	Yuri Malashev, Vladimir Aksenov
7	Soyuz 37	23 Jul 1980	Viktor Gorbatko, Pham Tuan (Vietnam)

8	Soyuz 38	18 Sep 1980	Yuri Romanenko, Arnaldo Tamayo Mendez (Cuba)
9	Soyuz 39	22 Mar 1981	Vladimir Dzhanibekov, Jugderdemidiyn Gurragcha (Mongolia)
10	Soyuz 40	14 May 1981	Leonid Popov, Dimitru Prunariu (Romania)

Salyut 7 resident crews

1	Soyuz T5	13 May 1982	Anatoli Berezovoi, Valentin Lebedev
2	Soyuz T9	27 Jun 1983	Vladimir Lyakhov, Alexander Alexandrov
3	Soyuz T10	8 Feb 1984	Leonid Kizim, Vladimir Solovyov, Oleg Atkov
4	Soyuz T13	6 Jun 1985	Vladimir Dzhanibekov, Viktor Savinyikh
5	Soyuz T14	17 Sep 1985	Vladimir Vasyutin, Alexander Volkov, Georgi Grechko
6	Soyuz T15	6 May 1986	Leonid Kizim, Vladimir Solovyov

Salyut 7 visiting missions

1	Soyuz T6	24 Jun 1982	Vladimir Dzhanibekov, Alexander Ivanchenkov, Jean-Loup Chrétien (France)
2	Soyuz T7	19 Aug 1982	Leonid Popov, Alexander Serebrov, Svetlana Savitskaya
3	Soyuz T11	3 Apr 1984	Yuri Malashev, Gennadiy Strekhalov, Rakesh Sharma (India)
4	Soyuz T12	17 Jul 1984	Vladimir Dzhanibekov, Svetlana Savitskaya, Igor Volk

ASSESSMENT

The return of Vasyutin and his colleagues concluded the main programme of Salyut 7's work. The first-ever handover of crews and the use of two large space station modules marked this space station as a significant advance over Salyut 6. Although the Salyut 7 station had experienced its fair share of difficulties—leaks, a launch abort, electrical failures, capped by the breakdown of the station commander—they had been patiently and, in the case of the Dzhanibekov–Savinyikh rescue, courageously overcome. Flight control and cosmonauts had demonstrated the ability to improvise, adapt and respond to a continuing series of problems, complications and mini-crises. Soviet practice in spacewalks, limited until 1977, had expanded enormously. These experiences provided a solid base for the next generation of orbiting station which was now ready.

10

Mir

Eventually, people will ascend into the expanse of the heavens and found a settlement there.

Konstantin Tsiolkovsky, 1897.

The successor to Salyut, a new third-generation station, was launched from Baikonour spaceport at night on 19–20 February 1986. It was called Mir, the Russian word for 'peace' but with semantic concepts of 'a commune', 'community' or a place where people live 'in harmony'.

PREPARING MIR

Mir was no larger than Salyut, but it embodied new concepts and possibilities. Mir startled observers by featuring no fewer than six docking ports, sufficient to receive a range of new modules, Progress supply craft and Soyuz manned ferries, and thus ensure permanent, uninterrupted occupation. Close to the ports was an arm called Lappa, which could manipulate modules from one port to another. The station itself had no scientific equipment, only control mechanisms and living quarters. Each cosmonaut had an individualized cabin with bunk, couch and table. Originally, the docking ports were to have housed small, seven-tonne scientific modules, the first of these being the astronomy module, Gamma.[98] However, the design bureau which built Mir, NPO Energiya, was ordered to use the much larger, 20-tonne TKS-based modules from the Chelomei OKB instead. This was to make the station grow much larger than its designers had originally intended.

For the Mir missions, new groups of cosmonauts were recruited.

Civilians selected from NPO Energiya, February 1984
_____

Sergei Yemelyanov
Alexander Kaleri

Civilians selected from NPO Energiya, September 1985

Andrei Zaitsev
Sergei Krikalev

Civilian selected from NPO Energiya, March 1987

Sergei Avdeev

Soon after, cosmonauts Leonid Kizim and Vladimir Solovyov took the plane down to the cosmodrome for the first mission to Mir. For the first time, a domestic launch was covered live. They flew up to Mir on 13 March and settled into Mir two days later.

Kizim and Solovyov comprised the pathfinder crew: their function was to iron out problems, difficulties and hitches on Mir before a permanent crew came on board. They were the first cosmonauts to benefit from the Louch (Russian for 'light') geostationary relay satellite Cosmos 1700. It provided 40 min stable communication each orbit. Ground listeners in Britain could make out the switch to the Louch system, when a series of pips opened the radio relay, with a slight humming sound and echo on the circuit.

Until Louch, cosmonauts could only contact ground control when over-flying the Soviet Union, or through one of the comships. Keeping comships at sea costs £3million a week, but 24 h satellites operating as data relays offered a cheaper, more convenient and effective alternative. The logic of Louch was that instead of communicating downward, Mir communicated outward, to one of three large comsats in geostationary orbit, which then acted as relays with ground control. Three Louch satellites between them could ensure global coverage. The Americans devised a similar system for the shuttle, called TDRS.

The first Louch launches took place in the Cosmos series until 1994 when the formal Louch designation was used. The first Louch was Cosmos 1700 in October 1985, located at 95°E, ready for Mir which was launched five months later. Subsequent Louch missions were Cosmos 1897 (95°E, November 1986) and Cosmos 2054 (346°E, October 1989). Louch coverage has been much less than what the Russians might have wished. Louch satellites seem to have insufficient fuel to stay on station as long as TDRS. From 1989 to 1994, only Cosmos 2054 was available, restricting communications to only short periods each day. Louch 1 was launched by Proton into 24 h orbit on 15 December 1994 and located at 95°E. Another followed in October 1995. Louch looks like a flying eagle—a 2.25 tonne bus with two giant 1.8 kW solar wings and three transponders which look like claws.

Soyuz T15 left Mir on 5 May. But it did not return to Earth. Kizim guided Soyuz T15 3000 km across space and fired its thrusters to switch from one orbit to another. Late on 6 May, having traversed the emptiness of space, the two cosmonauts arrived aboard the old Salyut 7, bringing with them 300 kg of cargo. On 28 May, they emerged from Salyut 7's hatch to erect a 15 m aluminium frame. On a second spacewalk three days later they welded its trusses together with an electron ray welder gun.

Even as they did so, a new spaceship arrived at Mir. The new craft was a new, modernized version of Soyuz, called Soyuz TM (modernized transport), on an unmanned proving

The Soyuz TM spacecraft, introduced in 1986.

flight. Soyuz TM carried a new navigation unit, power system, extra cargo space and advanced communication systems. Soyuz TM1 arrived on 23 May and returned after five days.

Soyuz T15 continued its virtuoso performance on 25 June. Kizim undocked from Salyut 7, activated the radar and set off once more in pursuit of Mir in a lower, faster, transfer orbit. With Solovyov he then spent a further three weeks aboard the Mir before coming down on 16 July after 125 days in orbit. Mir had been de-bugged.

Mir pathfinder crew Vladimir Solovyov (left) and Leonid Kizim celebrate their return after a 125-day mission in the course of which they put Mir in order, flew across to Salyut 7, made two spacewalks, navigated across space to Mir again and finally returned to Earth.

The orbital transfers were a spectacular exercise in space navigation. Soviet scientists began to talk of an 'archipelago' of space laboratories, with crews transferring from one to another as occasion demanded. In August 1986, Salyut 7 was fired into a 480 km high orbit. Air resistance proved much greater than expected and by the late 1980s Salyut was slipping inexorably back toward the Earth's atmosphere. Various options were considered, from plans to scuttle Salyut into the ocean and another to launch the Buran space shuttle to fit a manoeuvring block to Salyut. Such schemes were overtaken by events and Salyut 7 disintegrated in a violent fireball over South America in the early hours of 7 February 1991. Most of the debris ended up on the little-inhabited mountainous borders of western Argentina and Chile, but parts impacted on the municipal rubbish dump of Puerto Madryn, setting garbage on fire.

BUILDING THE STATION

Snow flurries filled the air as Yuri Romanenko and new cosmonaut Alexander Laveikin boarded Soyuz TM2 on 5 February, 1987. Searchlights bathed the night-time launch pad, and two and a half hours later the cosmonauts ascended on a pillar of orange and red flame as the Soyuz rocket sped aloft towards Mir. The mission heralded a long flight which would see the arrival of the first research module.

The first module, an astrophysical observatory, was duly launched on 31 March 1987. The cylindrical laboratory, called Kvant ('Quantum' in English) took six days to close on the station. The docking took a nail-biting six days in which the linkup came close to disaster on more than one occasion. At the first attempt to dock, the automatic control system broke down when the module was only 200 m distant. Kvant drifted away, apparently out of control. Several days were spent as ground controllers wrestled with the problem, anxious to try again, yet wary of any collision that might endanger the cosmonauts.

After further attempts, a soft docking was at last achieved. The module was linked to Mir/Soyuz TM2, but the tunnel with Kvant was not hermetically sealed. 40 mm separated the two vehicles, enough to make a crew transfer impossible. There was only one thing for it: a spacewalk. On 12 April cosmonauts Romanenko and Laveikin threaded their way down Mir to inspect the errant tunnel. They asked ground control to separate the modules to the limit of the connection between the drogue and probe connecting the stations. With a jemmy, Laveikin forced an object out of the tunnel, with Romanenko floating beside him with a tool box. After five attempts, the offending article was removed—a dirty plastic bag! Romanenko and Laveikin backed off and requested ground control to command a full docking. The spaceships clunked together perfectly. After five hours outside, Romanenko and Laveikin returned to their cabin, triumphant.

An important feature of Kvant was its gyrodines or gyros. Kvant carried six of these 165 kg units, whose task was to ensure that the Mir station was properly pointed, with an accuracy of 1.5 arc/min. Although heavy and bulky, they reduced the need for repeated thruster firings to orientate the station. The main features of Kvant were its Roentgen telescope, made by scientists in the USSR, Britain, the Netherlands, Germany and the European Space Agency; and the Glazar ultraviolet telescope, made in the Byurakan Astrophysical Observatory, Armenia, with the assistance of Swiss specialists. Roentgen

Yuri Romanenko, commander of the first long-term resident crew of Mir, who spent a record 326 days in orbit and whose spacewalk to Kvant saved the mission in April 1987.

comprised four X-ray telescopes to be pointed toward the galactic plane or areas of X-ray interest. One of the four telescopes was called the fine-resolution TTM and was made in Birmingham University. TTM stood for 'coded mask telescope' in Russian and was 2.5 m long, 40 cm in diameter and 100 kg in weight.

Kvant then dropped its rendezvous pack and engine motor to free the rear of the space station for further supplies. Progress 29 duly arrived at the end of April 1987, bringing fuel, food, water, supplies and more solar panels for Mir. Progress 30 followed in May, and in June, Romanenko and Laveikin spacewalked to erect the new solar panels so as to provide additional electrical power for Kvant.

Mir was visited by a Soviet–Syrian crew in July. Soyuz TM3 comprised Alexander Viktorenko, Alexander Alexandrov (the Soviet cosmonaut, not to be confused with the Bulgarian cosmonaut Alexander Alexandrov) and Mohammed Faris. Shortly before their visit, ground monitors had detected an irregularity in Alexander Laveikin's heart so, against his wishes and despite his protests, he was brought back by the visitors, being replaced on board by Alexandrov. Laveikin was transferred to the National Cardiology Research Unit in Moscow on his return but no serious problems were found. The visiting mission took Earth resources pictures of the eastern Mediterranean and Syria, which were sent to Damascus after the mission. Faris returned to the Syrian Air Force and Star Town never heard from him again.

The Soyuz TM3 crew of (left to right) Alexander Viktorenko, Alexander Alexandrov and Mohammed Faris.

LISTENING TO MIR

Even as *glasnost* advanced, amateur listeners played their part in decoding what was going on aboard Mir. Radio enthusiasts were able to rig up ordinary receiving devices to listen in to Mir, using conventional citizen's band radio equipment costing less than £1000. On an average pass over Britain, they would pick up 325 s of sound from the station, starting 1500 km out in the Atlantic. As well as the voices of the cosmonauts, there was a continuous background noise of carbon dioxide scrubbers, fans and ventilators (the turning off of these devices was always a sign that the station was about to be evacuated). Even without a knowledge of Russian, it was not difficult for English language listeners to know what was going on (not least when frustrated Russians swore, as the two languages are interchangeable). Lots of chatter often indicated preparations to go outside. A goldfish-bowl echo sound meant that the cosmonauts were spacewalking. At times, the cosmonauts adopted a zip-lip discipline (speak-when-spoken-to-only), which meant that they were scanning British military frequencies or the US fleet and re-broadcasting them. At times, the cosmonauts could be heard calling up tracking ships off the Sable Banks, Newfoundland (the *Yuri Gagarin*), the South Atlantic (the *Georgi Dobrovolski*) or the Canaries (the *Vladimir Komarov*). Sometimes the cosmonauts would start calling ground control early by mistake, a sign that their navigation system was malfunctioning. High-pipped squeaks in the background meant that the cosmonauts were communicating through the Louch comsat. Listeners could make out when Romanenko had a cold or, by listening to the downlink of Laveikin's heartbeat, know that the doctors were right to suspect something was amiss. Friday night and Saturday night were family times, and they chatted with the folks at home. One night, one of the cosmonaut's wives gave off at length about her Earth-bound troubles, her husband acknowledging with the occasional, tired monosyllabic *'da'* when he had the chance. Some of the early Mir cosmonauts were country music fans. As they flew over the US, they would pick up the sounds of the local FM country stations, record them and beam them down to other fans on the comship *Yuri Gagarin*—but they were careful to turn the recorder off once they came within earshot of Moscow ground control. Romanenko and Laveikin made an excellent singing duo—they had a guitar on board—and although they thought they were crooning for their own benefit, they had a wider audience down below.[99]

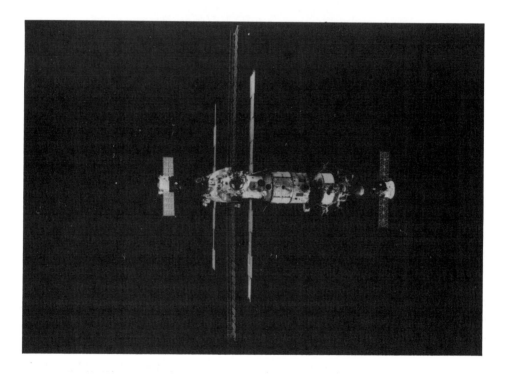

Mir space station—Soyuz at one end, Progress at another.

ROMANENKO RECORD

Romanenko and Alexandrov continued their mission, Romanenko setting a new en-durance record on 25 October. As he did so, Soviet engineers were preparing an even longer, year-long mission. Selected to break this important psychological hurdle were veteran cosmonaut Vladimir Titov and newcomer Musa Manarov from Daghestan. Also on board Soyuz TM4, which left a misty cosmodrome covered in light snow on 21 Decem-ber, was shuttle pilot Anatoli Levchenko on a short mission to give him experience in

On their way up for an epic mission—(left to right) Musa Manarov, Anatoli Levchenko and
Vladimir Titov. Manarov and Titov made the first year-long flight in orbit. Sadly, Levchenko
was dead by the time his companions eventually returned to Earth.

advance of flying Buran in space. He was selected at short notice—indeed, Romanenko
and Alexandrov had never met him before when he arrived on Mir.

The Soyuz TM3 cabin came down in the snow 50 km from Arkalyk on 29 December,
carrying Yuri Romanenko, Alexander Alexandrov and Anatoli Levchenko, all of whom
had been in space for different lengths of time. Romanenko had been no less than 326 days
in orbit, exceeding the previous record by 89 days. The cosmonauts were evacuated
through the top hatch at once, Romanenko being united straight away with his long-missed
family and relatives. Levchenko was brought to the nearest airfield and put at the controls
of a Tupolev 154 civil airliner, which he flew at once to Moscow, following the same
profile as Igor Volk in 1984.

The return of Romanenko and Levchenko had two footnotes. Romanenko was sent to a
sanatorium in the Caucasus to recover from his long and arduous mission, a decision
which sparked Western press reports that he had gone mad or was in acute depression. He
was brought back to a Moscow press conference in March to refute the rumours. Second,
on a sadder note, Anatoli Levchenko died suddenly of a brain tumour on 10 August 1988,
less than nine months after his return to Earth.

Meanwhile, on Mir, cosmonauts Titov and Manarov settled down to a year-long vigil
round the Earth, receiving a stream of Progress supply craft, conducting Earth resources
and astrophysical observations and carrying out medical experiments. They ran a standard

Earth-like day, rising at 8 a.m., breakfasting, three hours' work, an hour's exercise, lunch, three hours' work, an hour's exercise, supper, relaxation and some home repairs. They grew plants and studied the growth of biologically active substances. Each Progress brought up new items for the Mir library—videos, books, novels by the great classics. Each day they exercised 5 km on the treadmill and 10 km on a bicycle ergonometer. Titov and Manarov received two visiting missions: a Soviet–Bulgarian team in June 1988 (Soyuz TM5, with the Bulgarian Alexander Alexandrov) and a Soviet–Afghan mission in August (Soyuz TM6). The Bulgarian mission, the second from that country, was run as compensation for the failure of Soyuz 33 in 1979. Soyuz TM6 comprised 47-year-old veteran, Vladimir Lyakhov, a medical doctor, Valeri Poliakov (who was to be left on board), and 29-year-old Afghan Abdul Mohammed Mohmand. The Afghan flight was essentially a political one, the mission having been brought forward and flown before the hastily retreating Soviet forces left Kabul. The two crews received only six months training.

'A LONE BOAT DRIFTING ON A BOUNDLESS OCEAN'

The mission came close to disaster. Having left Poliakov on Mir to join Titov and Manarov, Lyakhov and Mohmand undocked from Mir in the Soyuz TM5 on 5 September. As they dropped off the orbital module of Soyuz and as they passed over the comship *Nevel* in the South Atlantic, they expected retrofire. The computer did not get the proper alignment with the horizon. Seven minutes later, the crew still puzzled why nothing had happened, the computer detected a proper alignment and retrofire took place. Such a late retrofire would have brought them down in Manchuria, so Lyakhov cut the engine out after 3 s. Three hours later, they tried again. This time, although the cosmonauts could not know this, the computer introduced its backup programme at a point where it was given the order for the already-achieved rendezvous manoeuvre and burned for only 6 s. Once it shut down, a frustrated Lyakhov restarted it manually, but the computer turned it off after 60 s. A total of 225 s was needed for a proper retrofire. Had the burn gone on much longer than 60sec, but still been aborted short of the 225sec, there was a real danger of an early, fatal improper entry trajectory and the cabin burning up.

As it was, Soyuz TM5 spiralled ever closer to Earth. Redocking with Mir was impossible because the orbital module, with its docking probe, had been jettisoned. Air supplies in the Soyuz cabin would last only two days. The cabin itself would burn up in the atmosphere in a few weeks. *Izvestia* that evening reported 'alarming hours in space'. Preparing the country for the worst, the paper referred to the cabin as 'a lone boat drifting on a boundless ocean'. Lyakhov asked ground control to play some music. Radio Moscow tried to reassure listeners. There was stable contact with the crew. Ground control was evaluating the situation carefully. There would be no panic. As controllers reconsidered the situation, the crew had to reconfigure Soyuz minus its orbital module. They managed to do so, turning Soyuz' panels to the Sun to recharge its batteries. Ground control diagnosed the problem, told the cosmonauts how to reprogramme the computer and its backup programme, and told them to try again the next day.

Early on 7 September, Lyakhov tried again. A thin red glow had come over the Kazakhstan dawn as helicopters gathered in anticipation. Cameras tracked the tiny cabin against the scrubby desert browns. There was no trouble this time. Lyakhov and Mohmand were out immediately, tired but grinning. They had endured a scary and uncomfortable day (there was little space to move in the cabin and they had no toilet facilities). An investigation began at once. At the time, Lyakhov blamed faulty computer programming, and it seems that he was right. In an important procedural change, the directors of the space programme took the decision not to jettison the orbital module until *after* retrofire in future. Abdul Mohmand returned to Kabul, bringing with him his spacesuit for a museum there. When the mudjahaddin later seized power, Mohmand, who is a Pushtun, fled to Germany and his spacesuit was seized as booty and sold off by the invading army.

A YEAR ON MIR

The Titov–Manarov team was nearing the end of its year-long marathon, now under the medical supervision of medical doctor and cosmonaut Valeri Poliakov. Instead of an eight-day handover, which would be normal, mission control planned a month-long handover as part of a Soviet–French mission. Soyuz TM7 was France's second joint mission and the French had sought a long-duration mission of a month, with a spacewalk. Selected for the mission was Jean-Loup Chrétien, who had flown the first Soviet–French mission in 1982 (Soyuz T6). To accompany him were Alexander Volkov and Sergei Krikalev. Watched by French President François Mitterrand, Soyuz TM7 left for Mir on 27 November. Highlight of the French mission was Jean-Loup Chrétien's 6 h spacewalk on 9 December, in the course of which he erected an $8 million truss structure called ERA, which had been developed by the French Space Agency, CNES, in Toulouse to test solar panels. At first, ERA refused to deploy, a problem solved by Volkov, who gave it a hefty kick. Chrétien was the first person to test an improved spacesuit. The new suit, called Orlan and

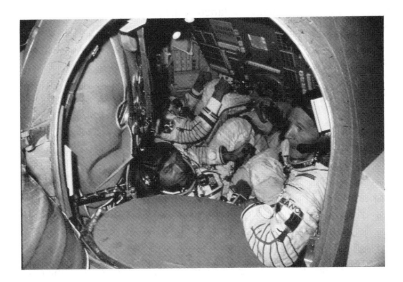

Jean-Loup Chrétien flies for his second space mission in the Soviet programme.

made by NPO Zvezda, was designed with French help. Orlan had improved visibility, dexterity and comfort and caution and warning systems. Ground controllers noticed a difference too: much improved communications from spacewalking cosmonauts. Gone were the sounds of heavy breathing, echoes (called the goldfish-bowl problem) and suit machinery which had previously been a feature of spacewalks. Like the Salyut suit first worn by Grechko, one enters Orlan by climbing through the back, closing the door and begins pressurization at once. It was lighter than the American shuttle spacesuit, which takes at least 15 min to don with the help of two other people.[100]

Titov, Manarov and Jean-Loup Chrétien returned to Earth on 21 December, their touchdown cushioned by soft-landing rockets firing into light winter snow. Doctors looked through the window and were greeted by a thumbs-up. Soyuz did not roll over, which meant the cosmonauts had to be hauled through the top, 'which put a lot of strain on the heart', Manarov later recalled.[101]

Titov and Manarov had orbited for 365 days and 22 h. They were flown by helicopter to Dzhezkazgan for transfer by airliner to Moscow. Though able to walk on to the plane, they had difficulty balancing themselves normally. An entire set of special equipment had been set up for Titov and Manarov to help them adapt to life on Earth. Swimming was an important part of the readaptation process. Within two days the cosmonauts announced that they were able to move normally and the doctors gave them the all-clear several weeks later.

Delays in the new modules scheduled for launch to Mir forced a change in plans for the operation of the station. Soyuz TM8 had been scheduled for launch in April 1989, but with no new modules yet available for them, the crew was stood down. Mission control decided to bring the Mir crew of Alexander Volkov, Sergei Krikalev and Valeri Poliakov back at the originally intended time and to leave Mir unmanned for the time being. Mir was duly mothballed, the crew soft-landing on Earth on 27 April. Poliakov had been in orbit for 240 days and Mir itself had been manned continuously for over two years, a new achievement in space station operation. The day after the landing, Poliakov was doing basic gymnastic exercises and was running two days later.

COSMONAUTS FOR THE NINETIES

At around this time, agreements were signed for further missions with France and the first missions with Germany and Austria and, representing Europe as a whole, the European Space Agency, ESA. Unlike the old Intercosmos series, commercial fees were charged. New groups of cosmonauts were recruited to take Mir operations into the 1990s. These were as follows:[102]

Air Force selection, March 1987

Vladimir Dezhurov
Yuri Gidzenko
Valeri Korzun
Yuri Malenchenko
Vasili Tsibliev

Air Force selection, January 1989

Sergei Kritchevsky
Yuri Onufrienko
Anatoli Polonski
Valeri Tokarev
Alexander Yablontsev

Civilians selected from NPO Energiya, January 1989

Nikolai Budarin
Elena Kondakova
Alexander Poleschuk
Yuri Usachov

Civilians selected from IMBP, January 1989

Vladimir Karashtin
Vasili Lukyanyuk
Boris Morukov

Air Force selection, May 1990

Salizhan Shapirov
Sergei Vozovikov
Sergei Zalyotin
Gennadiy Padalka
Valeri Maksimenko
Alexander Puchkov
Nikolai Pushenko

Civilian selection, NPO Zvezda, May 1990

Vladimir Severin

Kazakhstan government selection, 1990–1

Toktar Aubakirov
Talgat Musabayev

Civilians selected from NPO Energiya, March 1992

Alexander Lazutkin
Sergei Treshchev
Pavel Vinogradov

Civilians selected from NPO Energiya, April 1994

Nadezhda Kyzhelnaya
Mikhail Tyurin

Mir operations resumed at the end of the summer. On 22 August 1989, two teams of cosmonauts flew from Moscow to the cosmodrome for the next series of missions. The same day saw the launching of the new Progress cargo spacecraft to Mir. Called Progress M ('m' for 'modified'), it carried solar panels so as to permit a longer rendezvous pattern and most importantly, a recoverable capsule called Raduga (Russian for 'rainbow'). The capsule comprised a cone-shaped object measuring 1.47 m by 0.78 m, with a weight of 350 kg and a volume of 120 litres. The procedure was for Progress M to undock normally but for the capsule to be ejected at 130 km following which it would conduct a ballistic re-entry followed by parachute recovery. The main body of Progress M would then burn to destruction, as was the case with the previous Progress version. The announcement about the recoverable capsule proved confusing, for Raduga was already the title of several items of Soviet space hardware, and the capsule was not carried on every Progress M in any case. The Raduga capsule, which was slotted into the nose of the spacecraft, enabled up to 150 kg of materials to be returned to Earth from the station. Generally, the capsules carried the results of materials processing experiments, film and the cosmonauts' notes. The Progress–Raduga system again emphasized the evolutionary nature of the Soviet approach to spacecraft design and development.[103]

MANNED MANOEUVRING UNIT

Soyuz TM8 followed Progress M1 on 6 September, carrying Alexander Viktorenko and Alexander Serebrov. The purpose of their mission was to receive the first of the new large modules and to test the Soviet manned manoeuvring unit, a combined spacesuit, backpack and rocket manoeuvring unit which would enable cosmonauts to fly far from the space station and return. The Americans had introduced such a unit to their shuttle missions as far back as February 1984 on mission 41B, when it was first flown by Bruce McCandless.

A Soviet manned manoeuvring unit in fact dated back to the 1960s, when the first unit was developed by the Zvezda factory, directed by Gai Severin. The unit, made ready for flight in 1968, had 14 thrusters, could fly for four hours and weighed 90 kg, but it never reached orbit. In the mid-1980s, the factory developed the new model with 32 air-powered thrusters each producing 5 N of thrust. The system weighed 218 kg and could operate as far as 60m away. In some respects, its performance was superior to that of the American system. It was larger, bulkier, an integral part of the spacesuit, had a 50% higher thrust-to-weight ratio and could operate for up to eight hours.

The space station module, alternately called the D (*dushnashcheniye*, or 'additional') module or Kvant 2, was eventually launched on 26 November 1989 on a six-day rendezvous pattern. Problems developed soon after launch. A solar panel failed to deploy, thereby covering one of the manoeuvring engines and causing the module to tumble in orbit. This was sorted out three days later and by the 30th, Kvant 2 was crossing the night sky only one minute behind Mir. On 2 December, the space station and the module were only 20 km apart and preparing to dock when the Kurs navigation system switched itself off. Cosmonauts Viktorenko and Serebrov tried to carry out the docking manually, using Mir as the active spacecraft, but this was unsuccessful. Ground control commanded a separation as they tried to analyse the problem. In the event, docking went entirely smoothly on the next attempt on 6 December, the Lappa manipulator arm moving Kvant 2 to the side port two days later. This was no sooner done than Viktorenko and Serebrov boarded Soyuz TM8 and flew it around to the now free docking port.

Kvant 2 brought up the manned manoeuvring unit, new cameras, gyrodines, water regeneration equipment and a shower. The module had a purpose-built airlock designed to facilitate spacewalks. It carried a biological incubator and in March the first quail chicks hatched out.The manned manoeuvring unit, also called YMK and Ikarus, was given its first trial on 1 February 1990, when Alexander Serebrov flew it to 45 m from the Mir space station on a 4 h 55 min spacewalk. On 4 February, it was brought out for its second, 3 h 45 min, test by Alexander Viktorenko. For safety reasons, a 45 m tether was used. The YMK was never used again: nor was the American one, for NASA found the system extremely expensive to prepare and use.

KRYSTALL

The Viktorenko–Serebrov crew was replaced by Anatoli Soloviev and Alexander Balandin, who were launched on 11 February 1990 on Soyuz TM9. Their main task was to receive the third module, the T-module (*teknologia*, or 'technology'), popularly known as Krystall. Krystall carried a range of technological and materials processing equipment called Kratar 3, Optizon 01, Zona 02 and Zona 03; and two docking ports for use by Soyuz or the Soviet space shuttle. After some delays, Krystall was eventually launched on 1 June 1990 and, like the previous module, ran into immediate difficulties. A failure of the attitude control system led to the cancellation of the intended docking on 6 June, and the reserve system was brought into play the next day. This worked, Krystall sailing smoothly into the main docking port on Mir on 10 June. Two days later, the Lappa arm manipulated Krystall round to one of the side docking ports, freeing the main port to receive Soyuz spaceships.

Anatoli Soloviev and Alexander Balandin exited twice from Mir in July to resettle the insulation of the Soyuz cabin, some of which had worked itself free; though in the course of doing so they depressurized the spacewalk hatch of Kvant 2 so violently that it was damaged and bent. At one stage, there was Western press speculation that the Soyuz had been damaged beyond repair, prompting predictable 'stranded in space' headlines. The Russians announced that if the worst came to the worst, they could send up a solo Soyuz to bring them home. Four cosmonauts had trained for such a rescue mission and one was always on standby. They were Vladimir Lyakhov, who at this stage knew enough about emergencies, and Vladimir Titov, Alexander Volkov and Anatoli Berezovoi.

Soloviev and Balandin were duly replaced by Gennadiy Manakov and Gennadiy Strekhalov, who were launched on Soyuz TM10 on 1 August 1990. They returned to Earth with the first materials processing experiments carried out on Krystall. At this stage, Mir had settled down to a regular series of six-monthly occupations by resident crews of two cosmonauts. The last of the old-style Progress spacecraft, Progress 42, had left the space station in May and had been fully replaced by Progress M. The first recoverable Raduga capsule was sent down by Progress M5 on 28 November.

(a)

(b)

(c)

(d)

(e)

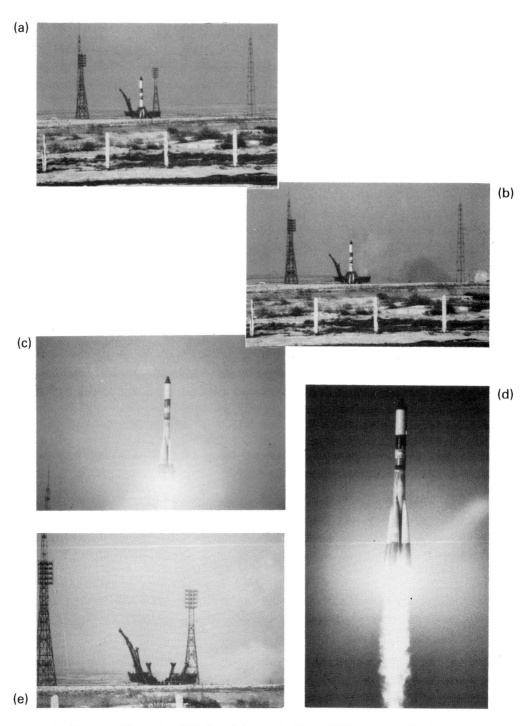

The successful operation of Mir depended on regular, bi-monthly Progress resupply missions.

JOURNALIST IN SPACE

Gennadiy Manakov and Gennadiy Strekhalov were replaced by Soyuz TM11 (2 December 1990), which brought up Viktor Afanasayev, year-long veteran Musa Manarov and Japanese journalist Toyohiro Akayama. The Japanese mission excited some interest, being paid for by the Tokyo Broadcasting Service (TBS), which chose its senior foreign news editor to fulfil the assignment. TBS paid the Soviet Union $12 million for the flight. Akiyama had to reduce weight and stop chain-smoking so as to claim his place on board (he was chosen in preference to a 27-year-old female camera operator, Ryoko Kikuchi) and even then became spacesick soon after he arrived on Mir. Although Akayama's broadcasts from Mir did not rivet the TBS audience in quite the way the station had hoped, he brought back some of the best colour movies ever taken from and in Mir.

The journalist-in-space mission excited the wrath of the Soviet press corps, who argued that the first journalist in space should be one of their own. Several newspapers clubbed together to organize a Soviet journalist in space. A squad of would-be journalist cosmonauts was recruited but, owing to a series of organizational and financial problems, the project fizzled (either Omelchenko or Mukhurtov would have been the lucky hack).

Journalist selection, 1990

Alexander Andryushkov, *Krasnaya Zvezda*
Valeri Baberdin, *Krasnaya Zvezda*
Yuri Krikun, Ukrainian TV and radio, Kiev
Pavel Mukhurtov, *Sovietskaya Molodyozh*, Riga
Svetlana Omelchenko, *Vozhduzhni Transport*
Valeri Sharov, *Liturnaya Gazeta*

FIRST BRITON IN SPACE

One of the most important tasks of the Afanasayev–Manarov crew was the erection, in January 1991, of a crane and mast on the outside of the Mir station. A bracket for the crane had been on the original Mir station. On 23 January, Afanasayev and Manarov made their way gingerly down the hull, carrying a 2 m container with the crane. The crane, when extended, was 14 m long with magnetic grips at the end. It weighed 45 kg, but could lift a mass of 700 kg. The spacewalk lasted 5 h 33 min. The crane comprised a base, rotation mechanism and arm. After testing it, the cosmonauts came back in. The purpose of the crane was to move large payloads from one part of the station to another and make possible the reconfiguration of solar arrays from one part of the station to another. On 26 January, in a 6 h 20 min spacewalk, they installed a telescopic mast on the outside of the Kvant 1 module, which would help in the relocation of solar panels.

Next was a Soviet–British mission, project Juno. Originally intended as a commercial mission for which a British company would pay £16 million, the financial package collapsed. The USSR flew the mission at its own expense, selecting 27-year-old science engineer, Helen Sharman. Soyuz TM12 was duly launched on 18 May 1991, carrying

Anatoli Artsebarski, Sergei Krikalev and Helen Sharman. A research technologist for the Mars company, Sharman carried out a number of medical, physical and chemical experiments on board, bringing up potato roots, seeds, snails, a lemon tree and ceramic films, and spoke to schools in Britain on amateur radio. Afanasayev and Manarov returned with Sharman eight days later.[104]

LAST SOVIET CITIZEN

Artsebarski and Krikalev carried out five spacewalks in July 1991 to erect a 14 m girder structure on the outside of Mir, as high as a four-storey building. Called sofora, the girder carried a new attitude control block for the better control of the space station. Sofora was constructed from two boxes the size of an electric cooker. Sofora was made from nickel–titanium alloys in tubular joints in 20 units. The cosmonauts topped their work by unfurling the Soviet flag at the top of the girder. By this stage, Krikalev and Artsebarski had spacewalked for 32 h 17 min each, bringing to 42 the total number of Soviet spacewalks.

The Soyuz TM12 mission attracted interest for two other reasons. First, it was the last *Soviet* manned space mission, and second, this and a variety of related factors conspired to keep the flight engineer, Sergei Krikalev, much longer in space than he had ever anticipated. 19 August was to have been the date for the signing of a new treaty to redefine the relationship between the member States of the Soviet Union. That morning, hard-line communists deposed President Gorbachev and put him under house arrest in his summer home in the Crimea. After five days of street fighting in Moscow, in the course of which Russia's President Boris Yeltsin had rallied the citizenry from atop a commandeered tank, the coup collapsed. Gorbachev returned to Moscow but his political authority had been fatally weakened. In the course of the coup, Ukraine and Belarus declared their independence from Moscow. The Communist Party was banned and the Soviet Union went out of existence at year's end.

Ground control was politically even-handed and relayed up news broadcasts from Soviet central TV (which supported the *putsch*) and Russian radio (which supported Yeltsin), thereby confusing the cosmonauts as to what was really going on. The operating manual specified that the cosmonauts must return in the event of war, but did not specify what was to happen in the event of a coup, so they stayed put until it blew over.

Ultimately these changes were to have profound consequences for the space programme. These were not apparent yet, but an inkling of what was to come was evident when Soyuz TM13 was launched on 2 October, the take-off observed by Nasultan Nasurbayev, President of the newly independent Republic of Kazakhstan. Soyuz TM13 had been originally planned as a joint mission with Austria, and Soyuz TM14 had been intended to fly a Kazakh cosmonaut. However, financial problems led to a merger of these two missions. Soyuz TM13 duly flew with a Russian commander, Alexander Volkov; a Kazakh, Toktar Aubakirov; and Austrian Franz Viehböck. The Kazakh, in effect, took Krikalev's return seat, so Krikalev was ordered to stay on the station indefinitely. Artsebarski returned on 10 October with the Kazakh and the Austrian. Sergei Krikalev remained on board with Volkov.

Sergei Krikalev still had his communist party membership card with him and he eventually became known as 'the last Soviet citizen'. It was a period heavy with symbolism. Back on Earth, the red flag, which had fluttered over the Kremlin since October 1917, was taken down on New Year's Eve, 1991, and replaced by the blue, white and red bars of Russia.

Krikalev was still on board to see the New Year in. Messages were sent up to him on board Progress freighters. Three months later, relief was in sight when Soyuz TM14 was rolled out to the pad on 15 March, decorated with the flags of Russia, Kazakhstan and Germany. Launching took place two days later, carrying Alexander Viktorenko, Alexander Kaleri and Klaus-Dietrich Flade for a week of medical, biological and engineering experiments devised by the German Space Agency. On 25 March, Alexander Volkov, Sergei Krikalev and Klaus-Dietrich Flade dropped away from Mir to land in calm, windless spring snow in Kazakhstan, to be met at once by recovery teams. Krikalev had been in orbit for 312 days, the longest ever unintended stay in space.

The third joint Russian–French mission, project Antares, began with the launch of Soyuz TM15 from Baikonour on 27 July 1992. On board were Anatoli Soloviev, Sergei Avdeev and Michel Tognini. The Frenchman had been backup to Jean-Loup Chrétien and in the course of his long period of training had married his physical education instructress, Elena Chechina. It was a two-week mission which concentrated on medical and biological research. In September, in the course of three spacewalks, Soloviev and Avdeev fitted a 700 kg manoeuvring block VDU on the sofora girder. The VDU had been brought up by Progress M14, from which it had to be extracted and then moved into open space. They attached cables around the sofora so as to connect the electrical commands that would control the VDU. The manoeuvring block would reduce the use of propellant by the station by a third.

French cosmonaut Michel Tognini in training.

LIGHTING UP THE NIGHT SKIES OF EARTH

The most politically symbolic moment of the mission took place on 7 September 1992, when Soloviev and Avdeev took down the Soviet flag from the sofora girder, replacing it with the Russian flag. It was the last Soviet flag flying anywhere in the solar system, though pennants and red stars from an earlier political epoch had by this stage been widely distributed on the Moon, Mars and Venus, presumably to be found by some future space archaeologist. They successfully hatched out quail chicks in the course of their mission. After 189 days in space, they were replaced by Gennadiy Manakov and Alexander Poleschuk, launched on Soyuz TM16 on 24 January 1993. Soyuz TM16 docked not with the main Mir docking port, but with the docking unit on Krystall.

These missions attracted little public attention, partly because of their routine nature, partly because of the economic crisis gripping Russia. An exception was the mission of Progress M15, the cargo craft which arrived at Mir on 29 October 1992. Progress M15 undocked early on 4 February 1993. Then an experiment, which had been planned for years, got under way. Filmed by Gennadiy Manakov and Alexander Poleschuk, Progress released a 5 kg, 10 m solar sail called Znamia ('banner' or 'flag' in Russian), which popped out of the hatch of Progress and unfurled like an umbrella. Progress began to spin against the blue oceans of Earth. As it entered the night-time skies over Earth, it was pointed downward and began to reflect the Sun's light onto Earth, testing the ability of objects in the sky to light up the ground. From an altitude of 250 km, Znamia cut a cone of light 5 km wide in a swathe from Toulouse through Geneva, Munich, Prague, Lodz, Brest and Gomel, where it could be seen as a bright diamond rapidly traversing the sky. The experiment was declared a complete success. The project had been funded by a Russian car company and a natural gas firm. Western experts had long doubted if it could be done. The idea could be traced back to Herman Oberth in the 1920s and subsequent theorists who dreamed of using artificial sunlight to light cities in the polar midwinter.

The fourth Russian–French mission took place in July 1993. The mission lasteed three weeks. Jean-Paul Hagnieré flew with Yuri Tsibliev and Alexander Serebrov on 1 July to replace Gennadiy Manakov and Alexander Poleschuk. Their mission had a busy start. In August, the station was peppered by tiny micrometeorite impacts from the Perseids meteor shower. In September, the cosmonauts spacewalked to erect a new truss on the outside of Mir. Called 'rapana', it was a 26 kg, 5 m long truss designed to carry antennæ, reflectors and solar gas turbines. The crew made five spacewalks and carried out materials processing experiments, astrophysical observations and observed the Earth.

The mission of Yuri Tsibliev and Alexander Serebrov lasted longer than anticipated, as the economic crisis hit home. A shortage of rocket motors prevented the launch of Soyuz TM18, originally slated for November. The new Soyuz did not get away until 8 January 1994, when Soyuz TM18 carried Viktor Afanasayev, newcomer Yuri Usachov, and veteran space doctor Valeri Poliakov. Five years after the record, year-long Titov–Manarov marathon, Russian space doctors now felt it was possible to break the duration record again with a mission of one-and-a-half years.

The delay over rocket engines which affected Soyuz TM18 was repeated in a similar manner when preparations to launch Soyuz TM19 began during the summer. This time the upcoming mission was postponed—though not for long—due to a shortage of

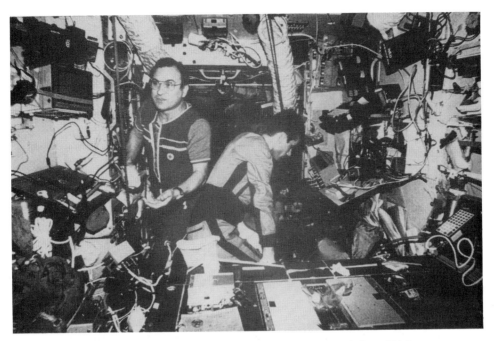

Dr Valery Poliakov on board Mir during his record-breaking mission, 1994-5.

nosecone fairings. Soyuz TM19 left Baikonour with an all-novice crew of Yuri Malenchenko, a 32-year-old air force pilot and a second Kazakh cosmonaut, Talgat Musabayev. Afanasayev and Usachov returned eight days later, leaving Malenchenko on board with Musabayev and the long-flying Poliakov.

MALENCHENKO SAVES THE MISSION

A reminder of the fragile state of the Russian space programme came at the end of August, when Progress M24 arrived alongside on 27 August with fresh supplies of food, water, air, fuel and experiments for the first mission with the European Space Agency, ESA. The docking was aborted at a distance of 150 m. Mission controllers made a second attempt on 30 August, but the automatic control system on Progress again cancelled the manoeuvre and the two craft began to drift apart once more. Progress had fuel for only one more attempt. If it failed, Mir would have run out of food and the station would have to be abandoned in mid-September, with little chance that there would be resources to re-occupy it. A third, desperate attempt was made on 2 September. Station commander Yuri Malenchenko took over when Progress closed to 150 m and guided the spacecraft in manually using a television monitor. All was well, and Progress maintained its 100% record of 67 successful dockings in a row.

The first of the European Space Agency missions, called Euromir, arrived on 6 October, when Soyuz TM20 reached the station carrying mission commander Alexander Viktorenko, flight engineer Elena Kondakova and European cosmonaut Ulf Merbold, a German who had already flown on the American space shuttle. The first of two Euromir missions, it lasted a full month. Merbold returned with docking hero Yuri Malenchenko and Kazakh Talgat Musabayev on 4 November, the cabin bouncing several times in a rough windy landing. Before coming down, the three men tested the rendezvous and docking equipment by undocking from Mir, backing away to 190 m and redocking.

Collaborative missions between USSR or Russia and Europe

Date	Spacecraft	Cosmonaut	Country	Duration	Mission title
Jun 1982	Soyuz T6	Jean-Loup Chrétien	France	8d	
Nov 1988	Soyuz TM4	Jean-Loup Chrétien	France	30d	Argatz
May 1991	Soyuz TM12	Helen Sharman	UK	8d	Juno
Oct 1991	Soyuz TM13	Franz Viehböck	Austria	8d	Austromir
Mar 1992	Soyuz TM14	K-D Flade	Germany	8d	Mir-92
Jul 1992	Soyuz TM15	Michel Tognini	France	8d	Antares
Jul 1993	Soyuz TM17	J-P Hagnieré	France	10d	Altair
Oct 1994	Soyuz TM20	Ulf Merbold	ESA	8d	Euromir 1
Sep 1995	Soyuz TM22	Thomas Reiter	ESA	179d	Euromir 2
Jul 1996	Soyuz TM24	Claudie Deshays	France	8d	Cassiopea*

*Assigned

YEAR AND A HALF IN SPACE

Elena Kondakova had now joined Poliakov in her own contribution to long-distance space flight. Just as Poliakov was trying to break the male long-duration record, she was trying to break the long-duration female record. Kondakova was only the third Russian woman in space. She was married to one of the leading mission controllers and Salyut veteran, Valeri Ryumin.

The three-person Mir crew saw in the New Year, carrying out a range of biological, technological and Earth observation experiments, but also spending much of their time keeping the ageing space station going. Soyuz TM21 was launched to join them on 14 March 1995, carrying novice mission commander Vladimir Dezhurov, veteran Gennadiy Strekhalov, and, for the very first time, an American astronaut, Dr Norman Thagard, under the new American–Russian programme for cooperation in space. All six worked together on the station for six days. The cabin of Soyuz TM20 re-entered the Earth's atmosphere on the morning of 22 March, coming down in snow 55 km northeast of Arkalyk, Kazakhstan. Kondakova had set a new women's duration record of 169 days, but Poliakov had circled the Earth for 438 days, seeing spring turn to summer, back to winter and a new spring begin again. He had orbited the Earth over 7000 times, passing through 14 000 sunrises and sunsets. With no further long-duration missions planned for some time, the record was likely to stand well into the twenty-first century. Against strong medical advice, he insisted on walking immediately, as if to prove that it could be done. The three cosmonauts were flown back to Moscow later that day. Doctors estimated that the bones of Valeri Poliakov would be completely recalcified within 15 months.

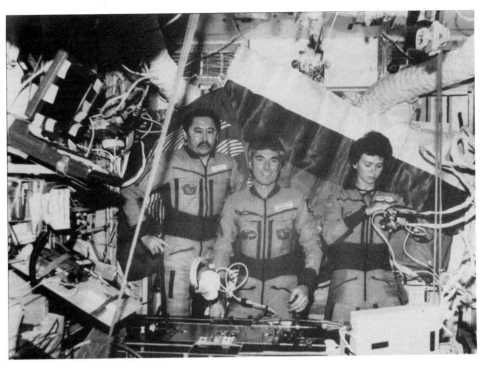

Talgat Musabayev, Ulf Merbold and Elena Kondakova on board Mir. Elena Kondakova became the most travelled woman in history, flying around the world for six months.

Space station endurance records 1971 -

Georgi Dobrovolski			
Vladislav Volkov			
Viktor Patsayev	Soyuz 11	June 1971	24 days
Alexei Gubarev			
Georgi Grechko	Soyuz 17	January 1975	30 days
Pyotr Klimuk			
Vitaly Sevastianov	Soyuz 18B	May 1975	63 days
Yuri Romanenko			
Georgi Grechko	Soyuz 26	December 1977	96 days
Vladimir Kovalyonok			
Alexander Ivanchenkov	Soyuz 29	June 1978	140 days
Vladimir Lyakhov			
Valeri Ryumin	Soyuz 32	February 1979	175 days
Leonid Popov			
Valeri Ryumin	Soyuz 35	April 1980	185 days
Anatoli Berezovoi			
Valentin Lebedev	Soyuz T5	May 1982	211 days
Leonid Kizim			
Vladimir Solovyov			
Oleg Atkov	Soyuz T10	February 1984	237 days
Yuri Romanenko	Soyuz TM2	February 1987	326 days
Vladimir Titov			
Musa Manarov	Soyuz TM4	December 1987	366 days
Valeri Poliakov	Soyuz TM18	January 1994	438 days

Dr Valery Poliakov gazes out of Mir's porthole. As the world passed below him, he saw five seasons come and go.

As doctors on Earth fussed over the condition of Valeri Poliakov, the new Mir crew prepared to receive the fourth of the large specialized modules due to fly to Mir. Under the original Mir schedule, Spektr should have flown to Mir in 1989. Falling financial allocations had first delayed and then grounded Spektr and its companion module, Priroda. But before Spektr arrived, there was work to do. On 19 April, Dezhurov and Strekhalov spring-launched a German microsatellite through the Mir airlock. Called GFZ, the microsatellite was 215 mm in diameter, 20 kg in weight and carried 60 reflectors for geodetic experiments. On 12 May, Vladimir Dezhurov and Gennadiy Strekhalov carried out the first of three spacewalks to move 14 m long solar panels from Krystall to the Kvant 1 module. There was a danger that the panels would cause an obstruction to the planned docking between Mir and the American space shuttle later in the summer: they would continue to provide power from their new location further back on the space station. Norman Thagard remained inside—and for the first time a Russian space station became the exclusive responsibility of an American. Further spacewalks were carried out on 17, 22,

29 May and 2 June, the panels being moved with the aid of the station's manipulator arm. Thagard, a shuttle veteran, was struck by the different pace of life on Mir compared to his own previous shuttle experiences. On short shuttle flights, time was at a premium; on long-duration Mir flights, there was a normal working day with time off in the evening, 'and weekends really were weekends'.

American shuttle veteran, Dr Norman Thagard, training for his flight aboard the Mir space station, summer 1995.

SPEKTR AND PRIRODA

Spektr was eventually launched on 20 May on a seven-day rendezvous pattern, though it had fuel for 90 days of independent flight. It entered a 337 by 221 km, 89.8 min, 51.7 deg orbit slightly ahead and above Mir and gradually descended to match the station's orbit.

Despite the nerve-wracking attempts to dock the first three large modules with Mir, the new module Spektr docked flawlessly with the Mir manned orbital space station first time on 1 June. Spektr weighed 23.5 tonnes, including 1.7 tonnes of fuel, and had enough resources for three docking attempts. Spektr had an internal volume of 63 m^3 and four solar panels with an area of 132 m^2. Spektr carried seven experiments: Oktava (sensing of Earth's atmosphere); Balkan (lower atmosphere); Faza, Feniks (spectral analysis of Earth's atmosphere); Astra 2 (gaseous composition of Earth's atmosphere); Taurus, Grif (X and gamma rays); Ryabina 4P (radiation sources) and a cargo of 880 kg of laptops, ergonometer and centrifuges for NASA. It carried a small 2 m manipulator arm called pelikan.

More than nine years after it was launched, Mir is nearly complete. This picture was taken after the arrival of Spektr, summer 1995.

Spektr's companion large module is the Earth resources module Priroda, developed in the mid- to late-1980s by the USSR, GDR, Czechoslovakia and the other socialist countries. It carried eight instruments:

— Ikar, a set of passive and active microwave polarization radiometers;
— Travers, a two-frequency synthetic aperture radar;
— Istok-1, a 64-channel infrared radiometer, to study the Earth's oceans;
— Ozon-M, a spectrometer to measure ozone and aerosol concentrations;
— MOZ-ozbor, a 17-channel spectrometer to measure reflected solar radiation;
— MSU-SK, medium-resolution and MSU-E high-resolution scanners;
— Centaur, to interrogate geophysical stations; and
— an aerosol lidar called Alisa.

By the time Spektr had arrived, Mir was scheduled for a further three years of operation—far beyond its originally scheduled lifetime when it was launched in February 1986.

Modules to Mir

Name	Launch	Arrival
Kvant	31 Mar 1987	12 Apr 1987 (hard dock)
Kvant 2	26 Nov 1989	6 Dec 1989
Krystall	1 June 1990	10 June 1990
Spektr	20 May 1995	1 June 1995

Mir: resident crews

1	13 Mar 1986	Soyuz T15	Leonid Kizim, Vladimir Solovyov
2	5 Feb 1987	Soyuz TM2	Yuri Romanenko, Alexander Laveikin
3	21 Dec 1987	Soyuz TM4	Vladimir Titov, Musa Manarov, (Anatoli Levchenko)
4	26 Nov 1988	Soyuz TM7	Alexander Volkov, Sergei Krikalev, (Jean-Loup Chrétien)
5	5 Sep 1989	Soyuz TM8	Alexander Viktorenko, Alexander Serebrov
6	11 Feb 1990	Soyuz TM9	Anatoli Soloviev, Alexander Balandin
7	11 Aug 1990	Soyuz TM10	Gennadiy Strekhalov, Gennadiy Manakov
8	2 Dec 1990	Soyuz TM11	Viktor Afanasayev, Musa Manarov, (Toyohiro Akiyama)
9	18 May 1991	Soyuz TM12	Anatoli Artsebarski, Sergei Krikalev, (Helen Sharman)
10	2 Oct 1991	Soyuz TM13	Alexander Volkov, (Franz Viehböck, Toktar Aubakirov)
11	17 Mar 1992	Soyuz TM14	Alexander Viktorenko, Alexander Kaleri, (Klaus-Dietrich Flade)
12	27 Jul 1992	Soyuz TM15	Anatoli Soloviev, Sergei Avdeev, (Michel Tognini)
13	24 Jan 1993	Soyuz TM16	Gennadiy Manakov, Alexander Poleschuk
14	1 Jul 1993	Soyuz TM17	Vasili Tsibliev, Alexander Serebrov, (Jean-Paul Hagnieré)
15	8 Jan 1994	Soyuz TM18	Viktor Afanasayev, Yuri Usachov, Valeri Poliakov
16	1 Jul 1994	Soyuz TM19	Yuri Malenchenko, Talgat Musabayev
17	3 Oct 1994	Soyuz TM20	Alexander Viktorenko, Elena Kondakova, (Ulf Merbold)
18	14 Mar 1995	Soyuz TM21	Vladimir Dezhurov, Gennadiy Strekhalov, (Norman Thagard)
19	26 June 1995	Atlantis	Anatoli Soloviev, Nikolai Budarin
20	3 Sep 1995	Soyuz TM22	Yuri Gidzenko, Sergei Avdeev, (Thomas Reiter)

Mir: visiting missions

1	22 Jul 1987	Soyuz TM3	Alexander Viktorenko, Alexander Alexandrov, Mohammed Faris (Syria)
2	7 Jun 1988	Soyuz TM5	Anatoli Soloviev, Viktor Savinyikh, Alexander Alexandrov (Bulgaria)
3	29 Aug 1988	Soyuz TM6	Vladimir Lyakhov, Valeri Poliakov, Abdul Mohmand (Afghanistan)
4	26 Nov 1988	Soyuz TM7	Alexander Volkov, Sergei Krikalev, Jean-Loup Chrétien (France)
5	2 Dec 1990	Soyuz TM11	Viktor Afanasayev, Musa Manarov, Toyohiro Akiyama (Japan)
6	18 May 1991	Soyuz TM12	Anatoli Artsebarski, Sergei Krikalev, Helen Sharman (Britain)
7	2 Oct 1991	Soyuz TM13	Alexander Volkov, Franz Viehböck (Austria), Toktar Aubakirov (Kazakhstan)
8	17 Mar 1992	Soyuz TM14	Alexander Viktorenko, Alexander Kaleri, Klaus-Dietrich Flade (Germany)
9	27 Jul 1992	Soyuz TM15	Anatoli Soloviev, Sergei Avdeev, Michel Tognini (France)
10	1 Jul 1993	Soyuz TM17	Vasili Tsibliev, Alexander Serebrov, Jean-Paul Hagnieré (France)
11	3 Oct 1994	Soyuz TM20	Alexander Viktorenko, Elena Kondakova, Ulf Merbold (ESA)
12	14 Mar 1995	Soyuz TM21	Vladimir Dezhurov, Gennadiy Strekhalov, Norman Thagard (USA)

ASSESSMENT

Mir is the most durable single achievement of the Soviet, now Russian, space programme. While part of the evolutionary process of building space stations goes back to the first-generation Salyut (Salyuts 1 and 4) and the second-generation Salyut (Salyuts 6 and 7), Mir was the station which made possible the permanent occupation of near-Earth space. With the exception of a brief period in 1989, Mir was manned permanently ever since its first long-term resident crew arrived in early 1987. Cosmonauts have flown continuously on Mir since 1989. While less glamorous than landing men on the Moon, it is no less an achievement in its own right. The quality of Mir's design was confirmed when it carried out a mission more than twice as long as originally intended, becoming home to modules, experiments and tasks quite different from those originally planned. At a time when American shuttles could fly for only two weeks at a time, Mir was home to missions which averaged half a year and the home of cosmonauts who pushed back duration in space to 326 days, 366 days and a year and a half. These long-duration missions represent the furthest frontiers of medical science and space medicine.

Sustaining the permanent occupation of near-Earth space required a considerable industrial and organizational commitment. The regular replacement of crews, the frequent Progress resupply missions, the year-long round-the-clock operation of flight control, the recovery of crews and capsules, the Louch communications network, all represented a commitment to quality, standards and sustained effort. By 1996, 20 resident crews had been placed on Mir; by the same time, the Progress freighter had made 73 successful dockings in a row, proof if it were needed that the Russian space programme can reach the highest standards of reliability.

Mir also demonstrated the ability of the space programme to cope with difficulty and the unexpected. Building orbital stations may once have appeared easy to the uninitiated, in comparison to flying men to the Moon. The many setbacks experienced by the Soviet Union during the early Salyut programme laid that notion to rest. Mir encountered its fair share of problems—modules which would not dock, low power supplies, manoeuvring difficulties, the tricky re-entry on the Afghan mission. Despite that, these difficulties were overcome. Designers devised one means after another to improve the station, such as rapana, sofora, the VDU, the reconfiguration of the solar arrays, all of them made possible by the extensive spacewalking of intrepid cosmonauts. Mir's experience indicates that construction of future, more complex, space stations will require similar reserves of resourcefulness and adaptation.

11

Cooperation: the International Space Station

there are none of the disorders and conflicts from which our poor Earth suffers

Konstantin Tsiolkovsky, describing a space colony, in
A change in Earth's relativegravity, 1894.

ROUND ONE: APOLLO–SOYUZ

No sooner had America's second Moon crew of Charles Conrad, Richard Gordon and Alan Bean returned from the Moon in November 1969 than public enthusiasm for the Moon programme waned. By 1972 the Apollo Moon programme had ended. All that was left was three flights the following year to a converted Saturn upper stage, Skylab.

The earliest the shuttle could fly was 1978 and NASA soon realized that there would be a gap of four years when no space missions at all would be scheduled. As early as September 1970, NASA internally considered three options: a flight between Skylab and Soyuz (its preference); a flight between Soyuz and Apollo; and a flight between the American Apollo and a Soviet station. In October 1970, during a visit by NASA officials to Star Town, sketches were swapped of what a compatible docking system might look like.

1972 was a year of *détente* between the United States and its communist adversary, following the improved relations between the US and China that resulted from President Nixon's visit there in 1971. After Frank Borman and Neil Armstrong visited Moscow and after some Soviet cosmonauts visited the United States, a space journalist floated the idea of the joint American–Soviet space flight. No one could think why not.

Pressure for a joint flight was stronger from the United States to start with, a position which was ultimately to be reversed. From NASA's point of view, a joint flight held three distinct advantages. It used up at least one of its surplus spaceships. Second, there would be few funding difficulties, as the President and many members of Congress saw the exercise as politically acceptable. Third, by bridging a gap during which no Americans would otherwise be flying in space, it enabled NASA to hold astronaut and flight control teams together who would otherwise leave the agency.

PLAN, PEOPLE, MACHINES

So it was that in February 1972, NASA and the Academy of Sciences agreed on an Apollo docking with a Salyut in 1975. It would be the first Salyut with two docking ports—Soyuz would arrive at one end and Apollo at the other. The joint flight was ratified in Moscow on 24 May 1972 by President Richard Nixon and Prime Minister Alexei Kosygin. The plan envisaged a joint flight in two years and a second mission after that. Yet suddenly the USSR withdrew the Salyut part of the mission. A two-port Salyut would simply not be ready in time, it said. The linkup would have to be between Apollo and a two-man Soyuz instead, a much less ambitious project.

NASA announced its crew to man the Apollo–Soyuz Test Project (ASTP as it was now being called) in January 1973. Commander was to be Tom Stafford of Apollo and Gemini fame; and the other members were Donald Slayton, the only Mercury astronaut who had never flown; and Vance Brand. But the USSR held off a final crew announcement. In retrospect it is easy to see why. Their main crews were tied down in the upcoming double Almaz–Salyut mission. The crews were finally announced on 4 June—after it was clear that there would be no space station mission. The prime crew was announced as Alexei Leonov and Valeri Kubasov, who had been waiting for a mission together for two years. Altogether, eight cosmonauts were allocated to the project.

With all the Almaz, Salyut and Soyuz mishaps, the USSR felt that success was at a premium in the upcoming ASTP. It must be seen to be at parity with the United States. Nothing must be left to chance. While the Americans allocated one spacecraft and six astronauts, the Russians allocated eight cosmonauts and seven Soyuz spacecraft. Four un-manned tests took place as Cosmos 613, 656, 638 and 672. Of the manned version, one was for a technical test before the flight; one was for the mission itself; and another was to stand by as reserve.

ASTP required new hardware—a docking unit which would enable the two spacecraft to link together. Because there was spare weight capacity on the American Saturn IB rocket, but not on the R-7, this was NASA's responsibility. The Americans constructed the docking unit—a 3.15 m long, 1.42 m diameter, 5907 kg box-shaped tunnel. As prepara-tions for the mission went ahead over 1973-4, cosmonauts were regular visitors to Cape Canaveral and Houston; American engineers and astronauts were seen in Star Town. To-gether they worked on the problems of pressures, optical and radar methods of navigation and docking and tracking. The Americans even got used to being bugged in their rooms in Moscow: it amused them more than angered them. At one stage in their rooms they com-plained loudly about the lack of coat hangers: next morning they miraculously appeared. Tom Stafford made a visit to Baikonour to inspect preparations there, a condition of the mission: his demand was met, but he was flown in and out by night so he would see as little as possible.

The USSR's pre-mission technical test took place from 2 to 8 December 1974. It was flown by Anatoli Filipchenko and Nikolai Rukavishnikov, and was designated Soyuz 16. They flew the 142 hours profile planned for the ASTP and carried out 20 experiments, mostly relating to the docking tunnel, atmospheric pressures, and frequencies. Soyuz 16 was tracked by the NASA network and communicated through mission control in Hous-ton.

'IT'S A GOOD SHOW, TOM!'

In early July 1975, preparations reached a climax. Alexei Leonov and Valeri Kubasov flew down to the cosmodrome on 3 July. Soyuz 19 was moved out to the pad on 12 July and the backup vehicle the next day with a second crew on standby (Vladimir Dzhanibekov and Boris Andreyev). Press interest in the flight reached a level not known since the days of the Moon landings. In the West there was amusement and a certain disbelief at the notion of the old rivals getting together. Western news coverage was made easier by the principal characters involved—greying old-timer Donald Slayton getting his first flight at 51; the straight-talking Tom Stafford; and joking, easy-going Alexei Leonov, one of the most personable of the cosmonauts.

Alexei Leonov, commander of the first joint Soviet–American mission in 1975.

The Soviet press felt obliged to advertise the whole mission in advance. It made the best of this and announced plans to broadcast the launch live as 'a novel departure from the Soviet tradition.' Well they might. They made a virtue of necessity and ran the show with all the razzmatazz of an American network, even if the style was a little stilted. Full flight details were released some weeks ahead. Some alert State enterprises even marketed Apollo–Soyuz cigarettes and perfume as exclusive once-off brands.

The flight got smoothly under way on the afternoon of 15 July. Alexei Leonov took Soyuz 19 up into a clear blue sky. A vanishing cottony vapour trail was all that could be seen over the steaming pad when it was announced that Soyuz 19 had safely reached orbit. The next step depended on the Americans.

NASA's astronauts were in fact asleep when Alexei Leonov and Valeri Kubasov entered orbit. Once woken, they watched a video tape of the start of their comrades' mission. They dressed, were driven to the pad and boarded what was to be the last Apollo. Like the Skylab missions, Apollo ASTP used the smaller Saturn IB rocket rather than the Saturn V Moonrocket, but it used the Saturn V tower. It was perched on pad 39 on a special trellis. Long flames could be seen coming from the base of the Saturn, reaching down to the ground like a gas flame on a cooker upside down. Then it lifted skywards.

'JUST ABOVE THE THUNDERCLOUDS'

Late that night, the rendezvous chase was under way across the entire hemisphere. Apollo was 6000 km behind and closing fast. At 200 km altitude it was flying unusually low for Apollo, so low that Donald Slayton gasped, with probably a little poetic licence: 'those thunderclouds down below nearly reach up to us'.

By midday on 17 July, Apollo command module pilot Vance Brand, peering through his docking module window, had spotted Soyuz 50 km away, with its red, green and white lights flashing. He braked Apollo's closing speed with a burn of 0.8 s. By 5 p.m. they were 150 m apart. Pictures taken by Apollo showed the winged Soyuz against the curving background of the Earth's horizon. Soyuz rolled, to align the communication systems. 'Remember to turn off your engines!' joked Leonov as Apollo headed in for capture and docking which took place over western France. Not long afterwards Tom Stafford and Deke Slayton began the procedure of depressurizing the docking module to Soyuz' level. The cameras went on, pointing down the tunnel. It was like a pit rescue when men entombed for days are about to be pulled out.

HANDSHAKE

So it was that at 8.17 p.m. the hatches opened and the smiling figure of Alexei Leonov could be made out in his communications softhat and light coveralls. He stretched forward his hand and the immortal and long-awaited handshake in space at last took place. Deke Slayton followed Tom Stafford into Soyuz, where they joined Alexei Leonov, who played the perfect host. The good-natured bonhomie was interrupted by a brief message of congratulations from Leonid Brezhnev and an embarrassingly long telephone call from President Gerald Ford.

The two spacecraft stayed docked together for two days. There were four series of crew transfers. Tom Stafford took Moscow TV viewers on a tour of the Apollo cabin. Press interviews were given. There were some fairly limited experiments. The hatches between Soyuz and Apollo were closed for the last time on the 18th. The spaceships separated the next day. Apollo drew 50 m away from Soyuz so as to eclipse the Sun, thereby enabling Soyuz to photograph the solar corona. They then redocked in a manoeuvre which had its moments, for the first time only one docking latch caught. Soyuz slewed around several times before docking hard again. Then they separated finally.

The landing of Soyuz on the morning of the 21st went as smoothly as the rest of the flight. Taking heart from the success of earlier live coverage, Soviet TV fitted cameras to the large Mil recovery helicopters. One of them picked up Soyuz high over the town of Arkalyk just after the parachute opened. Other cameras followed it down in the seven-minute descent. A stiff wind blew it across the brown steppes like a glider on a cross-country race. A whoosh of dust blew up as the retrorockets fired. It was over. Flight control applauded wildly. The two cosmonauts emerged, signed the side of their capsule in chalk, chatted to pressmen and were flown off. When mission doctor Boris Yegorov heard that they had got only 15 h of sleep since take-off six days earlier he ordered them to bed at once.

APOLLO–SOYUZ EPILOGUE

For the Russians, Apollo-Soyuz gave them parity with Apollo in the eyes of the world after six years of setback and disaster during which time the Americans had truly conquered the Moon and flown three times to their own orbiting Skylab space station. Under the full glare of the world's press, the USSR had flown a mission to high standards of technical competence and had not been found wanting.

Apollo continued in orbit till 24 July. The instrument section of Apollo had been converted to fly a wide variety of Earth resources experiments, and astronauts Stafford, Slayton and Brand spent the rest of their mission gazing down on icebergs, sand erosion in the Sahara, the Pyramids of Egypt, anchovy fisheries, and in carrying out electric furnace welding.

The aircraft carrier *USS New Orleans* took the last Apollo out of the Pacific Ocean. Only a few minutes after the three astronauts had walked across the flight deck of the aircraft carrier did it transpire that they were in the intensive care unit, poisoned. As soon as the parachutes had opened, astronaut Vance Brand had thrown a switch to dump unused fuel. This was a normal procedure. But instead of venting outside, the fumes were blown back into the cabin. All three astronauts began to lose consciousness. Tom Stafford just managed to get his oxygen mask on and managed to help his colleagues. The three only stopped coughing and spluttering once the hatches were opened up and the fresh sea air of the ocean blew in. The medium-term effects of the toxic poisoning were severe and the astronauts were not declared out of danger till the 28th. They left hospital on the 29th.

Despite allegations to the contrary, the Russians probably learnt little about the American space programme and its technology, and nothing that they could not have found out through the open technical literature. The Americans, by contrast, got a grandstand view of how the Soviet Union ran its space missions, warts and all.

Although the Americans had to design and build a special docking module, the adventure probably cost the USSR more financially. After all, they built no less than seven spacecraft for the flight, flying six of them (the backup orbited as Soyuz 22 the following year). There were numerous advantages to the Americans: it bridged a gap which in the end lasted seven years between Skylab 4 and the first Shuttle; it enabled NASA to hold on to many good engineers and astronauts for longer than would otherwise have proved possible; and the Earth resources package on Apollo 18 would alone have justified the flight.

SEQUEL: FLIGHT THAT NEVER HAPPENED

The ASTP had been envisaged by the Americans as the first of two joint flights. However, in October 1973, the Russians made it clear that they did not wish to discuss a second flight until the first had been successfully accomplished. Notwithstanding, NASA deputy administrator, George Low, floated the Russians the idea of a follow-up mission the following year, 1974, suggesting the shuttle fly to a future Salyut in the 1980s and that together the two nations build an international space station in 1990. In May 1975, with the joint mission only two months away, George Low again proposed a further joint mission, an astronaut/cosmonaut swap, space station linkup studies and cooperation in other areas. At this stage, NASA was desperate to keep its ASTP team together. Otherwise, it would face certain disbandment the moment Apollo 18 splashed down.

The Soviets did not respond for over a year. Approval for their own second-generation space station with two docking ports was not given until November 1975. A year later, on 27 November 1976, NASA received a positive response, proposing an American shuttle with spacelab module dock with their second-generation Salyut.

In May 1977, NASA and the USSR signed a second agreement for a joint flight, replacing and updating the 1972 texts. Two working groups were set up—one for experiments, the other for operations. The experiments' working group was soon considering proposals for the future mission: the USSR put forward 11 possible experiments, the Americans four. The task of the operations' working group, which met in November 1977, was to prepare a joint flight for 1981. NASA was confident that it could carry out such a mission even within its existing shuttle development budget and without having to ask for extra money from Congress. The working group discussed joint experiments and devised communication arrangements: the shuttle was to use the TDRS, and the second-generation Salyut was to use a new Molniya system.

The second working group meeting was scheduled for spring 1978. It never took place. The political climate worsened sharply during this period. It appears that President Carter cancelled scientific visits to the USSR because of the treatment of dissidents there. NASA tried again for another meeting in October 1979 to revive the flagging project, but the State Department again objected. The mission was never officially cancelled: it just died.[105]

RESUMING RELATIONSHIPS

The resumption of joint Russian–American spaceflights 20 years later was the combination of different factors at work in both Russia and the United States. The renewal of the relationship took place in two phases: the resumption of joint missions, first; and the building of an international space station, second.

The resumption of joint flights was the outcome of the much improved political relationship between East and West. From 1989 onwards, the Soviet Union began to withdraw its troops from eastern Europe. In 1991, the communist government collapsed and the new State of Russia began the uneven transition to democratic government and the market economy.

On 15 July 1992, following approval by both their governments, the first agreements were signed between Russia and the United States, providing for a cosmonaut to fly on the shuttle, an American to fly on Mir, and for the shuttle and Mir to link up in 1995. The signatories were Yuri Koptev for the Russian Space Agency and Dan Goldin for NASA. The purpose of these missions was the sharing of expertise and experience. Ironically, the agreement differed little from what George Low had proposed nearly 20 years before.

SPACE STATION

Coinciding with this agreement, the United States was experiencing considerable difficulties in developing its space station. Although announced in 1984 by President Reagan, the space station Freedom was by this stage seriously over-budget and many years from flying. In February 1993, within a month of taking office, President Bill Clinton ordered a complete redesign of the Freedom. He directed its costs to be cut from $30 billion to $10 billion, for a shorter lifetime, fewer assembly and resupply missions, and this review to be completed by 1 June.

In the event, NASA came back with three redesigns, popularly called the A (labelled 'austere'), B (labelled 'basic') and C (and which some simply called a 'can'), all budgeted in a range of $12 billion to $13.8 billion. President Clinton proposed that the station be kept in the budget whilst he considered the options. Just how little room for manoeuvre he had became evident later that month when the station survived a House of Representatives budget vote by 216 to 215. Clinton ordered NASA to come back to him in mid-September with a scaled-down version of option B, but to come in at between $10.5 billion and $11 billion. He also gave permission for negotiations to take place with Russia to see if cooperation would be possible and if that would reduce costs.

AGREEMENT

These negotiations came to a head sooner than expected and on 5 September Vice-President Al Gore and Russian Prime Minister Viktor Chernomyrdin signed an agreement. There were two parts. In the first, called phase I, the United States would pay Russia $400 million for joint operations on Mir for the period to 1997. In return, Russia would provide two years' astronaut flying time on Mir. In effect, the 1992 agreement was radically extended in a purposeful way to lay the ground for a bigger project. In phase II, the American space station and the projected Russian Mir 2 space station would merge in a joint international space station, which would have common controls and environmental systems. The new station would be jointly assembled by the United States and Russia using the space shuttle and Proton rockets respectively. The United States also relaxed some of its restrictions on the commercial uses of the Russian Proton rocket on the world satellite market.

An example of how joint working saved costs was the Assured Crew Return Vehicle (ACRV). The United States had always wanted there to be a lifeboat, a spacecraft which the space station's crew could use to return to Earth in an emergency, for example a fire breaking out on the station. The Americans had always planned to design their own Apollo-class ACRV, but the Russians offered to make available one or two Soyuz permanently docked to the space station as an ACRV. So Soyuz became the ACRV, thus saving considerable developmental costs and replacing it with a proven system. Indeed, the Russians made an early test of the ability of Soyuz to operate as an ACRV. Progress M17, which arrived at Mir in April 1993, was undocked in September that year for half a year of independent flight orbiting about 10 km distant from Mir at an altitude of 390 km. It burned up in the atmosphere on 3 March 1994.

On the Russian side, a joint approach offered considerable advantages. The summer of 1993 saw the suspension of the Energiya–Buran programme. At the same time, the first metal of the Mir 2 station was being cut at NPO Energiya, but there was a real risk that unless some financial stability were restored to Russia's space enterprises, it might never fly.

NEW DESIGN

NASA resubmitted its new space station design in November 1993. The four basic elements in its design were two American nodes, Mir 2 and a Russian functional block called the Salyut FGB which would be built on contract for the Americans for $215 million.

The International Space Station.

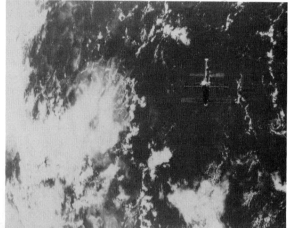

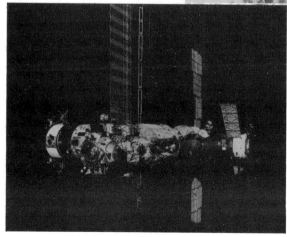

Nearer and nearer: *Discovery* closes in on Mir, February 1995 in the mission popularly known as mission Near-Mir.

The Salyut FGB is the first element of the station to fly and dates to Vladimir Chelomei's Almaz space station designs of the 1960s. The FGB is a 23 tonne module, 12.8 m long, 4 m in diameter, with a volume of 55 m^3. It has two solar panels of 28 m^2, able to supply 6 kW of electricity. It has four docking ports, three at one end, one at the other. The rear end will take Mir 2, the front end America's node 1. The FGB carries two 417 kg main engines, 20 rendezvous motors of 40 kg thrust and 16 stabilization motors of 1.3 kg thrust. Its design lifetime is a minimum of 13 years (to 2010). Its principal function will be to stabilize the station and provide it with electricity until the station's main power system is constructed. Although buried by his rivals during his lifetime, it was Chelomei's ship which became the core of the world's largest scientific project ever undertaken.

NEAR - MIR

Phase I of the Gore–Chernomyrdin involved four years of preparatory missions in which the two nations learned how to work together in space. In practical terms, it meant a Russian flying on the shuttle, an American flying on Soyuz, a shuttle–Mir rendezvous, and then nine joint missions when the shuttle would dock with Mir. This would give the United States two years' flying experience on Mir, crucial for long manned space station missions and crucial for the United States, whose longest mission to date was 84 days, set by the Skylab 4 crew as far back as 1974.

The *Discovery* crew (clockwise): Vladimir Titov, Michael Foale, Janice Voss, Bernard Harris, James Weatherbee and Eileen Collins.

The first of the joint missions took place on 3 February 1994, when veteran Soviet cosmonaut Sergei Krikalev joined the crew of STS-60, the space shuttle *Discovery*, which carried the Wake Shield experiment, Spacelab 2 and a German free-flying satellite. The second occurred just over a year later on 3 February 1995, when the shuttle *Discovery*, on mission STS-63, flew a rendezvous profile with Mir (inevitably, it was popularly named 'mission near-Mir'). The Russian cosmonaut on board this time was Vladimir Titov, and the purpose of the mission was to test the ability of the shuttle to close in on the space station. At 11.55 a.m. on 6 February, Vladimir Titov spotted his old home in space from the shuttle window from a distance of 338 km. Seven hours later, shuttle commander James Weatherbee and pilot Eileen Collins let the shuttle drift in to within 10 m, being ever so careful that the two did not collide. For the next hour, the shuttle and Mir flew in a gentle space ballet, crew members waving to each other through the portholes, exchanging greetings in Russian and English. Television pictures of the linkup were stunning, showing the shuttle closing in on the Russian space complex as it glided slowly over the blue and white background of the planet Earth. With the rendezvous over, the two spaceships separated, *Discovery* pursuing an independent mission before returning to Cape Canaveral on 11 February. A month later, the exchange was reciprocated when American doctor Norman Thagard flew to Mir for three months of experiments on board Soyuz TM21.

The American space shuttle docks with the Mir space station.

SECOND HANDSHAKE

The rendezvous was a rehearsal for the first of nine docking missions. Heart of the system was a new docking unit called Orbiter Docking System (ODS), modelled on the one first flown in 1975 on the Apollo–Soyuz Test Project. ODS weighed 1.7 tonnes and included a capture ring made in Moscow by RKK Energiya and sold to Rockwell for $18 million. The ODS is to be the basic system for the International Space Station.

Atlantis was the first shuttle to test the new docking system, eventually leaving Cape Canaveral on 26 June 1995 after two cancellations due to summer thunderstorms in Florida. Veteran shuttle commander Robert 'Hoot' Gibson brought the *Atlantis* close in to the Krystall docking unit on Mir, the two large space objects meeting slowly but firmly and exactly on schedule. Gibson brought *Atlantis* in just 1 km under Mir, astronaut and Mir trainee Bonnie Dunbar calling out the closing rates in Russian to the Mir crew. Flying over the Caspian Sea, they were 10 m apart. Five minutes later, over Lake Baikal, they had capture. It took two hours to equalize the pressure between the two spacecraft. 'Hoot' Gibson opened the hatch and floated through to be greeted by Mir commander Vladimir Dezhurov, his Russian companion Gennadiy Strekhalov and fellow American Norman Thagard, who had been on board Mir for three months. Besides gifts of chocolate, sweets and flowers, 'Hoot' Gibson brought with him the new Mir crew, Anatoli Soloviev and Nikolai Budarin, the first time the Mir crew had ever been changed by courtesy of an

Second famous handshake: 'Hoot' Gibson and Vladimir Dezhurov.

American spacecraft. The combined assembly of Mir/*Atlantis* weighed a record 230 tonnes, the largest single object ever assembled in space. *Atlantis* brought Mir new supplies of water and air.

END OF THE SPACE RACE

When the ten astronauts and cosmonauts posed for their group photograph in the Mir cabin on the afternoon of 29 June, that moment could be said to mark the true end of the space race. The shuttle undocked from Mir on 4 July, spending 90 min flying around Mir at a distance of 1 km and going on to make three days of independent flight before returning to Cape Canaveral. Thagard returned from Mir to Cape Canaveral in the shuttle with a new American endurance record in space, 115 days. The most serious problem the mission encountered was a bureaucratic one. No one had thought to get permission for returning Mir crew members Vladimir Dezhurov and Gennadiy Strekhalov to enter the United States, and the US Customs Service, considering itself now in the business of inspecting arriving space shuttles at Cape Canaveral, insisted the Russians have visas. These were duly brought up to them in time so they could present them at Cape Canaveral when they came down from space, duly classified as aliens.

The end of the space race—the group picture of all the American and Russian astronauts and cosmonauts involved in the linkup between *Atlantis* and Mir, June–July 1995. Clockwise from bottom centre are Gregory Harbaugh, 'Hoot' Gibson, Charles Precourt, Nikolai Budarin, Ellen Baker, Bonnie Dunbar, Norman Thagard, Gennadiy Strekhalov, Vladimir Dezhurov and Anatoli Soloviev.

Later missions were scheduled, over the 1995–7 period, to bring up prototype solar panels to Mir and for joint spacewalks. By 1996, preparations were well underway for the building of the international space station. Boeing had completed the first American hardware of the station, node 2, and node 1 was in progress. On the Russian side, the Salyut FGB had passed its critical design and engineering tests in Moscow.

BUILDING THE INTERNATIONAL SPACE STATION

The first missions for the international space station are scheduled for the end of 1997, the Salyut FGB being the first component to launch. This will be followed by a docking unit (delivered by Soyuz TM), by America's node 1, Mir 2 (prosaically renamed 'the service module') and the Soyuz Assured Crew Return Vehicle the following year. Next in line for delivery are the universal docking unit (sent up by Zenith rocket), the American laboratory, the small Italian module, America's node 2, the Japanese module and the European module. In all, 13 Russian and 16 American missions will be required to build the station, not to mention up to five cargo flights a year. In the course of 1998, construction will begin of the large power truss and turbogenerators that will power the station. Three Zeniths will be required to ferry up the large solar electric array which will be complete in 1999. Russia plans to moor three scientific modules at the station in the course of 1999–2001.

The first crew of the International Space Station will be Russian and American (May 1998). In 2000, the crew of the station will be expanded from three to six. A corps of nine European astronauts will be selected, of whom six will be allocated to NASA and three to the Russian Space Agency. The total airtight volume will reach 1200 m^3. The mass of the station, when complete in 2002, will be 200 tonnes. The station will orbit at 444 km, 51.6 deg, making it observable in the Northern Hemisphere from the United States, most of Europe, southern Britain and southern Russia. The cost to the United States will be about \$2.1 billion annually, with \$17.4 billion committed over the period 1994–2002.

The new Russian unmanned cargo craft, Progress MT, will be introduced in 1998, riding on the Zenith rocket from Baikonour. Progress MT comprises a service module, long cylindrical cargo module, solar panels and androgynous docking unit.[106]

The summer 1995 docking and the international agreement to build the space station gave the Russian space programme the confidence and stability to move ahead once more. By mid-1995, the cosmonaut squad had shrunk to 34—17 air force pilots, 12 engineers from RKK Energiya and five doctors from IMBP. In 1996, they began to put together their first set of four crews to train for the International Space Station for work with the FGB and the service module.

CONCLUDING REMARKS

When it is built, the International Space Station will be the fulfilment of the vision of Konstantin Tsiolkovsky in the nineteenth century and the great pioneers of the twentieth. The Soviet and Russian exploration of space has been characterized by a relentless pursuit of dreams and ideals and ideas, which have transcended the setbacks, disappointments and

disasters that inevitably accompanied such a great undertaking. Let Konstantin Tsiolkovsky himself have the final word:

> Mankind will not remain forever on the Earth. In pursuit of light and space he
> will timidly at first probe the limits of the atmosphere and later extend his
> control throughout the solar system.
>
> The impossible of today will become the possible of tomorrow.

Endnotes

These notes indicate the primary sources used and also refer the reader to useful secondary material.

1. A description and evaluation of his work may be found in A Kosmodemiansky: *Konstantin Tsiolkovsky*. Nauka, Moscow, 1985.
2. An excellent description of early Soviet rocketry may be found in Michael Stoiko: *Soviet rocketry—first decade of achievement*. David and Charles, Newton Abbot, 1970. For a Soviet perspective, see Evgeni Riabchikov: *Russians in space*. Weidenfeld and Nicholson, London, 1971.
3. VP Glushko: *Rocket engines GDL-OKB*. Novosti, Moscow, 1975.
4. Two early Soviet biographies of Korolev were Pyotr Astashenkov: *Academician Sergei Korolev—the life and times of the designer of Soviet spaceships*. Sputnik, 1971/1; and the more reminiscent A Romanov: *Spacecraft designer—the story of Sergei Korolev* (Novosti, Moscow, 1976). Neither, however, gives an account of the purges.
5. Dave Shayler: 'Where blue skies turn black'. Paper presented to the British Interplanetary Society, 3 June 1995.
6. Joel Powell: 'Animal precursors to manned space flight'. *Spaceflight*, Sep–Oct 1980.
7. For a history of the origins of the R-7, see Timothy Varfolomeyev: 'Soviet rocketry that conquered space'. *Spaceflight*, August 1995.
8. Contrary to Western popular opinion, the launching of Sputnik was well heralded in advance by open Soviet publications and media. See Martin Caidin: *Man into space*. Pyramid books, New York, 1961.
9. Brian Harvey: ' "I was last to touch the Sputnik"—top Korolev aide tells of how Sputnik 1 was launched and built'. *Spaceflight*, January 1991.
10. 'How about a trip to Mars?' *Science in the USSR*, 1988/6.
11. G Salakhutdinov: 'Once more about space'. *Ogonek*, **34**, 18–24 August 1990.
12. Roald Z Sagdeev: *The making of a Soviet scientist*. Wiley, New York, 1994, 158.
13. An account of the early days of unmanned lunar and interplanetary exploration may be found in Kenneth Gatland: *Robot explorers*. Blandford, London, 1972. For un-

successful Soviet missions during this period, see Curtis Peebles: 'Soviet launch losses'. *Spaceflight*, April 1987.

14. The first Russian work which made significant reference to his work was *Zagadki Zvezdikh Ostrovov*. Moscow, Molodaya Gvardiya, 1987.

15. For an account of early Soviet manned spaceflight, see Kenneth Gatland: *Manned spacecraft*. 2nd edition, Blandford, London, 1971.

16. There are two prominent historians of Soviet and Russian cosmonauts. Rex Hall, FBIS, has been published extensively in the *Journal of the British Interplanetary Society* (JBIS), *Spaceflight* and *Zenit*. The most recent summaries of his work are 'The Soviet cosmonaut team' in JBIS, **44**, no 9, 1991 and 'Civilians in the Soviet cosmonaut team', JBIS, **46**, no 10, 1993. The second is Gordon Hooper, FBIS. His two exhaustive compendia of the cosmonaut squads are Gordon Hooper: 'The Soviet cosmonaut team', vols 1 and 2 (2nd edition), GRH Publications, Lowestoft, 1990. See also *Zenit Supplement*, Jan 1989. My thanks are due to Rex Hall for his comments on the lists of cosmonauts provided in the text.

17. Yaroslav Golovanov: '*Cosmonaut no. 1*'. *Izvestia*, 2–6 Apr 1986, trans. by Jonathan McDowell.

18. Mikhail Rebrov: 'The difficult path to April 1961, or why we're not finding out the entire truth about the flight of Yuri Gagarin until today'. *Krasnaya Zvezda*, 28 March 1992.

19. The principal post-*glasnost* Russian review of its interplanetary space programme is available in Timothy Varfolomeyev: 'The Soviet Venus programme'. *Spaceflight*, February 1993 and 'The Soviet Mars programme'. *Spaceflight*, July 1993.

20. There are now several accounts of the Nedelin disaster. A Radianov: 'The time has come to tell: the first launch of a new rocket—how Marshal Nedelin died'. *Krasnaya Zvezda*, 24 Oct 1990; S Averkov: 'Explosion at Baikonour'. *Rabochnaya Tribuna*, 6 December 1990; James E Oberg: 'Disaster at the cosmodrome'. *Air & Space*, December 1990/January 1991. Much of the credit for exposing this disaster should go to James Oberg who wrote about it and other Soviet space mysteries long before *glasnost*, especially in *Red star in orbit*. Harrap, London, 1985.

21. JD Ratcliffe: 'Amateurs with their eyes on space'. *Reader's Digest*, May 1965.

22. Dwayne Day: 'Lifting the veil—US/Soviet competition and cooperation in space prior to Apollo'. *Spaceflight*, August 1995.

23. The most useful history of this episode and the subsequent spying by the two super-powers on one other may be found in William E Burrows: *Deep black—the secrets of space espionage*. Bantam, London, 1986.

24. The most useful description of Soviet and Russian space hardware dating back to this period may be found in David S Portree: 'Mir hardware heritage'. NASA, Johnson Space Flight Center, Houston, Texas, 1995.

25. Gordon Hooper: 'Secrets of the women cosmonauts'. *Space Flight News*, November 1989.

26. 'The 1965 journalist in space project'. *Space Flight News*, May 1990. For an account of the other planned Voskhod missions, see Phillip S Clark: 'The Voskhod programme: cancelled missions'. *Zenit*, **22**, December 1988.

27. There is now a substantial literature detailing the efforts of the Soviet Union to reach the Moon first. The principal Soviet texts are as follows: Sergei Leskov: 'How we didn't get to the moon'. *Izvestia*, 18 August 1989, translated by Charles E Noad; VP Mishin: 'Why we didn't land on the Moon'. *Znaniya*, **12**/1990; Mikhail Rebrov: 'But this is how it was'. *Krasnaya Zvezda*, 13 January 1990, translated by Charles E Noad; 1B, Afanasayev: 'Unknown spacecraft'. *Znaniya*, **12**/1991, translated by Ralph Gibbons; Andrei Tarasov: 'Space flights—fancy and reality', *Science in the USSR*, 2/1991. The principal Western texts are: Gordon Hooper: 'USSR's secret race to the Moon'. *Space Flight News*, November 1990, December 1990; Phillip S Clark: *The Soviet manned lunar programme and its legacy.* Space policy, Butterworth-Heinemann, 1991; and Nicholas L Johnson: *The Soviet reach for the Moon.* Cosmos Books, 1994.

28. A reconstruction of the UR-700 design is available in Phillip S Clark: 'More Soviet space secrets revealed'. *Jane's Intelligence Review*, Europe, September 1992; and in Phillip S Clark: 'Designing the UR-700 launch vehicle by computer'. *Zenit*, **62**, August 1992. Details of the RD-270 are available in Charles Vick: 'Russia, Energomash reveal F1 class rocket'. *JBIS*, **47**, no 9, 1994.

29. Andrew J Lepage: 'The mystery of Zond 2'. **JBIS**, **46**. No 10. 1993.

30. Phillip S Clark: 'The mystery of Luna 10 and Luna 11'. *Spaceflight*, December 1979.

31. Hugo Young, Bryan Silcock & Peter Dunn: *Journey to tranquillity.* Jonathan Cape, London, 1969.

32. Several accounts exist of the flight of Soyuz 1. The first *glasnost* account appeared in Leonard Nikishin: 'Soviet space disaster on the revolution's anniversary—how and why cosmonaut Komarov died'. *Moscow News*, 1–8 March 1992; see also Neville Kidger: 'Early Soyuz history recalled'. *Spaceflight*, September 1992.

33. *Moscosky Komsomolets*, 19 October 1994.

34. A detailed Russian description of the lunar lander, LK, is available in VM Filin: *Vospominaniya o lunnom korable.* Moscow, 1992.

35. B. Hendrickx: 'Soviet manned lunar programme'. In *JBIS*, **46**, pp. 207–8, 1994.

36. Paper presented by commander of the Military Space Forces Vladimir Ivanov, presented to parliamentary hearings on 23 February 1995 in the *Duma*; reported by ITAR/TASS, 23 February 1995.

37. Anatoli Stepovoi & Viktor Filipov: 'A terrestrial glance at Plesetsk'. *Izvestia*, 6 October 1994.

38. Vladimir Li: Problems: 'Leninsk—a closed city open to the winds of change'. *Kazakhstanskaya Pravda*, Almaty, 26 December 1992.

39. P Mills: 'Energiya and Buran at Baikonour'. *Spaceflight*, November 1989.

40. James Asker: 'US firm says Baikonour improving slowly'. *Aviation Week & Space Technology*, 31 July 1995.

41. For a pre-*glasnost* perspective on Russian rockets, see Kenneth Gatland: *Missiles and rockets.* Blandford, London, 1975.

42. FA Beswick: 'The Proton launcher at Baikonour'. *Spaceflight*, September 1992.

43. S. Sergeyev: 'Domestic space hardware—Tsyklon'. *Aviatsia i Kosmonavtika*, Mar/Apr 1994.

44. The introduction of the Zenith may be traced in Phillip S Clark: 'The first missions of the Soviet medium-lift launch vehicle'. *JBIS*, **41**, No 3, 1988. See also Phillip S Clark: 'New SL-16 and Energiya information released'. *Zenit*, 28, June 1989.

45. Serafim Saratov: 'Missile Complex Pioneer'. *Russian Magazine of Science and Technology* #1; Alexander Ryazhskikh: 'Space missile complexes'. *Russian Magazine of Science and Technology*, #1.

46. A detailed description of MAKS is available in Mark Hempsell & Bob Parkinson: 'MAKS—eastern promise?' *Spaceflight*, March 1993.

47. Stanley W Kandebo: 'Russians want US to join scramjet tests'. *Aviation Week & Space Technology*, 30 March 1992.

48. *Flight International*, 15–21 June 1994.

49. Phillip S Clark: 'Soviet rocket engines'. *Zenit special*, Astro Info Service, Halesowen, 1989; Phillip S Clark: 'Soviet rocket engine overview'. *Spaceflight*, July 1990.

50. Mikhail Chernyshev: 'The path of progress—from the bicycle to Buran'. *Segondya*, 15 December 1994.

51. C Wachtel: 'The chief designers of the Soviet space programme'. *JBIS*, **38**, 1985; Steven Zaloga: 'Soviet strategic missile development and production'. *Jane's Intelligence Weekly* 30 May 1987; 6 June 1987; Asif Siddiqi: 'Soviet space programme organizational structure'. *Spaceflight*, August, September 1994.

52. Russian tracking systems are reviewed by Phillip S Clark: 'Space debris incidents involving Soviet/Russian launchers'. *JBIS*, **47**, No 9, 1994; and by Henk HF Snid: 'Soviet command and control'. *JBIS*, **44**, No 11, 1991.

53. Bert Vis: 'All at sea with the Soviets'. *Space Flight News*, December 1990.

54. Christian Lardier: 'Menaces sur le programme spatial russe'. *Air & Cosmos*, 17 mars 1995.

55. Craig Covault: '95,000 Russian layoffs, launch breakdown feared'. *Aviation Week & Space Technology*, 15 November 1993.

56. Alan Postlethwaite: 'Opening doors'. *Flight International*, 18-24 April 1990. Tom Harpole: 'Can Russia's space program survive?' *Air & Space*, February/March 1993; Tim Furniss: 'Red star wars'. *Flight International*, 3–9 March 1993; Tim Furniss: 'Culture shock'. *Flight International*, 4–10 November 1992; Michael Lemonick: 'Space programme for sale'. *Time*, 16 March 1992; Craig Covault: 'Russian Proton challenges Ariane'. *Aviation Week & Space Technology*, 24 April 1995.

57. Valentin Khalin: 'Entrepreneurship—a commercial wheel for the space wagon'. *Delovoi Mir*, 30 April 1994.

58. Anatoli Pokrovsky: 'Reward for obedience'. *Pravda*, Moscow, 4 September 1993.

59. 'Aerojet, Lyulka push D-57 for SSTO validation'. *Aviation Week & Space Technology*, 11 October 1993. For a broader look at collaborative ventures, see *Aviation Week & Space Technology*, 23 August 1993.

60. Paul Mann: 'US, Ukraine sign space pact'. *Aviation Week & Space Technology*, 28 November 1994.

61. For a history of the Cosmos programme, see Robert Christy: 'Cosmos 2000'. *Space Flight News*, June, July 1989.

62. The most recent review of this part of the Soviet programme is Phillip S Clark: 'The Soviet reconnaissance satellite programme, 1982–90'. *JBIS*, **44**, no. 11, 1991.

63. Gary Bennett: 'A look at the Soviet nuclear power programme'. NASA, Washington DC, 1989, reprinted in *Zenit*, **40**, June 1990.

64. Yuri Atserov & B Konovalov: 'Space beacons'. *Science in the USSR*, **2**/1990.

65. P Daly: 'An introduction to the USSR GLONASS navigation satellites'. *JBIS*, **46**, no 10, 1993.

66. Christian Lardier: 'La Russie lance un satellite OKO'. *Air & Cosmos*, 2 juin 1995.

67. Joel Powell: 'Nauka modules'. *JBIS*, **41**, No 3, 1988; see also Joel Powell: 'Research from Soviet satellites'. *Spaceflight*, January 1983, which outlines scientific payloads within the Cosmos programme.

68. A good example of the declassification process was the publication 'The USSR in outer space—the year 2005'. *Novosti*, Moscow, 1989.

69. A most useful description of the series may be found in Phillip S Clark: 'Resurs F and related recoverable polar orbit satellites'. *Zenit*, **53**, July 1991.

70. Phillip S Clark: 'Soviet geosynchronous satellite activity October 1991 - May 1992'. *JBIS*, **46**, No 10, 1993.

71. Phillip S Clark: 'A review of the Soviet geodetic satellite programme'. *Zenit*, **44**, October 1990.

72. R. Kremnev, A. Smirnov, I. Saimagambetov: 'Project Interbol'. *Aviatsia i Kosmonavtika*, **8**/1993.

73. Plans for Russian Moon rovers had been articulated as far back as July 1957 in *Trud*. See Wilfred Burchett & Anthony Purdy: *Yuri Gagarin*. Panther, London, 1961. p. 125.

74. ITAR/TASS news announcement, 5 June 1994.

75. Roald Z Sagdeev: *The making of a Soviet scientist*. Wiley, New York, 1994, 232–243.

76. Nicholas Booth: 'Phobos 2: what went wrong'. *Space Flight News*, June 1989; Marina Lapina: 'Phobos mission—food for thought'. *Science in the USSR*, **2**/1990.

77. Peter Bond: 'Phobos debrief'. *Space Flight News*. February 1990.

78. The evolution of the mission may be traced in Yuri Zaitsev: 'Destination Mars'. *Space Flight News*, March 1989; Peter Bond: 'Soviets revise Mars targets'. *Space Flight News*, February 1990; Christian Lardier: 'Le nouveau programme martien russe'. *Air & Cosmos*, 21–7 septembre 1992; James Asker: 'Cheaper, faster Mars missions in sight'. *Aviation Week & Space Technology*, 12 April 1993; Craig Covault: 'US, Russia plan new Mars mission'. *Aviation Week & Space Technology*, 6 June 1994.

79. Christian Lardier: 'Revision des futurs programmes martiens'. *Air & Cosmos*, 12 mai 1995.

80. Details on early Soviet spaceplanes may be found in IB Afanasayev: 'Unknown spacecraft'. *Znaniya*, **12**/1991, translated by Ralph Gibbons. Among the most important articles in Western literature are 'Soviet mini-shuttles' in *Space Flight News*, January 1989; VM Petrakov: 'Two projects of VM Myasishchev'. *JBIS*, **47**, No 9, 1994; Peter Pesavento: 'Russian space shuttle projects, 1957–94.' *Spaceflight*, May, June, July, August, 1995; Curtis Peebles: 'The Soviet space shuttle'. *Spaceflight*, May 1984; and Dennis Newkirk; 'Soviet spaceplanes'. *Spaceflight*. October 1990.

81. Valentin Bobkov: 'Space sandal'. *Krylya Rodiny*/**11**, November 1991.
82. There are few histories of these cancelled programmes. Two that are recommended are Curtis Peebles: 'The origins of the US space shuttle—1'. *Spaceflight*, November 1979; and Curtis Peebles: 'The manned orbiting laboratory'. *Spaceflight*, April 1980.
83. Mikhail Rudenko: 'Star wars—history of the death of a unique spaceplane'. *Trud*, 26 August 1993.
84. V Ageyev: 'Unknown pages in the history of the space programme - BOR'. *Aviatsia i Kosmonavtika*, 1/1992, January 1992.
85. A fuller description may be found in Piotr Bukowski & Jay Miller: *OKB-MiG*. Midland Counties Publications, Leicester, 1991.
86. For a further exploration of these differences, see *Zenit*, **25**, March 1989.
87. Anatoli Kirpil & Olga Okara: 'Designer of space planes: Vladimir Chelomei dreamed of creating a space fleet of rocket planes'. *Nezavisimaya Gazeta*, 5 July 1994.
88. Richard DeMeis: 'Soviet blackbirds and a shuttle killer'. *Aerospace America*, July 1991.
89. 'New leap in space quest'. *Soviet Weekly*, 23 May 1987.
90. Phillip S Clark: 'Polyus—an Energiya-launched orbital production plant'. *Zenit*, **54**, August 1991; Lucien van den Abdelen: 'Soviet space at the crossroads'. *Spaceflight*, November 1991.
91. Charles Vick: 'Soviet orbital station designed in 1965'. *JBIS*, **47**, No 9, 1994.
92. The origins of the Almaz programme were published in IB Afanasayev: 'Unknown spacecraft'. *Znaniya*, **12**/1991, translated by Ralph Gibbons. A new Russian perspective is available in VM Petrakov: Soviet orbital stations. *JBIS*, **47**, no 9, 1994. Perhaps the best Western account is Neville Kidger: 'Almaz - a diamond out of darkness'. *Spaceflight*, March 1994.
93. One of the best overviews of the Salyut programme is 'Salyut—Soviet steps toward permanent human presence in space, a technical memorandum'. Congress of the United States, Office of Technology Assessment, 1983.
94. Mikhail Rebrov: 'Bitter aftertaste of glory'. *Krasnaya Zvezda*, 9 September 1994.
95. 'How emergency system saved cosmonauts in 1983 pad mishap'. *Krasnaya Zvezda*, 30 May 1987.
96. V Golovachev: 'Vladimir Shatalov answers queries about space programme's results and next steps'. *Trud*, 26 January 1989.
97. Vladimir Dzhanibekov gives an account of the rescue in Vladimir Dzhanibekov: 'The rescue of Salyut 7'. In David Whitehouse (Ed): *Man in space*. New Scientist, IPC publications, 1986.
98. A drawing of Mir with this configuration appears in 'The USSR in outer space—the year 2000'. *Novosti*, Moscow, 1989; and in *Soviet science and technology*, Novosti Press Agency Almanac, Moscow, 1987, p. 198. In the event, Gamma was flown on an independent mission.
99. J Branegan: 'Simple analysis of space station downlinks'. *JBIS*, **41**, No 3, 1988; John Branegan: 'Mir communication'. *Spaceflight*, March 1988; John Branegan: 'Keeping track of Mir'. *Spaceflight*, April 1988.

100. A comparison of the spacesuits of both countries is given in James Asker: 'US, Russian suits serve diverse EVA goals'. *Aviation Week & Space Technology*, 16 January 1995.
101. George Spiteri: 'Marathon men'. *Space Flight News*, December 1990.
102. The status of the cosmonaut team in the mid-1990s was reviewed by Sergei Voevodin: 'Cosmonaut status'. *JBIS*, **47**, No 9. 1994.
103. Phil Mills: 'Progress modified'. *Zenit*, **36**, February 1990.
104. Helen Sharman & Christopher Priest: 'Seize the moment'. London, Victor Gollancz, 1993.
105. DJ Shayler: 'The proposed USSR Salyut and US shuttle docking mission c. 1981'. *JBIS*, **44**, No 11, 1991.
106. Christian Lardier: 'Nouvelles utilisations de la fusée Zenith'. *Air & Cosmos*, 4 November 1994.

Index